The Definitive Donkey

A Textbook on the Modern Ass

By Betsy and Paul Hutchins
Revised and Edited by Leah Patton

For Longear Lovers and Owners,
from Miniature Donkey to Standard to Mammoth Jackstock

ISBN 0-9659312-0-X

Dedicated to *El Burrito Platero* and his longeared friends throughout the world.
Thank you for being a part of our lives and letting us share our joy of donkeys.

Melissa Hutchins and *Platero*

The Definitive Donkey
A Textbook on the Modern Ass
by Betsy & Paul Hutchins,
Revised & Edited by Leah Patton
Original Copyright 1981   Renewed 1999
Hee Haw Book Service

The Authors (and friend)
Betsy Hutchins, *El Burrito Cupid's Beau*, and Paul Hutchins.

THE DEFINITIVE DONKEY -

A TEXTBOOK ON THE MODERN ASS

INTRODUCTION by Betsy Hutchins

In this book we hope to try to cover all possible aspects of the modern donkey, from the single family pet, to the show animal, to the breeding herd, for all sizes of ass.

We hope that the book will be in a down to earth, easy to understand style that will suit donkey lovers for easy reading in front of the fireplace.

This book is a direct outgrowth of our 30 + years work with the American Donkey and Mule Society. When Paul and I founded the organization in 1967, and later incorporated it with Carl A. Wilson II, in 1968, there was no really organized body of literature or any organized groups of people who were actively promoting donkeys. There was a minimally active Miniature Donkey Registry, and the Standard Jack and Jennet Registry had been in existence for many, many years, but no real activity was taking place. Contrast that to today's busy world of donkey fanciers! There are now multiple registries for donkeys, although the ADMS remains the only all-breed registry. There are shows for both donkeys and mules in every section of the country. Countless people who thought donkeys were both stupid and stubborn have changed their minds, the journalistic coverage these animals have had in the last 30 years is tremendous and all complimentary. The American Donkey and Mule Society in cooperation with the existing registries and the ever growing Regional Clubs has indeed accomplished wonders for both donkeys and mules.

In those years we have both published and carried in our bookstore quite a few books about donkeys. We have never been satisfied with the amount of information in any one book. For that reason, we have decided to try to combine all the information we can get from: MR. LONGEARS and BRAYER articles, THE DONKEY AND MULE AS A BACKYARD HOBBY, the ADMS DONKEY SERIES (Training, Breeding, Judging, Breeds of the World) plus the many books that have been written and published in England and Australia, into one huge DONKEY TEXTBOOK. We have deliberately called it a text on asses, because the proper and universal name of this animal is ass. However in the text of the book we will refer to most of these animals as donkeys, as it comes more easily to the tongue of the English speaker. We do not use burro because we do not speak Spanish. Also because over the years it seems to have acquired a totally undeserved derogatory feeling around it.

A word about thank you's. Our unbounded thanks to the literally hundreds of sincere donkey lovers who have contributed work through the years which has gone into this book. None of the writers or the artists you will find represented here have been paid for their work, either at the first printing in the donkey magazines or in this book. They have donated their work, and poured out their knowledge for you out of love for the animals and a great desire to see them properly appreciated and cared for. We fervently hope that this book will help to fulfill this desire and thus carry on the generous tradition these writers and artists have started.

Special thanks go to the various registries and clubs you will find listed in this book for the special literature they contributed. Also many thanks to the magazine MR. LONGEARS AND FRIENDS for their generous help.

Another special thank you goes to the artists. The principal artists represented in this book are BONNIE SHIELDS "The Tennessee Mule Artist" who contributed so many illustrations to so many of our books and articles, and CINDY POLLOCK of Laveen, Arizona, whose original illustrations from Definitive Donkey we have carried over, and Leah Patton who is our current in-house artist!

We have tried in this revision to go back and add in lore, legend, and more advanced overall training and general care which we did not have a chance to add into the original version. New information on donkey color genetics has come to light which we happily include! We hope you will find the expanded information useful and also entertaining.

"Kissing Cousins" - Frosted spotted white Mexican Burro "*Blossum*" and spotted Mexican Burro "*Confetti*". The parents were Frosted Spotted White burros. These foals were born at Skylar Farms, Newport TN.

Chris and Myryha Patton on *Cupid's Beau*, a Large Standard Donkey gelding owned by Paul & Betsy Hutchins. Donkeys are great saddle animals!

CHAPTER ONE

Donkeys Around The World

AN ASS VOCABULARY

In dealing intelligently with any subject it is necessary to be able to speak in the jargon of the people who are "in the know". With donkeys and mules terms vary from place to place in our country, and even from neighborhood to neighborhood. The American Donkey and Mule Society conducted studies to find out which terms were proper and decided on a group of definitions which mean the most to the most people. Some of what follows are horse terms, which fit in with donkeys because they are equines and their diseases and parts of the body are the same. You will find more terms useful for judging purposes in the judging section of this book.

Ass This is the animal we are dealing with in this book. It is the separate equine species known to scientists as "Equus asinus". It is an equal member in the equines with the horse, zebra and wild ass species. The ass is counted as a different species from the horse because of several physical characteristics. The main ones are: tufted tail; braying voice; short upright mane; different pelvis shape; different hoof shape; long ears; different hair and skin texture; and different chromosome number.

Donkey Donkey is the common name that English speaking people have for asses. Its derivation is supposed to be from the older English words *dun* referring to its color, and *ky* a diminutive meaning small. Since most donkeys are pony-sized, the animal became known as the dunky, the small dun colored animal. Even today the largest numbers of English donkeys will be the typical "gray-dun" (slate) color with dorsal stripe and cross. Some British nicknames are "Moke" and "Neddy".

Burro This is the other common name for the small ass in the United States. It is the Spanish equivalent in usage of our donkey. It is the name for the everyday working animal that is so common in Spanish speaking lands. The Spanish have a large vocabulary for asses with several terms for breeding herd, breeding jack, breeding jennet, mule breeding stock etc. However when they want to talk about the animal carrying the water jars down the street he is the burro. This term has come into common use in the Western part of the United States. The important thing to remember about it is that burro-donkey-ass they are all the same animal, and the burro isn't aseparate breed, just a separate term. Burro, however is not considered proper to use when referring to large Jackstock or to the Miniature Mediterranean donkey.

Standard The American Donkey and Mule Society refers to these medium size indigenous asses as "Standard Donkeys". They may be further divided for show and breeding purposes into **SMALL STANDARD DONKEY**, standing from 36.01 inches at the withers to 40", **STANDARD**, 40.01"-48" tall, and **LARGE STANDARD DONKEY**, 48.01 inches to 54 inches. After these heights come the "Mammoth Asses" (or "Jackstock") which run 54 inches for females and 56 inches for males.. A donkey which is a MALE and which is 48-55 inches tall is considered to still be a LARGE STANDARD whereas a female which is 54 inches is a "Mammoth" or American Standard Jennet.

"Mammoth" Jackstock For a full understanding of this remarkable breed you should consult the breeds section of this book. However it should be stated that this is the most well bred, well developed largest ass breed in the modern world. The technical and registry name is The American Mammoth Jackstock Registry (formerly called American Standard Jack and Jennet). These animals must measure 54 inches at the withers for a female and 56 inches for a male. Males should have a 7 1/2 inch measurement around the cannon bone below the knee for proper registration with their own registry. These, as with all breeds may be registered with the American Donkey and Mule Society as well as with their specific breed registry. One important note:

These animals are never referred to as burros or donkeys. They are always called Jackstock or Jacks and Jennets or "Mammoth stock".

Miniature Donkey These small donkeys, which should be no more than 36 inches at the withers were originally imported from the islands of Sicily and Sardinia. There is a separate registry for them run by the ADMS. They make excellent pets. For a full explanation of these and other breeds see the BREEDS SECTION of this book.

Spanish Jack As with burro, this is a descriptive term, not a breed designation. This usually is used to refer to a large jack or jennet, which obviously has Spanish blood in its veins, but is not large enough to be designated a true "Mammoth". This term usually is used to refer to a large animal with a good deal of refinement which would be suitable for breeding saddle mules. Often they may bear a resemblance to other Spanish Breeds. Many of our American asses show obvious traces of foreign blood. One of the most obvious being a large animal with curly luxurious brown hair, even to the extent of hair dripping out of the ears, and with perhaps pendulous lips and big feet. These were traits of the famous Poitou Asses of France and show up in many of our North American donkeys, usually the hairy trait being the strongest. In any case the "Spanish Jack or Jennet" is usually a tall animal of good quality, balance and style.

Jack The proper name for the male ass, as stallion is the proper name for the male horse. JACKASS is also proper but the added "ass" is not necessary.

Jennet The proper name for the female ass, the equivalent of mare in the horse. There was a breed of horse in Spain in the Middle ages, spelled *Jineta*, which is sometimes translated as jennet, but this animal is extinct. Also the British sometimes call a **hinny** a jennet, but Jennet is only used properly to mean a female ass.

Jenny This is a more colloquial form of the word jennet. It is frequently used as it seems to come more easily to the tongue and it is perfectly all right to use it provided you know it is the informal term and that Jennet is the proper term.

Jack Colt Young male ass under 3 years of age.

Jennet Filly Young female ass under 3 years of age.

Mule A hybrid and sterile, though sexually normal animal, produced when the jack is crossed with the female horse. Mules can be male or female! **It is not true** that all mules are male and hinnies are female!

Hinny A hybrid and sterile although sexually normal animal, produced with the donkey jennet as the mother and the stallion horse as the father. Some hinnies are indistinguishable from mules, others look quite a bit more horselike in the head and ears. The voices of both the mule and hinny vary considerably from animal to animal and are quite different from the bray of the ass and the whinny of the horse. They are usually an interesting combination of the two and each animal has its own vocal style.

Bray The "hee-haw" sound made by the ass. It is made by a sort of bellows action of the chest and belly. The neck and head are extended and the ears are usually but not always laid back for the full bray. The ass also makes several sounds which correspond to the nicker of the horse, made by drawing in its breath in small amounts. Various small sounds of pleasure or greeting are made in this way. A jack when in breeding excitement almost roars rather than brays, a very loud and amazing sound. Each donkey's bray is different and owners can tell their individual animals by the sound of their voices. However they do not vary as greatly among individual animals as do mule and hinny brays.

Mare Mule Proper term for the female mule.

Molly Mule Colloquial term for the female mule, used in the same way as jenny is for donkeys.

Horse Mule Proper term for the adult male mule, a mule of this type is also properly but unnecessarily referred to as a gelding mule. Jack mule is not proper.

John Mule Colloquial term for the gelded male mule.

Mare Hinny, Horse Hinny Terms for female and male of the hinnies.

Stud Mule As both the male mule and male hinny are sterile, they should be gelded, as unaltered male mules show often dangerous and uncontrollable behavior. They should never be allowed in the show ring as a stud. The words "rank" and "stud mule" are often linked.

Stallion Mule   Ungelded mule over 3 years old, very hard to handle and often dangerous. (Stud Mule)

Mule Sterility   Mules although sexually normal are sterile for a very simple biological reason. To reproduce, the sire and dam must contribute the exact same amount of the gene carrying bodies known as chromosomes. This is because the chromosomes must pair up and divide exactly to make a new individual in the offspring. The chromosome numbers of the horse and ass are different, therefore the chromosomes are not able to pair up during the reproductive process and are unable to divide properly to create a viable offspring. Mule mares will sometimes conceive and abort. Very infrequently they have been thought to have offspring, which would be perfectly possible if they were lacking a chromosome or if some other defect of that type was present.

Mule Filly and Mule Colt   Terms for the young female and male mule up to 3 years old.

Ass Colors   The typical "donkey gray" is not gray at all. A true gray horse or ass is born dark or black and gets lighter with age. A gray ass is not unusual nor is a white one, some of these will be dappled also, and some will and will not show the dorsal stripe. However the color that is called donkey gray is the color of the ancestral North African Wild Ass, and is really a "gray-dun" or slate color. Some animals of the slate pattern may be true duns, a dilution of black. Names for this color differ in different areas, it has been called mouse, grulla/grullo, smoke, blue, blue-dun, silver and others. We prefer slate/gray-dun as this describes both the color as it appears to the eye and the genetic color (probable dun). The color is a silver gray often with buff or brown tones (sometimes described as oatmeal) and comes in all shades from very light to very dark. Many spotted asses have their spots this color and have the dorsal stripe and cross as well. This color is accompanied by those "primitive" markings in a marked degree, and often by leg, fetlock and ear stripes as well.

Asses are found in many horse colors including chestnut (sorrel) of all shades and Overo-type pinto marked. The ass does not come in the true creme (red to yellow) dilutions (palomino, buckskin, cremello and perlino) or in appaloosa patterns. Bay is less common, and those animals who appear bay lack the rich red shading of the horse. The next common colors in most of the world to gray-dun are black and brown. Of course the majority of all asses have a light colored muzzle, eye rings, belly and inside of the legs. Some asses, almost always the black or dark brown colors, are born with no white on them at all which gives them a most unusual appearance in the ass world. In some parts of the world such as the Middle East and Egypt, white is the predominant ass color, the animals having been bred for this color and large size from Biblical times. Asses differ from horses also in that they also lack chestnuts on the hind limbs and the males have vestigial teats on the sheath (see the chapter on color and genetics for more information).

The Cross   This refers to a line of darker hair, starting in the mane and travelling down the line of the back to the tip of the tail. This is usually crossed by another dark line at right angles on the withers, and this line may be short or come very far down the shoulders, be narrow or broad. The dorsal line actually may have short beginnings of stripes coming out from it in an interesting ladder effect. The ADMS often sees jennets and their foals with the same shoulder marking. This cross also will appear on some mules, especially those that inherit the dun color. The cross may be seen very faintly on all colors, although sometimes it does not seem to appear at all, at least to the naked eye. There are many Christian legends about the cross being given to the ass for its various services to Jesus. (see Appendix)

White Points   This is the term used to describe the white muzzle, eye rings, belly and inner leg surfaces in asses. These areas can vary in color from white, to roan to very dark. Most animals have them, some dark brown or black animals are born without. Some spotted donkeys show them clearly and some do not. Those without are said to have "no light points" and it is a recessive gene to the light points.

Mule Jack   This is the term used to describe a jack used to breed to mares to produce mules. Do not confuse with horse mule. Also use it only with people who understand its use or you will confuse them.

Jennet Jack   Term used to describe a jack used to breed to jennets to produce more asses.

British Terms   There has been a thriving donkey society in Great Britain for many years, and just recently a well organized British Mule Society has also arisen. Some terms vary a bit in England. For instance they have adopted the term stallion for jack and mare for jennet. Also in some cases they refer to a hinny as a Jennet. Their terms for color (colour) vary as well, using oatmeal for tan, and broken-coloured for spotted.

Other Breeds   It is common practice for a pet owner, or a breeder standing a jack at stud to refer to his animal as some breed, such as "Nubian" or "Catalonian", "Maltese" or "Andalusian". Don't argue with him, but take this with a grain of salt. What he really is trying to convey is that his animal may resemble one of these breeds of ass. Probably it does indeed have bloodlines of these breeds and in some cases can be quite an authentic "throwback". Please, use the proper terminology of "Mammoth" or Mammoth Jackstock, Standard Donkey, Large Standard Donkey, or Miniature Donkey. Try not to get involved in calling your own animal by any breed unless you have a pedigree, registration from another country or import papers listing the breed name. It is permissible to say that he has many features which make him resemble a certain breed, if you know the features correctly and can explain them. This will educate people, and give an idea of your donkey's type as well. Remember that in most cases although pure breeds were heavily imported they were blended together purposely to form the American Standard ("Mammoth"), or accidentally to form the "burro" of the west. Few if any were kept as separate breeds.

Type   A term used to refer to an ideal or standard of perfection which combines all the characteristics which contribute to the animal's value and efficiency for the purpose for which it is intended. For instance the "breed type" of the Mammoth Jack is completely different from the "breed type" of the miniature jack, but both have certain ideals they strive to live up to in type.

Breed Character   The specific variations in bodily development of such characteristics as color, height, ears, heads, bone etc., which separate breeds. In other words, the prominent breed character of the Poitou Ass is the heavy coat; of the Andalusian, the Roman nose and dappled coat.

Symmetry   A balanced development of all parts. A donkey with a heavy Roman nosed head and a light goose rump is not symmetrically balanced.

Quality   Is used to indicate freedom from coarseness. Quality involved refinement in the texture of bone without a sacrifice in size of bone, and smooth clean cut features throughout that contribute to the beauty, neatness, activity and ability of the individual to do work well and to wear well. There are many quality donkeys and no one who wishes to have one need settle for a coarse and underbred type instead.

Substance   Commonly understood to refer to the amount of bone present (heaviness of bone as opposed to thin legs and build) and the general ruggedness and wearing ability of the conformation.

Scale   Refers to size and development. If too much of the weight is due to fat and not growth, or too much of the height is due to legs and not depth of body, the animal lacks in scale.

Style   Degree of grace with which an animal shows itself, either while moving or at rest. A sluggish donkey will not possess style. Style is an expression of pride or interest an animal displays in itself and its surroundings.

Constitution   Chest capacity which is determined by the length and fullness of the foreribs and the width of the chest floor. A robust constitution is possible only when there is ample room for heart and lungs.

Finish   Degree of fatness, condition of hair coat, general presentability of the animal.

Purebred   Literally defined as one whose sire and dam are both registered and of the same breed. It can also be taken to mean one in whom there is no trace of alien blood. In this sense all donkeys are purebred donkeys. However, when referring to breed such as Miniature or Mammoth, a pedigree of several generations of the breed to which the animal belongs on both sides and not crossbred is generally considered "purebred".

Crossbred   The breeding of an animal whose dam and sire are of different breeds (such as breeding Standard to Miniature). This is not so much a fault in donkeys as it would be in crossing two horse breeds (such as a Clydesdale to a Morgan).

Pedigree   A record of ancestry, and the value of the pedigree provided it is complete in recording all ancestors of the first five or six generations depends upon the merit of the individuals recorded. When making out the pedigree as much information as possible should be recorded for all the animals listed, such as color; height; breed, etc.

Purebreeding   A system of breeding in which animals of the same breed are bred only to one another, and proper records of each breeding and ancestry are kept.

Inbreeding   The mating of animals more closely related than the average of the population from which they came (includes closebreeding and linebreeding). Close-breeding is the mating of closely related animals; such as sire to daughter, son to dam, and brother to sister. It might appear that closebreeding is predominantly harmful in its effect - often leading to the production of defective animals lacking in vitality. However the animals that result of this plan *that are superior* can be expected to be homozygous for a greater than average number of GOOD genes and thus more valuable for breeding purposes. Closebreeding had best be confined to use by the skillful master breeder who is in a sufficiently sound position to endure rigid and intelligent culling and whose herd is both large and above average in quality. Closebreeding should be done only by one familiar with pedigree and genetics, and accidental breedings should be avoided.

Linebreeding   Linebreeding is that system in which the degree of relationship is less intense than in closebreeding, and in which the matings are usually directed toward keeping the offspring related to some highly admired ancestor. The degree of relationship is not closer than half brother and half sister, or matings more distantly related; cousin matings, grandparent to grand-offspring, etc. Linebreeding may be practiced in order to conserve and perpetuate the good traits of a certain outstanding jack or jennet. Because such descendents are of similar lineage, they have the same general type genes and therefore exhibit a high degree of uniformity in type and performance. It is a more conservative and safer type of program, offering probability that small breeders can use it to their advantage. Usually a linebreeding program is best accomplished in breeding to an outstanding sire rather than outstanding dam because of the greater number of progeny of a sire. The success of linebreeding depends on having desirable genes with which to start and on an intelligent intensification of these genes.

Outcrossing   Outcrossing is the mating of animals that are members of the same breed but which show no relationship close up in the pedigree for at least the first 4 to 6 generations. This is a relatively safe system of breeding for it is unlikely that two such unrelated animals will carry the same undesirable genes and pass them on to their offspring. Defects in inbred animals may best be remedied by introducing an outcross through an animal or animals known to be especially strong in the characters which need strengthening. In general however, continued outcrossing offers less hope for improvement than inbreeding of different types.

Grading Up   That system of breeding in which a purebred sire of a given breed is mated to a native or grade female. The purpose is to impart quality and increase performance in the offspring.

Crossbreeding   Mating of two animals, both of which are purebreds, but of different breeds.

SOME TERMS OFTEN COME ACROSS IN BUYING ANIMALS

Crampy   When the head is elevated and the animal compelled to move backwards he raises his tail and shows a quivering of the flanks, soreness of the loin and an inclination to drag his feet. Don't buy.

Curb   An injury or strain of the ligament at the back of the hock which often causes an enlargement.

Cribber   Not a wood chewer, which is common in donkeys, but a wind sucker which is rare. The animal bites against something and sucks in air, a vice of boredom, but the animal can never keep weight on and is unpleasant to be around.

Fistula   Since donkeys have low withers this is rare, but it is an abscess on the withers. Any sore or odd enlargement of the withers area should be avoided.

Founder   Laminitis. Donkeys can founder, usually from overeating. Inflammation of the feet causing lameness, sole will possible be concave (dropped) instead of convex, and feet will be very tender. Hoofs may be overgrown, but donkeys can have extremely overgrown feet without being foundered.

Cutting   Also called Forging.   Feet interfering with one another. Striking the fetlock or cannon with the opposite foot as it passes. Interfering is striking with the foot on the same side, rare in donkeys, but to be avoided.

Winging   Paddling. Common in donkeys whose feet turn outward, the feet do not go straight back and forward but are seen "winging out" to the side. This trait should be examined by someone familiar with the movements and gaits.   Some gaited horses perform this movement, but a true gaited donkey is rare.   Even given that the donkey might be gaited, it should travel straight and true with the forelimbs under the body and not circling to the side.

Weedy   Bone too light for size of animal, common in underbred donkeys.

Bowed Tendon   Enlarged tendon back of the cannon, often due to working too young and too hard, when fresh is very sore and tender, will heal but if severe, animal may never be as sound again. Do not work donkeys until age three.

Capped - usually in reference to the elbow or hock. An unsightly swelling on the point of the hock or elbow, usually from injury or repeated pressures.   Not usually crippling, but may indicate a vice (such as kicking the stall). Not preferred in potential halter stock, but should not be prejudiced if the rest of the animal is of breeding quality.

Ouchy - an animal that is stiff-moving, minces, or acts slow, surly and grouchy. Altogether, usually an animal that is difficult to work with for a number or reasons.

Other Equine Terminology:

As with any sport, hobby, or aspect of science, there are unique terms that refer only to that particular field of interest.   There are terms used in working with equines that are peculiar to this specific group of mammals.   A few of the most general and commonly used terms are indexed below.   Colors of equines, which have varied and descriptive names, will not   be shown here, as they are discussed in depth in the following chapters.

ASS - a member of the equine family, containing the wild and domestic donkeys. Characterized by longer ears and a hee-hawing vocal noise called a bray

BARS - the bars of the mouth - there is a gap in the equine mouth where the bit rests. Hoof bars are the rear edge of the hoof and regulate expansion of the frog and absorb shock.

BRAY - the peculiar vocalization of the ass family

BREED - a specific type of equine with similar characteristics. If members of the same breed are mated, the result is another purebred with the same body type, colors, etc.

BURRO - colloquial term for a small donkey, also the Mexican type or wild donkey.

BY - Sired by.   Baby (Daddy x Mamma) is read as "Baby, by Daddy, out of Mamma".

CANTER - a three beat gait of the horse, in essence a slow, easy paced run.

CASTRATE - to alter, or geld (remove the testicles) of a stallion or jack. The animal is then known as a gelding and is sterile (cannot reproduce).

CHESTNUT - One of the common colors of horses. Also the horny growth on the inside of an equine's leg. Horses have large chestnuts on the forelegs, smaller ones on the rear. Donkeys, wild asses and most mules lack rear chestnuts.

COLLECTION - The equine is rounded up under itself, the hindquarters used efficiently and the action coming from behind. Collection between the aids - the rider's hand and leg - is essential in English type riding styles, especially dressage. Opposite of Extended.

COLT - the young male equine up to the age of three. Colt is a specific term, whereas foal is general. Both terms may be used together, a colt foal (very young male equine).

DAM - the mother of a foal.

DONKEY - a particular type of equine, a cousin of the horse, from a desert origin. Characterized mainly by differences in conformation and chromosome counts. Most notable are the longer ears, upright mane with no forelock, tasseled tail, braying voice.

DWARF - An animal with genetic defects causing extreme proportion problems. Usually characterized by oversized heads, very short forelegs, knobby joints, elevated (rabbit) rumps, and other undesirable characteristics.

EMASCULATOR - the tool used in castration, having both cutting and crimping surfaces. Used to crimp, and then cut the spermatic cords and blood vessels when removing the testicles in the stallion or jack.

ENTIRE - the male breeding equine, the stallion or jack. Not castrated, in possession of both testicles.

ERGOT - small horny growth on the back of the fetlock. May be a reminder of when horses had multiple toes.

EQUID - A colloquial (localized or slang) term for equine.

EQUINE - of the family of mammals Equus - namely the horse, ass and zebra.

EXTENDED - moving forward with a larger stride, not necessarily faster in pace.

FERAL - not true wild equines, but those descended from wild or domestic stock and living in a wild state. American Wild Mustangs and Burros are feral stock as they have domestic ancestry.

FETLOCK - the ankle-like area in the equine. In actuality, the fetlock corresponds to the human knuckle in hand and foot.

FILLY - the young female equine - usually under three years old.

FOAL - the young of any equine.

FROG - the spongy inner (soft) sole of the hoof, v-shaped.

GAIT - any of the forms of locomotion in the equine. These include the walk, trot, jog canter, lope, gallop, pace, rack etc.

GALLOP - the fastest natural gait of the equine, a four beat extended run.

GELDING - the castrated (neutered) male equine.

GET - the offspring of a male (stallion or jack) equine.

GIRTH - the ribcage (circumference) area of the horse, also the leather or web strap used around this area to hold the saddle on.

HAND - the unit of measure used in determining the height of a horse. One hand equals 4 inches. Ponies are under 14.2 (fourteen two - or fourteen hand and two inches) hands. Most saddle horses are in the 15 to 16 hand range, while drafts may be as large as 18.2. or 19 hands. Miniature stock may be smaller than 9 hands.

HINNY - the opposite hybrid cross than the mule. The hinny has a horse (stallion) sire and a donkey (jennet) dam.

HOCK - the back-ward facing hinge of the hind leg, corresponding to the human heel.

HOOF - the horny "fingernail" on the end of the equine leg. The equine actually walks on its fingertip.

HORSE MULE - the male mule, gelded. Colloquial terms for horse mules may include "john mule". ALL male mules should be gelded, they are sterile anyway.

HYBRID - a cross between two distinct species. The most commonly known equine hybrid is the Mule, a cross between a male donkey and female horse.

INBREEDING - the practice of crossing closely related horse (mother x son, etc) in breeding in order to strengthen or concentrate a bloodline for certain traits.

JACK - the uncastrated male donkey or ass. In England called the stallion.

JENNET, JENNY - the donkey or ass mare, the female .

JOG - the slow, two-beat gait of a Western style horse. Technically the same as a very slow trot in pattern, but with less action.

LIGATE - Tie off. In castration of donkeys, it is advisable to ligate the blood vessels, as the emasculator does not always compress them fully.

LINEBREEDING - crossing certain related lines of horse (with the same bloodlines and common names in the pedigree) in order to strengthen and concentrate certain traits. Common in the Arabian bloodlines.

LONGE LINE /LUNGE - the long strap used to exercise a horse. The horse works in a circle (created by the line attached to a headpiece on the horse) around the trainer on the ground.

LOPE - the canter (Western term). Must remain 3-beat. Slower than a normal canter.

MANE - the long hair that grows down the ridge of the horse's neck. Donkeys, zebras, and other Asses have coarse, upright manes.

MARE - the mature female horse, the breeding female

MODEL - in the show ring, the Champion of a division. Model may also refer to a figurine, a scale-model replica in a variety of mediums shaped to resemble a certain type or even a specific individual of the equine (portrait model).

MOLLY - the female mule, often termed a mare mule (mare mules are physically normal, having complete female parts, but cannot reproduce due to inherited chromosome imbalance).

MULE - the hybrid offspring of a donkey jack and a horse mare. The mule combines trait of both parents. With the exception of one-in-a-million cases (still under scientific scrutiny and verification), the mule is sterile.

OUT OF - refers to the dam. Baby (Daddy x Mamma) is read as "Baby, by Daddy out of Mamma".

PACE - a unique gait in horses, where both legs on the same side move forward at once (laterally). A two beat gait that can be either very rapid or slow and ambling. One of two harness racing gaits, pacers wear hobbles to help keep the gait steady.

PARK - a particular type of horse or riding style, characterized by high, showy action. Saddlebreds, Arabians and Morgans with the correct action are usually considered to be Park horses. Breeds with low action (such as Quarter Horses) are not suitable for Park classes.

PARKED - the way in which a Park or Gaited Show horse stands, with the forelegs under the body or slightly out in front, and the hind legs thrust away from the body. Tennessee Walking horses Park with the legs more up under the body.

POITOU - a particular breed of donkey. Once famous for the part-bred mules sired by Baudets (jacks), now nearly extinct. Poitous are in excess of 15 hands, have huge ears and large heads and leg bone. The coat is characterized by the long, shaggy curls, and is always bai-brun (dark brown).

POINTS - particular areas of the equine. When referring to color in the horse, points refer to the mane, tail and lower legs. In the Long-ear (donkey, mule) the term "Mealy points" refers to the lighter areas on the muzzle, belly, eyes, and inside of legs and flanks.

PONY - any of the breeds of smaller horse - technically any horse under the height of 14.2 hands is a pony. Most ponies have slightly different builds than the larger horses.

PRZEWALSKI HORSE - the Mongolian Wild Horse, a very primitive type of horse. The last actual wild Horse in existence.

PRODUCE - the offspring of a female equine, her young. When a mare is shown with her young, the class is Produce of Dam.

QUAGGA - a now-extinct species of Plains zebra. The Quagga had coloration different from other zebras, partially striped over a reddish body. They were killed by man and died off in the 1880's. A project in South Africa is attempting to use selective rebreeding to recreate the Quagga.

ROACHED - a mane that has been shaved close on the neck. Worn on some working breeds, saddle horses, and mules. Also a term for a hunched back, a fault.

ROMAN NOSE - the convex (overhanging) nose. The facial bone is curved.

RUMP - the rear of the equine, the term is usually applied to the haunch or hip area.

SIRE - equine term for father. A donkey jack is the sire of a mule. When stallions or jacks are shown with their offspring, the young are referred to as get, the class as Get of Sire.

STALLION - the mature male horse or zebra, the breeding animal.

STOCK BREED - Types of horses developed for ranch work, although now used for much more. Most are typified by heavier, more muscular build, with straight necks and faces.

STUD - the stallion used for breeding. In England, the Stud is the farm where equines are bred. The term At Stud refers to advertising a stallion or jack for breeding.

TOLT - The unique "flying" 4-beat gait of the Icelandic Horse. Each foot hits the ground separately. When performed at speed, the tolt can be as fast as a racing trot or canter. (There is no equivelant gait in donkeys and no known Icelandic mules.)

TROT - the intermediate gait of most equine breeds, a two-beat gait which can be smooth or very bouncy. The legs move in diagonal pairs (right front and left rear). Trots can be slower than a walk (the Western Jog) or racing speeds, (as performed by a trotting Standardbred.)

WITHERS - the bony portion sticking up at the end of the horse's neck. The mane hairs end at the withers where the back is joined. Donkeys, asses, and zebras do not have much, if any, withers.

X - used in denoting a cross, whether or two breeds, or of 2 specific individuals. Some donkeys may be Miniature x Small Standard (both parents are not pure Miniatures)

ZEBRA - a particular branch of the equine family, originating in Africa. Zebras are closer relations of the ass than the horse. They have stripes in varied degrees and patterns over the body.

ZEBRASS - the registry term for the zebra/ass or zebra/donkey hybrid.

ZEBROID - a zebra hybrid, a slang for the zebra/horse cross. Zebrass, zedonk, zony, and zebrorse are also local terms used, respectively, for zebra x ass, zebra x donkey, zebra x pony crosses and zebra x horse crosses.

ZORSE - The registry term for the zebra/horse hybrid.

MAMMOTH JACKSTOCK

The Mammoth (or American Standard Jackstock) resulted from the careful breeding and selection of asses in the states of Kentucky, Tennessee, Virginia, and Missouri. Interest in the jacks grew out of the demand for mules, especially after Southern farmers found that mules fit well into the Agriculture of the South. The demand for mules created a demand for the type of jack that could be mated with the usual farm mare to produce a type of mule most useful in this work. After 1940 the mule suffered as did the draft horse in a decline of interest - only to begin coming back in the late 1960's at which time the demand for this jackstock began to revive. At this time however very few purebred mammoth jacks and jennets were left and the breed has had to rebuild itself over the last few years.

ORIGIN:

All jackstock introduced into the U.S. came from the Southern European area, mostly from the Mediterranean area. All of this stock was descended from the wild asses of North Africa. The various breeds were blended into one breed in this country. The Mammoth jack is a distinct breed as compared to its components, and is decidedly superior in usefulness for mule breeding. Most of the breeds that were used to produce this strain are either extinct or close to it - or their breeding has been totally neglected over the years. The Catalonian stock from Spain was considered to be the best and was used the most. The Andalusian was very acceptable in many ways but American breeders did not favor the gray or gray-dun colors, because of the subsequent production of gray-dun mules or roan mules.

FOUNDATION BREEDS:

Catalonian, From Catalonia, Spain 14-15.2 hands, black, brown, white points, good heads, style.

Andalusian, Andalusia, Spain 13-2 to 15 hands, gray, large, good heads.

Majorcan, Island of Majorca 14.2-15.2 hands, black, large, sluggish.

Maltese, Island of Malta, 13-14.2 hands, black, brown, very refined, small.

Poitou, Poitou, France 15-16 hands, black or brown, very drafty, long hair, large coarse heads.

Italian, Italy, 13-14 hands, black, small, inferior bone.

IMPROVEMENT IN THE U.S.

Prior to the Revolutionary War, some ordinary Malta Jacks had been introduced into the New England states, but did not prove very successful. George Washington was interested in the possibilities of the mule as a draft animal, and in 1787 the King of Spain sent him a gray jack, "*Royal Gift*" and two jennets. General Lafayette sent Washington a black Jack, "*Knight of Malta*" and several jennets. Washington crossed his two strains to become the very first American Breeder of Jackstock. The next noted importation of American Jack stock was by Henry Clay of Kentucky who began his importations in 1827 by bringing in some Maltese stock which included "*Warrior*", the second most important foundation sire. The best foundation sire brought to the U.S. in the early days was imported "*MAMMOTH*" whose name has been given as a secondary name to the breed of jacks he helped to found. He was landed from Catalonia, Spain in 1819 and was used with great success by J. R. Brockett of Mt. Sterling, KY. He and his produce crossed espcially well with descendents of the Clay stock.

Imported "*MAMMOTH*" was a very large jack, standing over 16 hands high, and many of his offspring were as large or larger. He introduced much of the size demanded by American Jack Breeders, and although he was somewhat coarse, the blood of his descendents blended well with the more refined stock, and before long a distinctive type of American jackstock was produced. Nearly all jackstock traces to this great imported sire and there has been considerable line breeding directed to him. Between 1830 and 1890 several thousand jacks and jennets of the various European breeds were brought into the U.S. The Civil war stopped most stock breeding and it was not until 1885 that large importations were again made. In 1937 Berry and Arrington of Stillwater, Okla. imported the Poitou jack "*KAKI*". He was a 16.2 hand (66") jack of superior conformation, and one of the few jacks of this strain that lived to reproduce in the U.S. Many jackstock breeders felt the Poitou did not give as much to the breed as it might have. The animals were hard to obtain, and although possessed of huge bone, the offspring of the third generations were often coarse.

Jack men speak of JENNET JACKS and MULE JACKS. Jennet jacks are considered the most valuable and are used to reproduce their own kind (to produce more jackstock/donkeys). They should be superior in size and build. Mule jacks are used to breed to mares to produce mules. The modern Mammoth Jack should be a large, well balanced animal with conformation approaching that of the heavy saddle or the draft horse. The best types usually range from 15 to 16 hands and weigh from 1075 to 1200 pounds. Females are slightly smaller. Great extremes in height and weight are sometimes found, but often the larger specimens lack the balance, symmetry and quality of those less extreme in size. Mammoth stock is registered by measurements and those from unregistered parents can be registered if the measurements are correct. The height for jennets is 13.2 hands (54") high, and for jacks 14 hands (56"). (Or 56 &58" respectively with the American Mammoth Jackstock Registry) There are also bone and girth measurements that should be met. The heartgirth should be at least 60 in. The circumference of the fore cannon should be at least 7 1/2 in. for jacks. Jennets must be 58 in. in girth and 7 in. in cannon bone. Jacks are not usually as smoothly turned as horses. However, they should be well balanced and as high in quality as possible without unduly sacrificing size and ruggedness.

The topline should be straight and strong. They should be short-coupled and smooth over the hips, carrying a long, well muscled croup. The shoulders should be well sloped, chest wide and deep and the ribs deep and well-sprung to give depth and capacity to the middle. Heavy muscling should be evidenced not only over the top line and croup but also through the chest, forearm and gaskin. The set and quality of the legs is important and should be as nearly correct as possible. The bone and joints should be large but clean and flat. The feet should be deep, round and large and show considerable evidence of good wearing qualities. Most breeders have favored a black color with white points in the past but other colors are highly favored for modern mules including the many shades of red. More recently, spotted jacks are being seen, but the gray-dun (slate) color is still frowned on. No matter the color, the coat should be fine and glossy.

Jack breeders have always been very particular about heads. The head should be well shaped, carried alertly and well balanced. The ears should be long, well set and carried erect. The eye should be large and open and the face straight with only a slight "roman" nose. The animal should have alertness and style in its manner and gaits. Breeders constantly practice selection to avoid such faults as, sluggishness, flat ribs, long, easy toplines, steep croups, weak, dipped loins, lack of muscling and general roughness through shoulders and hips. They carefully watch legs and feet. Measurements of a typical good jack are: 15.3 hands high; 1300 lbs.; ears from tip to tip horizontally 34 inches; around face and jaw 39 inches; around throatlatch 36 in.; around arm 21 in.; around cannon 8 1/2 in.; around girth 70 in.; length from poll to tail 84 in.; around body at loin 67 in.; around hoof at hairline 16 1/2 in.; around back cannon in rear 8 ½", above hock 17 1/2 inches.

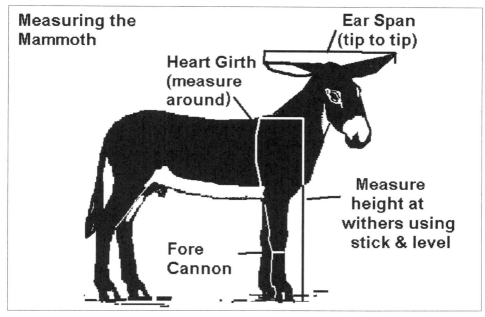

Measuring the height, heart girth, ear span, and bone on Jackstock.

THE MINIATURE DONKEY
By Arnold and Carol Sorensen & Betsy Hutchins

ORIGIN

The miniature donkey is native to the Mediterranean islands of Sicily and Sardinia. They are identified as either Sicilian or Sardinian donkeys depending on their ancestry, although the two types do not differ in any respect. There are very few left in their native habitat due to importation demands in the past. At least one animal in the original importation was from Abyssinia (Ethiopia). There are about 50,000 of these donkeys in the United States today, but there is no accurate count of them because many are not registered. Some of the animals used in creating the Miniature as a breed type were undoubtedly undersized small Standard donkeys as well. The Miniature donkeys have become very popular over the years. A registry was established in 1958 by the original importers, Daniel and Bea Langfeld of Danby Farms. The Miniature Donkey Registry is still run by the American Donkey and Mule Society.

CHARACTERISTICS:

The miniature donkey is by nature one of the friendliest and most affectionate animals of its type. They are very tame and gentle. They love their owners and seek attention. They do this with friendly nudges and brays and funny little sounds designed to get you to pay attention to them. The Miniature donkey is extremely intelligent, docile and is easily trained. Geldings or jennets make the best pets - jacks enjoy braying and may become excited in the presence of jennets.

The size of these donkeys averages from 26" to 36" in height at the shoulders with the average size around 34". (As of 1998 the smallest known mature jennet was recorded at 25", the smallest mature breeding jack at 26 ½", but these are extremely rare animals. 29" is considered to be the smallest viable size for a breeding jack or jennet). Breeders have worked very hard to keep the height down, and the smaller the donkey the more valuable it is accounted to be.

Conformation of these animals is supposed to be a sort of Miniature draft donkey. The leg bones should be large in relation to the size, the ribs well sprung, the chest wide, and the heart girth deep. Many of the donkeys have backbones that stick up (roached) rather than lie slightly curved or straight, and this is a fault, as are heads too big for the body, flat ribs, extremely short legs, and crooked legs. The average donkey will weigh from 200 to 400 lbs. The hair ranges from flat to long and shaggy, and in texture from smooth to wiry. Some foals will have a soft furry coat and others will have a curly wiry coat. These donkeys can come in fancy colors. The most prevalent color is gray-dun/slate (a mouse or grulla color) with line back and cross. Other Miniature colors are brown, and black/brown. True black with no visible cross and stripe is quite rare.

More recently the trend has been to breed for sorrel (or chestnut), but the sorrel colors in the donkey are paler, or more brown, lacking the bright red tones in the horse. Ivory (blue-eyed white) does occur in purebred Miniatures but is extremely rare. Spotted miniatures can be of any base color, though most are brown or slate. The red-and-white spotted animal is a breeding goal, but has not been recorded yet. The debate still flourishes whether the spotted Miniature is purebred (from original lines) or if the spotting gene was bred down from Standard donkeys.

The distinguishing mark on these donkeys is the dark stripe down the back and across the shoulders. This marking forms a cross on the back of the donkey. Larger donkeys have this marking also, which is inherited from the wild ass ancestors of the domestic donkey. The nose of these donkeys along with the belly is usually white, although dark noses are not uncommon. A donkey with dark nose and belly is rare, due to a recessive gene, but it can occur on all of the colors including sorrel and spotted. It is most striking on the dark colored, black or dark-brown, animal. One particular bloodline also has large white stars on dark-coated animals with No Light Points. Life expectancy for Miniature donkeys is around 25 to 30 years with good care. They are truly a lifetime companion.

The males and females usually display the same friendly characteristics but an ungelded jack may become aggressive in the presence of females. Also two older jacks will fight and must be kept apart. The females have no problem getting along in any size herd.

USES

The Miniature donkey has many uses, one of the most popular is that of a pet. They make excellent pets for both children and adults and can be trained to come into the house without causing a fuss or mess. They can be easily trained to pull a cart or wagon, singly, in pairs or as a team. One man has a team of 20 of them that pull a miniature Borax wagon. He drives a team of 8 in parades and in shows and they compete with miniature mules and win! They can pack a moderate load for the backpacker's companion, and can be trained easily for smaller children to ride.

As a pack animal, the average Miniature can carry 100 pounds of well balanced cargo, if it is well fed and properly conditioned to firm up its muscles first. Other uses include petting zoos, exotic game farm display, breeding for sale, display in zoos and showing.

The Miniature donkey has been used on small pony and miniature horse mares to produce tiny miniature mules, but the market for mini-mules should be evaluated before starting on this endeavor. Mules of this size require different handling than either of their equally small parents.

"OVERSIZED" or Class B Miniature Donkeys

Some of the original donkeys imported from Sicily and Sardinia were up to 38" in size. However, when the stud book was handed down, the acceptable size limit was mistakenly recorded as 36". That height has been approved by breeders, and the original studbook of the Miniature Donkey Registry (MDR) accepts animals as Miniatures if they are 36" and under. Provisions have been made for animals that do go over the 36" mark. If the animal has both parents registered with the MDR as Miniatures, the 36.01-38" donkey can be listed in the MDR as oversized. It cannot be shown in approved Miniature Donkey classes as it is over the allowed height. As there are very many good miniature jacks under the approved 36" height, it is not recommended that oversized jacks be used for breeding purebred miniatures. The private IMDR registry in Maryland has decided to create a "Class B" listing for oversized animals, but these animals are not accepted as purebred miniatures for show or breeding purposes with ADMS and the National Miniature Donkey Association. Since the trend is toward smaller, there is little sense in using larger animals in a breeding program. In addition, since the registry is by size, the 34" offspring of a 32" jack and a 40" jennet would be eligible to be registered as a miniature donkey. This is well and good for the addition of new blood, but that 40" height could show up in offspring four generations later. If you are breeding for small size and especially for bloodlines, check the heights of animals in the pedigree of stock before you breed!

THE STANDARD DONKEY

This is the animal that ranges in size from 36.01 to 54" and comes in a rainbow of colors, a variety of conformation and is often called "burro" by the public. As we have noted before, burro is simply the Spanish term that means donkey, or ass. We generally use "Miniature Mediterranean" Donkey to describe that particular breed, "Mammoth Jackstock" or "American Standard Jackstock" to describe the very large breed of mule breeding asses, and Standard Donkey to describe the animals that fall in between. The only time the ADMS uses the term "burro" is to describe animals wild caught off the open range. We have adopted this term because it is the official one that the United States Government uses for these animals. We would normally then, refer to them as "Wild burros" or "Feral asses". The term Standard Donkey was adopted because this is literally the standard size for asses all over the world. Anything larger or small is unusual and specialized.

The term Standard, when describing Mammoth Stock (American Standard Jack) is used differently. It was put there to indicate that the animals were "Bred up to a certain standard" in height, weight, and bone. We know the terms are somewhat confusing, but once you have learned them you are not likely to confuse them. After all the term donkey is never properly used for mammoth jackstock. Like all of their brethren however, the term ass is perfectly proper although not usually used for them. Registration rules for donkeys including Standards are shown in Chapter 2. The Standard donkey in the United States is a mixture of many imported breeds. Most of these were from Spain, but there are many others also. In the following pages we will attempt to describe some of the breeds of ass that originated in the world, many of which may be in the bloodlines of your Standard donkey.

LARGE STANDARD

As with Standard, this is not really a breed, but a convenient size description. The Large Standard is from 48 - 54/56" tall (dependant on sex). They may be of any color or body type, from the lighter saddle-type to the heavier Mammoth. Some may indeed be of Jackstock descent that are too small, others may be Mammoth x Standard crosses.

THE CATALONIAN ASS

These animals come from the Province of Catalonia in Spain and are famous- for large size, 14-16 hands, black, glossy coats, great style and action, and a good deal of refinement about the bone and head. It is said to be primarily to this type of ass that the mammoth jacks of the United States owe style, action, finish and smooth flat bone when they have it. The Catalonian is all but extinct in Spain with only a tiny population still known. A few Mexican-Catalonian jacks are known, with a very few known in the US, but pedigree is essential if purchasing an animal listed as a Catalonian.

THE ANDALUSIAN ASS

This animal came from the Northern part of Spain from the area known as Andalusia. It had been bred in that country since at least 700 B.C. The breed was usually a white-gray or dapple gray-roan. These animals were large and rangy with large, firm bones and good quality bone in the legs. Many modern Mammoths of Sorrel, red roan or gray-roan color bear a strong resemblance to the ancestral type. The head is impressive, with roman noses, very large ears, all on a muscular neck. They have powerful forequarters, good withers and long bodies. They are of quiet disposition and have graceful and free movement. Size 14-151/2 hands on average.

THE MALTESE ASS

The smallest asses used in breeding the American Mammoth Stock, the Maltese came from the Island of Malta, but is now extinct there. Seldom taller than 141/2 hands they were black or dark brown, slender with good bone with very large, hard hooves. They had fiery dispositions and the jacks were sometimes very hard to handle. The Maltese would do well in a show ring today as Large Standard donkeys because they had style, well balanced conformation and refinement.

THE MAJORCA ASS

This was the largest of the European breeds of asses, competition being given only by the Poitou. They came from an island environment and because of limited terrain and great exportation are probably extinct. The size of the jacks was from 14-16 hands with correspondingly large bodies and bone. The color was usually black but the coat is more harsh than silky or glossy. The head was very large with very long ears. The Majorca was a drafty animal with no real style in appearance or action but was very powerful with a rather sluggish disposition. He was the true equivalent of the Draft horse in donkeys.

THE POITOU ASS [pwa-too]

This is probably the most unusual ass ever bred, and also probably the most famous. In appearance the animals were unusual because they were encouraged to grow extremely long silky coat, they had a long mane which fell to the side and a well haired tail. The breeders in Poitou France where it originated never allowed the animal to shed its coat and rarely if ever groomed the coat, so it collected upon the animal like an old mattress throughout its life. The ears were full of hair, the head was coarse and Roman nosed with a drooping lower lip. The ears while very hairy were very large. Sometimes they were so huge they flopped because of their weight and the hair inside. These animals had huge feet, very heavy large bone and good muscling and were famous for siring excellent mules from a special breed of horse kept only for that purpose. This was the only breed of asses that we know of that was bred solely to raise mules and was not worked in the fields or otherwise. The height was from 13 ½ hands to 15 hands the breed is actually recorded in centimeters) but some came much larger. The color is always black or dark brown (bai-brun), other colors being rigidly culled. The Poitou should never bear a cross and stripe. The neck is strong, thick, broad and short, the shoulders are upright, the chest very wide, the body long and the belly huge. Knees and joints are extremely large, and the feet are very large and the legs are short. There are less than 200 purebred animals in existence worldwide, with efforts being made to attempt to revive the breed. Estimates in 1998 were a breed population (pure and part-bred) of between 300-500 worldwide. Some 30-40 purebred animals are in the

United States today, with the number of good part-bred animals numbering about 40-50.

MALLORCA ASS
Native to the Balearic Islands in the Mediterranean this animal is apparently somewhat related to the Catalonian Ass and was valued for mule breeding as far back as the 10th century. The jacks vary in height from 138 to 160 centimeters, have a large head, broad hoof and are smaller and finer boned than the Catalonian asses. They are usually black and have very kind dispositions as do the mules they sire.

ZAMARANO-LEONES ASSES
These asses come from Western Spain in Zamora. There are very few left but they are a large and historically valued mule breeding ass. They are black or brown usually, quite tall and heavy and weigh about 700-800 lbs. They do not have much style but are heavy boned and strong bodied and produce strong and valuable mules.

WHITE EGYPTIAN ASS
This is the most famous breed of riding donkeys in the world. It has been known as a white or gray breed since Biblical times and is used typically for riding although in these poor countries it is used for packing or anything else the owner needs. It was originally called the White Damascus Ass and was the mount of kings. The height is from 12 to 14 hands. Three local varieties in Egypt are: Saidi of upper Egypt, Hassawi, the common saddle animal, and Baladi of lower Egypt. In previous times these animals were bred as carefully and valued as highly as the Arabian Horses. Although the breed has been allowed to deteriorate, any visitor to Egypt can see many examples of it - some very excellent in the cities and countryside.

AFRICAN BREEDS
Since the donkey arose in North Africa from wild asses, there are dozens of local breeds. The following lists some of them:

Israel Local Breed: 10-14 hands, gray, black, brown, no careful breeding.

Muscat Donkey: South of Persian gulf, white or dun, saddle animals, graceful, well built.

Sudan Donkey: Small, poorly built, dun.

Sudanese Riding Donkey: Bred along the Nile north of Kartoum, 10-11 hand, gray, white or dark brown. Often has no cross. They have spread and developed into other reeds such as ATABAI, Nubian desert, reddish, middle sized; KASSALA, larger, reddish in color with cross; MASSAWA, almost white, saddle asses.

Sennar Asses of Ethiopia: Pale gray, excellent riding animals, good mule producers.

Native Ethiopian Ass: Small, dun to black, heavy head, roman nose, pack animals.

Somaliland Domestic Ass: 10 hands, coarse common, ordinary work.

East African Donkeys: Small 10 hands, poor conformation, hardy, gray, brown or reddish in color.

Maasai Donkey: Small, dun and well known belongs to Maasai tribe, used for pack etc.

Nigerian Ass: Small, dun, ordinary.

South African: Small, black, dun, brown, light gray, common.

Morocco: Light gray with pronounced dark stripes and striping on legs, 9-12 hands.

OTHER BREEDS
Cyprus Ass: Valuable, large, long legged, strong and well developed, dark color 11-12 hands.

Arabian White Ass: Large, refined, saddle type.

Turkish Ass: Small, sturdy, black or dun.

Afghanistan: Small body, large wide head, long ears, 8-11 hands, cross, dark gray. Second type is bigger, smaller head, finer hair, white or gray bushy mane and tail, no cross, 11-14 hands, saddle type.

Purgosh Ass; rare, excessive amount of long hair, 12 hands and reddish brown. Some are used for sturdy saddle animals.

Pakistan: Small, dun, common.

Indian: Small, dun, common, some so small to be of miniature status, MAHRATTA ass very small.

China: There are many mules and donkeys in North China. Indigenous asses are dark brown and reddish/chestnut. 13 hands. An improved breed is the SHANTUNG ASS, good mule breeder, almost black with light-points, 13 hands and has been esteemed for centuries for the Shantung mules.

Central Asia: Small, hardy, coarse and mostly dark colors.

Italy and Greece: Mostly local, small, unimproved races, but there are 3 improved breeds. MARTINA FRANCA ass, 13.2 to 14.2 hands, black or dark bay with light points. well formed bone structure, short straight back, short croup and strong joints, heavy head with large long ears. RAGUSAN ASS: most are in Sicily. 14 hands, dark bay with light points, strong and compact small head, well set on ears, good barrel and straight back, well proportioned legs with small, neat and supple joints, small feet with strong, high hoofs for mountain travel - mostly mountain pack asses. ROMAGNOLO, large and used for mule breeding.

South America and Mexico: Many local races, but all medium sized, not usually carefully bred, dun, brown or black. AUSETANO ass is from Catalonian blood and is used for mule breeding in Argentina. BRAZILIAN ASS: 12 hands, good conformation, many colors. PEGA ASS: white or light gray, some cream, registry was kept. Graceful, body fine and muscular, limbs long, strong bones, sloping pasterns, a gaited Ass. NORTHEASTERN: rare, used to breed mules.

EUROPE

Spain and France have been mentioned. Most European donkeys which have not been mentioned are of no particular breed, medium sized and usually dun. They are seen at their best in England where a stud book registry is kept. The English donkey often originated in Ireland where it was used for work and was a medium sized donkey, similar to the U.S. Standard donkey. A typical English donkey is small 10-12 hands, with strong legs, rounded body and neat, fine head. Most are dun but blacks and spotted animals are popular also, there are also some chestnut/sorrels. Most English donkeys are small, cobby, compact and stocky. The Miniature Mediterranean Donkey (most imported from American but some from Canada) is being introduced, and some Miniature Jacks are being crossed with the small standard and standard donkeys in England.

AUSTRALIAN DONKEYS

These are almost exactly similar to standard and large standard donkeys in the United States. Differences from imported English donkeys are quite startling. These asses are usually 11 to 14 hands, is strong and has good bone. Many have been running wild for generations and are quite similar in conformation to the "wild Burros" of the United States. A movement is being made by some breeders to import good Mammoth stock and upgrade the donkey in Australia.

THE WILD ASSES

From the National Geographic hook BOOK OF THE HORSE

The African ass is found in the wild state in Abyssinia (Ethiopia) , Nubia and other parts of northeast Africa between the Nile and the Red Sea and is regarded by zoologists as the progenitor of domestic asses. (Ed. Note: Although you can still see some of these breeds they are nearly extinct and are being protected and bred in zoos)

Its color and markings approach closely to those of the domestic ass. It possessed the distinctive shoulder stripe, running from the withers down to the fore leg, usually observed in the donkey. The ears of the African wild ass are somewhat larger than those of the Asiatic ass types. The bray of the African is identical with that of the domestic ass. The skeleton of the African ass shows only five lumbar vertebrae as compared with six in the horse. The chestnuts (soft horny growths) found on the inside of the hind legs of the horse are absent in those of the ass. The ass of Somaliland differs somewhat from the usual type of the African ass in being of a more greyish color and with the absence of the stripe across the shoulders, and in the presence of black stripes and markings on both front and hind legs. It also has smaller ears and a tendency to grow a longer mane. The presence of leg stripes has suggested to investigators a near relationship to the zebra. The African wild asses of the present day are divded into races according to their markings. The Nubian ass, which inhabits the country on both sides of the Atbara River, in the eastern Sudan, to the south of Nubia proper has a distinct shoulder stripe, with no dark markings on the legs, with the exception of a patch on the fetlocks. The Somali ass on the contrary has quite lost the dorsal and shoulder stripes but has the legs fully barred. In general character the wild asses resemble the domesticated breeds, differing mainly in having more slender legs and greater speed. The asses, both wild and domestic, male and female have a raucus bray. Unlike the Kiang they often have an aversion to entering water. They subsist on dry grasses found in the desert areas of northeastern Africa. Both breeds attain a height of about 12 hands. Their conformation clearly establishes their right to be considered as of the original stock from which have come the domestic asses."

SOMALI WILD ASSES - EQUUS ASINUS SOMALICUS
Dr. Ernst M. Lang

"... Our Somali Wild asses have a noble bearing, they are gray with a suggestion of pink when the sunlight falls on them. The ventral surface and legs are white, all four limbs bearing bold horizontal black stripes. A broad black stripe tapering towards the root of the tail extends along the middle of the back. Characteristics of this wild ass are the dark upright mane and almost black tip of the tail. Ergots lie on the inside of the forelegs and a striking feature is the large, dark eyes. The upper third of the long ears are dark on the back and the region around the mouth is white as is the belly. A hint of a vertical shoulder stripe in the form of 3 cm. long slender line can be seen on the shoulder of one of the mares but is completely missing in the other animals in the group."

Photo by Joan Byrne.

When burros were rounded up in large numbers. At the BLM holding facility.

HOW TO ADOPT A WILD BURRO
By Jet O. Lewis, Cushing, Texas

After reading and hearing about the plight of America's wild burros my wife and I decided that we would adopt some through the Bureau of Land Management. (You can call the National Program office at 702-861-6583 and request the necessary forms.) In a few days we received the forms and some literature which explained the program. Some of the highlights of the program are: 1.) There is a small fee for a health certificate, brand inspection fees, and transportation from point of capture to the distribution center. 2.) The federal government remains the legal custodian for one year. At that time, after an inspection and a request, the government will transfer legal title to the adoptee. If the jenny is carrying a foal, the foal of the property of the adoptee, as well as any subsequent foals. All animals are branded by the government. 3.) The BLM will check to make sure the animals are being well treated. If they are not being well cared for, they will be reclaimed and returned to the distribution center. 4. Distribution centers in Arizona, California, Colorado, Idaho, Montana, Nevada, New Mexico, Tennessee, Oregon, Texas, Utah and Wyoming. Other states may have been added. A phone call to 702-861-6583 will connect you to the Adopt-a-Burro (horse) office and they will be happy to give you the latest information on where you can pick up an animal. 5.) Only residents of the United States and its territories are eligible. 6.) You can adopt more than one animal - the number depends on your facilities and your financial ability to feed and maintain them (Usually you are allowed up to four).

After you submit your application it is screened as to your facilities and ability to care for the animals. (You may have to have your facilities inspected by the BLM before being accepted in some states.) You will be notified by letter if your application has been accepted or rejected. If accepted, your name will be placed on a register and you will be advised when animals will be available for pick-up and where. The length of the wait depends upon the number of roundups, the quantity of animals captured and the number of names on the register. What sex you decide on will also make a difference, as recently more jacks are being rounded up than jennets. At the last several adoption, only jacks, no jennets or foals, were offered. When you are notified by letter that an animal will be available, and you are given the name and location of the distribution center, you will be given a phone number to call and get an appointment for actual pick up. On the pick-up date, distribution is made on a first-come, first-serve basis. If you are third in line you will be the third one to select your animal(s) from those remaining. The secret seems to be to get there early and get a low number for selection - that's what we did. Be sure to call ahead and find out what the system is, as some adoption centers have gone to a different system of choosing order.

After you make your selection the distribution center personnel will help you load your prizes and get headed for home. I want to say that the people at the Valley Mills distribution center were the most friendly and courteous I have ever met anywhere. They were helpful and patient, sometimes under trying circumstances.

When you get back home the fun of gentling your animal(s) begins. We put ours in a sturdy corral with plenty of fresh water and a small amount of good hay. We carried high quality horse feed to our three and fed them small amounts at a time - we used the horse feed as a way to get acquainted with each of them. After two weeks we could use the curry comb on two of ours and the third was almost ready for currying. After two weeks we turned them into a one acre trap between the house and corral. At each feeding we closed the burros in the corral and proceeded with our gentling program. Within four weeks we could curry all three and two would eat out of our hands. At this state they seemed almost domesticated so we turned them into a pasture with access to a corral. Now we have a daily training program and we've had our three for four months and they follow us around when we are in the pasture. They are taking their training very well and getting slicked out into prime condition. We selected a jack and jenny with a colt, and the colt is the real darling of the trio. My wife and I have truly found that "Happiness is Adopting a Wild Burro".

THE FOLLOWING IS FROM THE THIRD REPORT TO CONGRESS,
June, 1980
ON WILD HORSES AND BURROS

(Wording in italic the editor's as known amendments or updates)

HISTORY OF THE WILD HORSE AND BURRO PROGRAM
ORIGIN:

During the last Ice Age, over 10,000 years ago, horses became extinct on the North American Continent. They did not reappear until horses and burros were brought to America's western plains by Spanish explorers in the 16th Century. Through the years, escaped or abandoned animals formed the first wild horse and burro herds.

Indians obtained horses from Spanish camps for hunting, fighting on horseback, and for transportation. As settlers headed West, they lost some horses which joined the wild herds. Sometimes, the cavalry released horses after Army posts were closed. Still later, ranchers released horses when they could not afford to keep them.

The sure-footed burros were used by early prospectors and sheepherders as pack animals because they could travel long distances and survive on desert vegetation. Some of them were later abandoned in favor of new forms of transportation. Others escaped to the open range.

Though today's horse and burro herds are wild, they all came from animals that were once tame.

ABUSE:

The herds continued to multiply and the number of people in the West increased too. The horses were often a nuisance to ranchers raising cattle and sheep, and because of this, some were destroyed. Also, commercial horse-hunters began rounding the animals up with trucks and airplanes as a source of pet food. Sometimes, herds were driven to exhaustion and destruction, then sold to canneries.

PROTECTION:

At first, man's abuse of wild horses and burros concerned only a few people. One person was the late Mrs. Velma Johnston of Reno, Nevada, who earned the title of "Wild Horse Annie" for her diligent campaign for legislation to protect the animals from abuses during roundups. Her campaign for legislation began in 1950 and resulted in the passage of Public Law 86-234, known as the "Wild Horse Annie Act" in 1959. This legislation prohibited the use of aircraft or motor vehicles and the pollution of watering holes for capturing or killing wild horses and burros. (Because of the danger to both the rider and his mount, this Act was amended by the Federal Land Policy and Management Act of 1976 to permit the humane use of helicopters in government roundups.) Continued efforts during the 1960's by concerned groups and national letter writing campaigns by schoolchildren ended in full-scale protection of wild horses and burros on public lands with passage of the Wild Free-Roaming Horse and Burro Act of December 15, 1971.

ADOPT-A-HORSE PROGRAM

The practice of removing wild horses and burros from the public lands and placing them in the custody of individuals began in Montana in 1973 when 23 excess horses were removed from the Pryor Mountain Wild Horse Range (established in 1968) and adopted. The next year, BLM began an adoption program in Oregon, followed by Nevada in 1975. Favorable public response in these states led BLM to launch the adoption program nationwide in the spring of 1976.

ROUNDUPS

Since the wild horse and burro management began in the early 1970's, the Agencies had captured almost 22,000 excess animals *(as of 1980)* . About 3% of the animals died or were destroyed shortly after capture, due to injuries, illness, or old age. A limited number of animals were released at the capture site or relocated to other wild horse and burro areas. Remaining captured animals have been placed or are awaiting adoption through the Adopt-A-Horse program.

Roundups have been increased in the last few years to remove excess animals and restore balanced use of public rangelands. Most of the Agencies' roundup activities have been concentrated in four States, because the pressures on the public lands are greatest there. Slightly more than 58 % of the wild horse population is in Nevada and another 19% is in Wyoming. The same problem exists with burros in California and Arizona, where they account for 51 % and 40%, respectively, of the total population.

A small number of animals have been rounded up because of their attraction to gardens and lawns or their amorous attentions to mares on nearby private lands. Because of the intermingled pattern of private and public lands and rapidly growing communities in the West, such conflicts are expected to increase.

A factor which may have significant effects on BLM's roundup program relates to recent litigation. As a result of a court ruling in Oregon, ROARING SPRINGS ASSOCIATES V. ANDRUS, BLM was required to remove wild horses from public rangelands which were unfenced and interspersed with private holdings. The plaintiffs were successful in invoking a provision of the Act which requires strayed wild horses and burros to be removed from private property upon the request of the landowner. Since most of the public rangelands in the West are intermingled with private lands, BLM cannot prevent herds from moving onto the private land. The only solution presently available is to eliminate entire herds in such areas.

Similar litigation against the BLM is pending in both Nevada and Wyoming. (1981).

ADOPT-A-HORSE PROGRAM

More than 20,000 wild horses and burros (mostly horses) have been adopted throughout the United States by some 7,000 (*as of 1980*) individuals, organizations, and groups. Some of the animals are trained for riding, showing, or working on farms and ranches, while others are used as family pets.

Once captured, the wild horses and burros are transported to nearby holding facilities owned or rented by the Agencies. There, the animals are examined by a veterinarian and given any necessary medical treatment. Blood samples are drawn and examined for diseases. Old, sick, or lame animals that are unable to fend for themselves are humanely destroyed under a veterinarian's or Agency personnel's supervision. Animals destroyed usually number less than 3 % of the total captured.

After the captured animals are examined, they are painlessly freeze-marked for identification as wild horses and burros. This system of identification was initiated by BLM in April 1978. Each animal is individually identified by a series of coded dashes and angles applied by a freeze mark and the left side of its neck. The symbol includes the animal's birth year and individual identification number.

Easy and permanent identification will help eliminate past abuses by hindering attempts to sell, trade, or make commercial use of freeze-marked wild horses and burros. Information about the identification system has been distributed nationwide to brand inspectors, slaughterhouses, and rendering plants. Humane organizations and associations monitoring the program have been alerted about the system.

Cost of adoption has been set at $75.00 for a burro and $200.00 for a horse. *(Please note that the prices have changed several times since 1980, both higher and lower than the amount stated in the report. At one time it was as low as $125 per horse. In '99 they accept bids on animals. See the BLM website at www.adopahorse.blm.gov)*

Forest Service adoptions are handled in one of two ways: (1) in areas with small herds, excess animals are adopted by local people on-site; or (2) when large numbers are involved, excess animals are processed through centralized Forest Service or BLM facilities.

BLM has expanded its distribution system for excess wild horses and burros to make the animals more accessible to potential adopters. Year-round facilities operate in Susanville, California; Palomino Valley, Nevada; Burns, Oregon; and Rock Springs, Wyoming. As other roundups are scheduled, centers are opened periodically in Arizona, Colorado, Idaho, Montana, New Mexico, and Utah. Supplementing these facilities are year-round BLM-contracted centers opened during 1978 and 1979 in Eugene, Oregon; Cross Plains, Tennessee; Valley Mills, Texas; and Spanaway, Washington. Almost 1,500 (*figure from 1980*) animals have been placed under adoption through the contract centers.

Humane standards and practices have been established by the Agencies for processing excess animals for adoption. The procedures were developed in consultation with State and local governments and humane representatives. Animals are put into separate pens according to age and sex. The number of animals which may be held at any given time is limited to avoid overcrowded conditions.

The Adopt-A-Horse program has been publicized nationwide to generate interest in adopting excess animals, and to inform people of the necessity for the program and its procedures and responsibilities. Media coverage has included numerous newspaper and magazine features, television and radio announcements, and news stories. European journalists have covered several of the roundups and adoptions for international papers and magazines.

As a result of the publicity, BLM's current computerized listing of applications totaled nearly 16,000 in April 1980, and the applicants have asked for almost 43,000 animals. In 1998 the numbers of animals placed were 6,507 horses, 1,337 burros for a total of 7,844 adoptions. Since the inception of the program, 138,947 horses and 25,812 burros (total 164,759) animals have been adopted. One problem associated with this is that the demand and supply do not match. More than half the applicants request female horses and primarily those of relatively young ages. Demand for stallions, again mainly younger ones, totals little more than 10,000 animals. Applications for male and female burros account for 5,700 animals. Although there are a number of applications, some distribution centers have reported that less than three out of ten applicants actually adopt animals. The best estimate is that 1 in 4 applicants actually adopt animals.

(The BLM has had a lot of publicity, both good and bad, over the years. The controversy over disposal of the horses and burros, humane treatment in holding facilities and by adopters, and other issues has shifted one way and then the other. However, the workings of the BLM are still in the best interests of the animals. Without the adoption services, many of these animals would have perished.)

Donkey jennet with BLM Angle freeze brand.

Read each angle to determine freeze mark number

Freeze Mark:

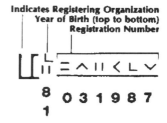

Indicates Registering Organization
Year of Birth (top to bottom)
Registration Number

The BLM Angle key. The first symbols of the freeze brand indicate the BLM, the two stacked are the year of birth, the rest an individual animal id number.

Feral donkeys may also have the "China Lake" anchor freeze brand on the neck.

Black Bart, a Champion Mammoth Jack. This jack has ideal conformation, and has sired many quality offspring.

A famous Mammoth Jack, "*Kansas Chief*", owned by Hineman's Jack Farm. This jack was the World's Champion in 1915, weight 1260 lbs. Note his large bone, good size, perfect topline, and refinement. Still a model for the Mammoth Jack of today.

Ivy League Fortunate William Robert, a handsome Large Standard Donkey gelding owned by Kelley & David Ward, Enumclaw, WA. He has been shown, participated in Parades, and is well-loved by all he meets! Photo by Creative Photo.

From large to small - donkeys (and asses) of all sizes have a friendly nature and win the hearts of whomever they meet! This is *The 'Ol Griz* 15 hh, and *No Jo Jo II*, 33 3/4", both owned by the Nissen's Lazy N Ranch, Corwith IA.

The Miniature Mediterranean Donkey is growing in popularity not only as a pet, companion and working animal, but in the Show Ring as well.

Photo by
Don Shugart

The breed we have come to know as the modern Mammoth has several distinct breeds blended in its background, but many will tend to look very much like the ancestral breed. This jack is quite similar to the true dappled-roan Andalusian type.

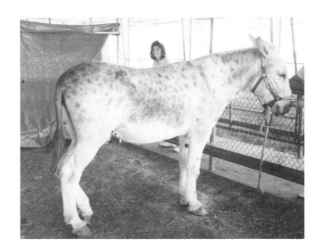

The famous jack *Texas*, whose blood can be found in the bloodlines of many donkeys, large and small today. He is resonsible for many of the striking spotted Standard donkeys and even some spotted Miniature donkeys in todays showring.

Texas was shown at halter, even sidesaddle and in Harness for many years. He even appeared at the Olympics in Los Angeles along with carriage horses.

A modern Mammoth jack who resembles the ancestral Andalusian type. This jack, owned by Garrett Jackstock, is producing superb Jackstock colts.

This is a famed jack, used on many jennets, but shows one of the typical faults of the breed, a long back connected into a sloped, light hip. In matters of height and bone, he was superb, but the hip should be improved on in the jennets bred to this type of conformation.

Ideal conformation has a level topline with more equal parts - hip, back and shoulder.

This animal is a modern Mammoth, but although the head and forequarters are appealing, it has faults which should not be passed along to breeding stock! Some taller Mammoths are used in breeding simply because they are large, or have nice coloration, but the long, weak back and loins in this animal are a fault.

A lovely small standard jennet, about 42" tall. She has good conformation, and is of the size most used as guard donkeys. She is owned by Chris Spira, Texas.

Headstudy of a modern patriarch of the breed - the Mammoth *Jen-Jack.* This outstanding jack is owned by Dr. Tex Taylor, College Station, TX. Photo by Dr. Suzanne Burnham

Crystamarq Mario, a large Standard Spotted Ass gelding. His pattern is typical of the spotted donkey, with a blaze and race, white over the barrel and rump, and small dark spots throughout. Owned by Colleen Covey, Dallas TX.

Peggy Reed and her Standard Jack *Beanie Burrito.* This jack rides and drives, and is siring beautiful mule colts.

Engraving - Catalonian

A Modern Catalonian Ass.

Old engraving of a Poitou

A modern Poitou Ass, (Baudet du Poitou) *Erable*, at 4 yrs old. Owned by Bruce Kovner, NY. Photo by Suzon Murray

The Majorca Jack

Catalan (Spanish) Jack

A Damascus Saddle Ass as compared to the common breed of Iran.

A one day old spotted foal "Merlin's Magic" G-1417, by a Spotted Jack out of a black Jennet.

Modern Mammoth jack,

The Andalusian Ass

CHAPTER TWO

OBTAINING THE RIGHT DONKEY FOR YOU

BUYING THE DONKEY

It is sometimes a shame to give people an ideal animal to look for when everything they can find for sale falls short of what they are told to buy. It should be said right at the beginning, that the best donkey for you is one who gets along with you, whom you get along with and who fills your necessities - no one else's! If you see a sway backed, spavined, droopy eared ancient jenny who immediately loves you and whom you immediately love, and you ask nothing more of her than to be your pet and companion - by all means ignore anything anybody might say and take HER, not the fancy priced one in the next lot, with whom you have nothing in common! Just analyze your own needs and go from there. The person hunting a high class breeding jack is looking for something entirely different from the person who wants a children's pet, or the one who wants an active show donkey.

In the rest of this chapter we are going to try to describe the **ideal** donkey because there is not much point in describing the less than good animal! Also you need to know what to look for. However use your own common sense and taste and the knowledge in this book to pick the donkey that is right for both your personality and your purposes.

Also keep in mind your needs when you think about what sex to buy. If you want a pet and using animal, your needs are not necessarily for a jenny, although if you are like the majority that is the first thing you will think of. You may be able to get a gelding more cheaply, and from my own and other's experiences we can tell you that the most satisfactory all-round family animal is definitely a gelding! If you are starting out for the first time and are offered a nice gelding or a jack colt to geld yourself at a nice reasonable price, we recommend taking him, he has no heat periods to make him cross, he does not have the headstrong disposition of a jack (plus the braying habits) and will make an even tempered pet growing more loving with age. Later perhaps when you are more knowing about donkeys you can pick a really nice jennet to breed, but remember, when she is pregnant and nursing she will not be useable - a gelding is useable all the time.

Jacks are NOT SUITABLE as pets. They are usually extremely good natured and kind animals, but they are headstrong and can bite or kick when they smell a mare or jennet on a person. Please do not get a jack unless you are very experienced and do not give one to a child as a pet. We cannot emphasize this too strongly, even the best natured jack in the world can be ungovernable and even dangerous when in the excitement of smelling a jennet in heat and only an experienced person should handle a jack. Some jacks develop the habit of bullying or even hurting other animals, jennets, geldings or horses which are kept with them, and all will breed a yearling jennet in her first heat. They should be kept apart in their own pens and we repeat, only handled by experience people no matter how kind and people loving they are. No matter if he is 29" or 17 hands, a jack is a stud, the breeding male, and he runs primarily on testosterone. They cannot help their own instincts, so allow for these instincts and you and the jack will both be happier. If you want a using and working animal have a gelding or a jennet, not a jack. See more in the chapter on breeding and jacks.

SELECTING A DONKEY

The first thing that most people think of when they are starting out to choose a donkey, if they are thinking of riding, it is size. Now, size is not as important in itself as is size in relation to rider. Size is not particularly important in driving unless you want a team, in which case the donkeys need to be more matched in size than not. Miniatures should be ridden by light children, and larger, heavier people should look for a donkey of 45" and up with sound good-sized bone in the legs and a stocky or strongly built body with a fairly short back. Height is not the criterion here so much as body build, and don't let fat fool you. Look for depth of chest, breadth of hind quarters and chest in the front and good bone if you are a heavy person (over 150 lbs.) and looking for a donkey to ride. Remember small, weedy underfed donkeys trot along briskly under a load and a rider in Egypt (with shorter usage- and life-spans), but you want to make sure you are riding an animal that can carry weight without any strain. Donkeys are extremely strong for their size as anyone who has seen them in actual everyday use can tell you. The English custom of limiting donkey riders to children is unnecessary.

Before you start worrying about looking odd on a small animal, just put that out of your head and get oriented to working with donkeys. If you need a large imposing mount just get a mule. However, the donkey pleasure classes at the shows are well filled with adults, sometimes long legged, or overweight adults, riding donkeys from 44 to 54 inches tall. They ride with light western saddles or with English style tack, and they neither look or feel undermounted if one first accepts the fact that they are riding donkeys and not horses. Some mule owners have this problem - they will spend up to a thousand dollars for 8 inches of mule! They have the feeling that height makes right, when a smaller and less expensive mule can perform as well or better, carry the same weight, but won't look quite as impressive. People with this particular hang up just shouldn't ride donkeys. But from our own experience most "donkey people" are a self confident bunch, and know better than to expect prestige from mere height or appearance. So if you are tempted to put all other considerations away at the expense of size in your donkey think twice. Size allied with all the other good qualities is wonderful, but size alone can be quite disappointing. The most crowned champion jack we have ever had in the Texas area, *"Texas"*, was just 45" tall. He was driven, and ridden by adults, and even carried a lady sidesaddle. He has superb action and style and never appeared small, almost everyone who was asked to estimate his size guessed him at several inches taller than he was! Other qualities can count more than size!

Donkeys can be quite elegant under sidesaddle. They have often been used as children's mounts before present day, and are still seen in the showring as a stylish ladies mount, no matter their size. Left, *Beanie Burrito*, a Standard jack.

COLOR

It may seem odd to worry about color, but it is very important to some people. Many people don't want anything but the classic slate (gray-dun) color with cross and stripe, while others want the most exotic they can get, the spotted donkey. The most important thing about color is that it be pleasing to you, the owner. If you are not happy with your donkey's looks you will never be quite satisfied with him.

Betsy: If I were picking MY ideal show donkey I think I would pick a spotted one, marked with even, well defined black and white or brown and white spots. This is because this type of animal is fairly rare and really catches the eye of judges, spectators and your friends.

Some people prefer white, but watch for pink skin because in sunlight or in a pasture with irritating plants it can break out into horrible eczema. An unusual color is any shade of sorrel (or chestnut) from light "pink" to deep mahogany (very rare). Dapple sorrel and dapple gray can also be found as can red roan and blue roan. Black and dark brown can be very shiny for the show ring, but tend to get sunbleached, as does any dark color including gray-dun, and have an unattractive brownish tinge. Any color is quite acceptable in the show ring, but the darker and richer and less washed out it is the better for show purposes. (See more on in the chapter on color.)

Three shades of red - the first sorrel Miniature Donkeys to be born in Europe. Left to right *Pepperoni of Marklye, Pizza of Marklye,* and *Salami of Marklye.* Owned and bred by the Lady Fisher, Marklye Stud, England.

Dark brown, no light points. This donkey has red tones in the coat, and the head and lower legs are distinctly blacker than the rest of the body. This visually resembles Bay in the horse, and research is ongoing to test for genetic bay in donkeys.

CONFORMATION

Conformation is the name used for the physical "build" of the animal. Buy your animal in warm weather if you possibly can. The best time to pick out a donkey is in mid-summer when, except for a baby, its long coat of winter hair is shed off. The best donkey can be hidden under a thick mat of winter hair, and the worst one will be disguised into cuteness. If you absolutely must pick your donkey in full, shaggy coat, you will have to rely on a careful visual and tactile examination of the head, backline (topline), depth of body, width of chest and quarters, line of neck, legs and rib spring.

Even when you get a good one and shed or clip him off, remember he may not look as good as he will after some hard work to muscle him up and some good food to fill him out if he is lean, and perhaps in some cases some time to grow and fill out. All donkeys go through a really gangly teen age stage sometimes in their second and sometimes in their third year, where they look pretty bad! When they mature in their fourth year they look quite different and usually the owner heaves a real sigh of relief.

If you want him for show, do not let the fact that he looks like a stuffed toy influence you to buy him if he has a roman nose, ewe neck, sway back or crooked legs!

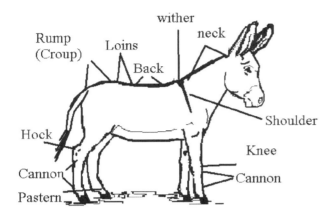

Parts of the equine are the same, whether Donkey, Mule or Horse. The main differences in conformation are in the shape of the parts, and the obvious ear length in the donkey.

For a more complete conformation chart, see the Appendix

BODY

When first looking at a donkey, stand back and look for balance and symmetry in his general appearance. Everything should blend well, head length and proportion, length of back and legs, length of rump, depth of body, length of neck, etc. If the animal looks unbalanced due to thinness you can make allowance for that. However, a mature donkey that is very narrow through the chest is built that way, not just thin. Foals will widen out somewhat, but avoid the narrow chested animal.

Withers, (top of shoulder where the cross is) do not protrude in donkeys like they do in horses, but if some wither shows it is so much the better as the saddle will sit better. The back should be strong, whether long or short and have a gentle dip. Donkey backs are much more straight than horse backs. A donkey will sometimes have a very sway back, and this is usually from many years of foal bearing or else some severe injury, perhaps from riding much too early. Sometimes the line of the back will stick up in a convex manner. This is called a **roach back** and must be avoided in a breeding, riding or show donkey, but for a pet or driving animal is allowable. Length of back should be in proportion to the animal's height. Many donkeys have backs that seem too long to a horseman's eye. It has been discovered by actual measurement, that if that particular animal had upstanding withers such as a horse has, the back would appear short! So just make sure the loin area is fairly broad and strong and not dipped and weak, and if the back is in decent proportion it probably isn't too long.

The loin area needs to be strong, broad and firmly coupled. It needs to be strong if weight of any magnitude will be carried by the animal, as it will suffer first if it is weak and overloaded. The line of flank should be low and the tail set fairly high. The top line of the croup (top of rump) should not slope down at an acute angle in a "goose rump" to the tail setting and should not have a high peak at its highest point. Such peaks are usually disguised fairly well by fat if the peak is not extremely pronounced. This is a typical donkey feature and comes from the pelvis of the donkey being of a different in shape from that of the flat crouped pony or horse. The smoother the donkey is in hips, top of croup and loin the better it will show in the arena.

The shoulder area should be clean cut (not smothered in fat) and as sloping as possible although straight shoulders are normal in donkeys as they are in draft horses. The chest and ribs should be deep and rounded for heart and lung room. Flat sides are a very common defect in donkeys and are often found with a very straight shoulder or a roach back. The breast, the part of the chest seen from the front, should be relatively wide in proportion to the animal, a weak and narrow chest is a common fault and undesirable from the point of weight carrying ability and endurance. Also this is heavily counted against in the show ring. You will note that the breast of the donkey is single-lobed , whereas that of the horse is clearly defined and double-lobed. The more width and definition you can get on the breast of the donkey, the better.

THE HEAD

The head should be short rather than too long and in proportion. Very long, heavy heads will make the animal appear out of balance. In the Miniature Donkey, care must be taken that in breeding stock animals head proportions match the rest of the body. Over-large heads are a sign of dwarfism. Current research supports that the forelegs of a mature animal should be longer than the head when measured from lip to poll. Heads the same length as the forelegs or only minimally (1") longer are probably indications of dwarf traits. (For now Disproportional animals should be noted as Visually Disproportional, or AVDS - Apparent Visual Disporportional Syndrome.)

The head should be wide between the eyes with a tapering muzzle and firm lips with large open nostrils. The profile of any donkey except a mammoth should be straight or slightly dished (it may be slightly convex or "Roman" in the mammoth). Eyes should be set "low" wide apart and be clear and healthy looking. In fly season a watery discharge is common from fly irritation and probably means nothing unless pus is present.

Jaws and teeth must meet properly and not be under or overshot (Parrot or monkey mouth. . Animals inherit this defect and if they have it ADMS will not register them. Features should be well defined and the eyes large, free of blemishes and of a kind or mild expression unless the animal is frightened. Jaws should be strong, generous and open and round with good width between them on the underside. The head should be deep through the jaws tapering to a fairly small muzzle. Remember that donkeys have larger heads in proportion to their size than horses or ponies, but the head should look correct on the donkey and not be so big as to be out of proportion. Ears should be long, clean cut, set upright and firmly. Notched ears, lop ears, broken ears should be avoided for show donkeys but not necessarily for pets.

Roman Nose
Straight face
Dished face
Face on, ears
lopped to side.
Arab (dished)

NECK

The donkey's neck is entirely different from that of the horse. Due to a difference in muscle structure the top line of the neck in the normal mature donkey is straight. A truly arched neck is not normal, as it is with horses, not even with jacks. Young animals may have necks more arched due to less muscle development. Also the donkey will have a "sausage roll" of muscle on the very top of its neck. In fat donkeys or older donkeys or donkeys that have been obese and lost weight, this roll will get very large as it is a storage area for fat. If allowed to grow too big the "crest" will be inclined to fall over to the side. This condition breaks down the cartilage that holds this area in place and if allowed to go too far cannot be corrected even if the donkey loses weight. The neck and head should be in proper proportion to each other and to the donkey. A heavy head needs a thicker neck than a light head. The neck should tend toward the long and refined side however, rather than being short and thick. A short, thick neck makes the animal more difficult to control in turns and stops.

Some donkeys have a "Ewe" neck. That means it is too thin to be in proportion to the head and has a pronounced dip or concavity in the top line. The underline of the throat will also be more pronounced and physically longer than the topline. Do not buy a donkey with this fault as it is a real weakness besides being highly unattractive. Most donkey's necks (and horses or mules) can be made to ewe if the head is forced up, it is when the animal stands normally or at rest that the neck shape should be judged. The ewe-neck is also most pronounced when a high-headed animal runs, with the neck forming a pronounced S-curve.

A few donkeys have a very pronounced dip in the neck just in front of the withers. This is quite unsightly and shows a lack of muscle development there, but if your animal is not going to be a show donkey it does not matter in any practical way. A well shaped and strong neck will allow the animal to hold its head up alertly. Nothing looks or feels worse than the animal that constantly holds its head low and pulls on the bit all the time, due to poor training, conformation or condition (weakness for some reason). When the donkey you are inspecting is walking on the lead at its ease, or in the pasture watch the natural head carriage closely. Do not buy a donkey that walks with its head down all the time or with its neck stretched straight out but look for one that holds its head up and looks alert and active.

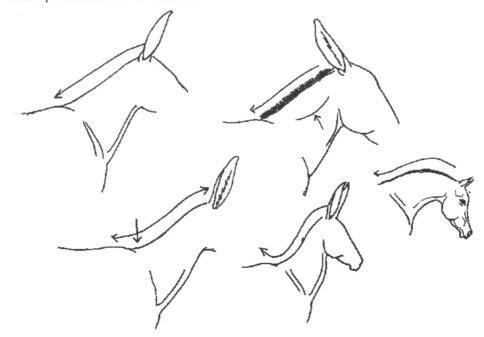

HINDQUARTERS

These should be as long from the point of hip to the point of the pelvic girdle (just by the tail where the bone sticks out) as possible and as flat on top as is consistent with normal donkey conformation. They should look fairly long on top also and should be well fleshed and plump without pones of fat. If the donkey you are inspecting is thin, look for this point of hip to point of buttock line. If it is long, and in proportion to the rest of him, and if the bone from the top of his quarters to the tail has a pleasing slope instead of a ski jump in profile, then fat will probably have him coming out looking well. Viewed from the rear, the wider and thicker all parts of the quarters and upper legs are, the better. Many donkeys are "cat hammed", meaning that the upper thighs are flat and lack any decent muscling. This actually is found in most working donkeys in the middle east, but you still do not want to see it in your donkey and some muscle and breadth from side to side and front to back in the upper thighs is extremely desirable. You want to find a donkey that is proportionally more "Square" in view than an inverted triangle - wide hips and narrow underneath.

1. Good, Straight.

2. Set close behind.

3. Severely cowhocked, toes point out sharply, hocks rubbing.

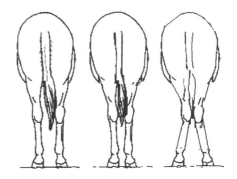

LEGS

Legs are very important in working equines and also in ones that will be shown in halter classes. The straighter the legs and the heavier in bone the better. Many an otherwise fine animal will be consistently placed down in halter classes because of some typically donkey leg defect. If you find a thin animal with straight well made legs, buy it in preference to a more well fleshed donkey with crooked legs, especially if you intend to show or breed it. DO NOT CHOOSE BREEDING DONKEYS WITH MODERATE TO BAD LEG FAULTS!!!!! Keep in mind that even baby donkeys should have their feet rasped and kept level from birth so that they do not grow up with preventable leg faults that would have been kept at bay by proper vitamins and nutrition and proper foot care! If the animal shows long, overgrown hoofs, even extreme ones they can usually be corrected by a good farrier with quite a few visits, correction taking a long time. However this animal may not be suitable for riding although it may be fine for breeding or a pet oeven driving. In other circumstances overgrown feet can be fully corrected and the animal brought back to full working condition. Much depends on the amount of leg twisting and bone damage the neglect allowed to take place. If you are not sure, have the animal examined by an equine veterinarian and/or a, good farrier before you buy. Feet should be rather narrow with a good cup in the sole, a good healthy frog, and the donkey stands at a much more upright angle on his feet than a horse, this is normal.

Here is the ADMS Standard for legs: Donkey legs to be straight and true with adequate bone in proportion to the animal. Knees flat and wide; cannon bones short; hocks set low and strong, clean and correct in shape. Hind legs set straight, front legs straight and properly set. Feet to be even and of good shape, narrowness being normal and should be properly trimmed. Feet to be hard yet elastic, clean, smooth, and tough. Size in proportion to the donkey. Donkey hooves are narrow but adequate; no tendency to low heels. Front foot oval, hind foot more elongated, frog small but well developed and not trimmed away except to take off ragged edges.

It is said by many breeders, especially of draft animals, that some degree of cow-hocks is better than the plumb-line true set you often see in textbooks. To the untrained eye, this can be quite confusing. Legs that follow the line of the gaskin down straight through the hooves are fine. This line will be narrower than in a horse. The hocks of the donkey may be set closer to each other since the undercarriage of the donkey is closer-coupled than mules or horses. True cow-hocks point strongly toward each other, and the degree of turnout in each leg may vary. Legs where the gaskins slope in, the hocks are touching, and the heels pointing sharply back out the other way again ARE cowhocked. This degree of angularity often causes interference with the way the animal moves, and hocks that rub together (even at rest!) should be strictly avoided in breeding stock.

1. Good hips, good line from tail to hock to ankle.

2. Dipped loins, steep rumps, leg set too far back in large donkey.

3. Roached back n large donkye, bullet rump and sloped croup, both camped under.

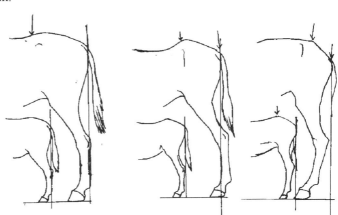

ACTION
To be level, straight, willing, active, light and smart not sluggish. High knee and hock action not necessary.

CONFORMATION FAULTS TO AVOID AND WHY

Ear: Set and quality determines the style and beauty of the animal. Ear cartilage may be damaged in older animal or weak in very young. Lopped ears are not desirable, except in animals of Poitou breeding.

Eyes: Small, light colored or dull may indicate poor vision and are unattractive.

Nostrils: Small, pale lining or discharge, the latter two signs of ill health. Small nostrils indicate lack of good breathing capacity.

Mouth: Except in Poitou throwbacks, drooping lips are usually a sign of age or a bad bite. Protruding or receding lower jaw is sign of inherited defect and ugly. Drooping lower lips may also be a sign of a bite defect, especially in monkey mouth (overshot jaw) where the lower teeth protrude past the upper ones.

Teeth: Must be in good condition to insure good health. If animal is thin, or dribbles grain, teeth should be "floated" by a veterinarian. Jaws which do not meet properly (overshot or undershot) in excess of ¼" should not be used as breeding stock. The teeth will not wear evenly.

Back: Too long or badly coupled is weak and likely to become sore or break down. Convex or "roach" is ugly, too short, prevents good leg action and saddle will not stay on. Roached back in small donkeys may be an indication of dwarfism. Sway is weak, ugly.

Loin: Too long interferes with transmission of power from hind legs forward and is weak and may become sore or break down. Dipped in front of hip is weak and will lead to other back problems. Common in Mammoths, should be severely penalized in evaluation of breeding stock.

Croup: Steep croup causes sickle hocks (displacing hind legs to the front thus causing them to bear too much of the body weight in an unnatural position). Thin goose rumps usually mean an animal with poor keeping qualities which will not fill out well. Also it is unsightly and out of proportion.

Knee.: Incorrectly placed (displaced frontward of backward Buck-kneed or calf-kneed) is weak and may break down with work.

Hocks: Cow hocks (turned inward toward each other) are weak and predispose to a twisting rotating action when moving which hurts legs. Sickle hocks are unsound and predispose to early break down. Hocks which are round on the back profile and not straight are weak from a tendon problem (curby hocks). Hocks carry great strain and have many problems in horses, although less in donkeys unless they are worked too hard at a young age. They should be large, clean and well set.

Plaiting: Putting one foot in front of another, dangerous at speed or turning corners. Common in donkeys of narrow build.

Winging - also called Paddling. Although gaited animals may have a small degree of paddling, extreme outward rotation of the limbs is not normal travel in the ass (donkey).

Pigeon toed: Toes turn out in front or back, also hard on legs and movement.

Heavy Topped: Body too fat and heavy for size of bone in legs, may break legs down.

Broken Angles - in reference to the hoof angle: long sloped pasterns than break downward from the pastern angle (coon foot) may become weaker as the animal ages or under heavy work conditions - this is the type most likely to have fetlock damage - also called "down in the bumpers". Underrun heels break the hoof angle on pasterns that are too upright and cause contraction of the hoof.

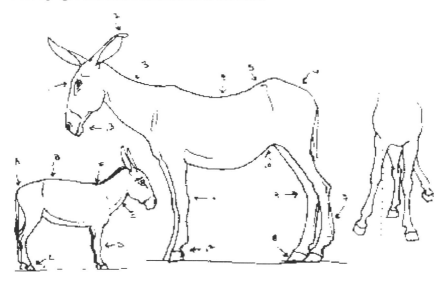

Mini: Bullet rump, roach back, dip at withers, ewe neck, back at the knees, stands under.
Large: small eye, broken eartip, ewe neck, sway back, weak loins, sloped rump, bowed tendon, stands under, underrun hooves, tucked up, clubfoot fore, back at the knees, probable underbite.

When experienced donkey or mule people judge a class they either consciously or subconsciously have a definite model in mind as they begin to place the animals. One must of course, realize that perfectly built animals do not exist. One of the first things to look for in the beginning of a halter class is the way the animal travels, BEING MINDFUL OF BREED STANDARDS. As you can see the whole framework of each animal you can compare proportions.

WHAT TO LOOK FOR IN THE FRONT VIEW

A. Head, in proportion to the rest of the body, refined, clean cut chiseled appearance, broad forehead, wide between the eyes, jaw broad and deep, ears large and long, clean and well carried, large bright eyes. These basics apply to mules and donkeys equally. Refinement and femininity in the jenny or mare mule, boldness and masculinity in the jack. Straight or dished profile in small and standard donkeys: slightly roman nose allowed in jacks in large standard, and moderate roman nose allowed in all Mammoth stock, but less in the female. Straight profile more desirable in modern mule breeding stock, and straight profile desired in all mules except large draft mules. Slightly dished profile allowed in saddle or mini-mules.

B. Chest deep and wide, but not so wide as to interfere with action. Mules have a chest which approximates the horse they are related to. Donkeys have a more narrow chest, which should simply be in proportion to the animal and not narrow and lacking in substance.

C. Legs, straight, true and squarely set on.

FAULTS IN FRONT VIEW

A. Head, plain, too long, drooping ears, drooping lips, dull eyes, too large for body, small eyes, narrow forehead, etc.

B. Jack too feminine, jennet too masculine looking, geldings may be in between.

C. Narrow chest, lack of bone in front legs, narrow front leg set, feet turned out or in.

WHAT TO LOOK FOR IN THE SIDE VIEW

A. Style and Beauty

B. Balance and Symmetry - Parts well developed and blended together.

C. Carriage of head, active ears, alert bearing.

D. Neck - Fairly long neck, clean cut throat latch, well set, donkeys may have straight necks as may mules, a slight arch is welcomed - over-heavy fatty crest to be discriminated against.

E. Shoulders - Shoulder slope as close to the ideal 45 degrees as possible. Donkeys and mules have straighter shoulder than horses, so this will be a comparison judgment among the animals in your class.

F. Topline - Short, strong, long and well shaped and well muscled croup, high tail set. Most donkeys have a sloping croup as a breed characteristic, if in proper symmetry with the animal and not excessive (goose) this does not count against, except in comparison with another animal in the class which may have a less sloping croup.

G. Coupling - Short and broad across the loins.

H. Midsection - Well sprung ribs, not too long in proportion to animal, deep heart girth.

I. Rear Flank - Deep (well let down) rear flank.

J. Arm, Forearm and Gaskin - All well muscled, broad, and strong looking.,

K. Legs, Feet and Pasterns - Straight and squarely set. Pasterns at approximately 45 degree angle, feet sized in proportion to body size, bone in legs in proportion to body size. Hoof angle should match pastern angle, without breakover at coronet.

L. Quality - Clean flat bone, clean joints and tendons, skin and hair fine, head clean.

M. Breed Type - Showing good type for the breed of ass or mule being shown. A Draft mule breed type is different from a saddle mule type, just as a mammoth jack is entirely different from a miniature. These animals may sometimes be judged together if BASIC CONFORMATION STANDARDS are used as the ideal.

FAULTS IN THE SIDE VIEW

1. No style or beauty.
2. Animal lacks balance or symmetry in certain parts.
3. Short, thick or long ewe neck.
4. Shoulders coarse and too straight for breed type.
5. Topline with a too long back, peaked rump and/or sloping croup, roach back weak, dipped loin, narrow loin.
6. Slab sided (not sufficient spring of ribs) common in donkeys, bad fault, wasp waisted, not sufficient heartroom (bad fault).
7. Flank cut up.
8. No muscling in gaskin, arm and forearm, these parts narrow and weak (bad fault).
9. Crooked legs and straight pasterns. (Most donkeys are somewhat sickle hocked - this when not severe is not the extreme fault it is in horses, although the judge is asked to discriminate against it if there is an animal with straight legs in the class.)
10. Lack of quality and refinement, coarse bone and head, ears droopy or thick.
11. Breed type, Poor breed type in: Miniature donkeys, mammoth donkeys, draft mules. All others have no really fixed breed type ideal and breed type does not count greatly in judging unless there is an obvious unsuitability.

WHAT TO LOOK FOR IN THE REAR VIEW

A. Width of croup and through rear quarters - Overall wideness of rear quarters, the wider the better as these tend to be narrow in donkeys and to a lesser extent in mules (do not confuse FAT with good conformation), heavy inner and outer muscling of quarter (will not be heavy compared to horses) and good muscling in gaskin.
B. Levelness of croup and tail set, level top as far as possible, most donkeys and mules slope to some degree, a well rounded and lengthy croup is more important. Length of croup is not measured along the top line of the croup, but along the side from the hipbone to the point of the croup.
C. Set of hind legs - Legs straight, clean cannons, clean deep hocks, well defined tendons.

FAULTS IN REAR VIEW

1. Cow hocked, sickle hocked, hocks turned out, lacking width of hock, coarse hind legs.
2. Sloping (goose rump), short rump, lacking in strength and proportion.
3. Rough hips with bones sticking out like a cow's, point at the top of the croup, croup out of proportion to rest of body.

WHAT TO LOOK FOR IN ACTION: Left - cowhocked. Right - good lines.

Walk

Easy, quick, balanced. Long stride in proportion to animal, each foot carried forward in a straight line, feet lifted clear of ground.

Faults At The Walk

A. Short step, not carried forward in straight line, feet not clearing ground, sluggish way of going. Animals rear not tracking with front, limp or favoring of one foot or side. Rapid, straight, elastic, joints well fixed

B. Winging, forging and interfering, not travelling in straight line, sluggish, feet dragging. Pronounced limp or head bob on alternate strides.

If you are fortunate enough to see the donkey canter before you purchase, or are calling for the canter (lope) in an under saddle class, the canter or lope should be a three (3) beat gait. Four-beating is a fault. The stride should be even on both sides, smooth, with little up-and-down movement.

EVALUATE THE UNSOUNDNESS AND BLEMISHES

DISQUALIFICATION
Blindness
Lameness

Bone Spavin
Stifled
Broken Wind
Stringhalt or Crampiness

DISCRIMINATION
Capped Hock

Cracked Hoofs
Filled Hocks
Bowed Tendon (serious)
Bog Spavin
Cocked Ankles (serious)
Curb
Hip Down
Parrot Mouth (serious)
Monkey Mouth (serious)

Remember also that there is eveidence to support that a bad bite (over or under bite, also called Parrot or Monkey Mouth) is inherited. Donkeys, especially Miniatures, with more than 1/4" of bite deviation should NOT be used for breeding stock.

Capped hock, bowed tendon, ringbone, hoof crack.

Bucked knees, back at the knee, capped elbow, dropped hip.

Popped stifle, filled hock, overgrown and underrun hoof.

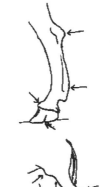

Even bite

Underbite (undershot, monkey mouth)

Overbite (Parrot mouth

PELVIC DIFFERENCES IN
ASSES AND HORSES

We would like to address those who are engaged in judging or breeding asses.

The best index for DETERMINING SPECIES (capitals ours) or subgeneric differences in the pelvis of the two animals would appear to be in the height of the two ilia as compared with the bi-iliac width (see diagram). In the true (Caballine horses, this index (H/E) is small, corresponding to a LOW BROAD PELVIS (croup). In the ASSES, zebras and hemioids the index is larger in conformity with a PELVIS THAT IS RELATIVELY HIGHER, STEEPER AND LESS BROAD. Therefore expecting the donkey to have a rounded croup like a horse is both unrealistic and un-donkey-like. Naturally the animal should not be out of proportion and badly put together - there are extremes to be avoided. but the steeper croup, sometimes with a peak on the top and narrower from behind is a SPECIES DIFFERENCE between the ass and horse and should be recognized as such. The marked difference in this respect between the pelvis of a Shetland pony stallion and a male domestic ass is shown in the diagram.

The hoofs are also valuable to help separate species. The difference in both size and proportion existing between the broad rounded hoofs of the horse and the small elongate hoofs of the donkey are such as to easily separate them into two species upon examination of the hoofs alone. When, in order to make a cross section I sawed through the foot of the donkey I was astonished at the solidity and toughness of the horny hoof. Even with a power saw, it was like cutting through ironwood!

There is also a vertex/basilar ratio of the skull and neck. A small ratio denotes unfavorable leverage of neck muscles on the head - this is characteristic of horses and explains the high, arched neck of stallions. This ratio is large in asses, zebras and hemionids and permits a lesser development of the neck muscles as results in the relatively flat necks typical of these species and the superior holding power of the jaws of a jack.

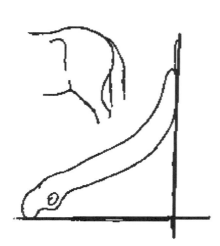 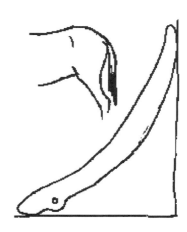

Left - the pelvis of a shetland Pony   Right - pelvis of the domestic Ass.

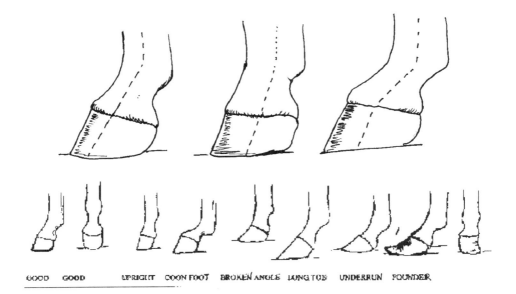

GOOD   GOOD   UPRIGHT   COON FOOT   BROKEN ANGLE   LONG TOE   UNDERRUN   FOUNDER

The shape of the Donkey hoof varies slightly from that of the horse. However, for the most part, the general shape and angle should be similar - no broken angles, severely upright or underslung, smooth surface, no cracks. More on hooves and hoof shape can be found in the chapter on Care.

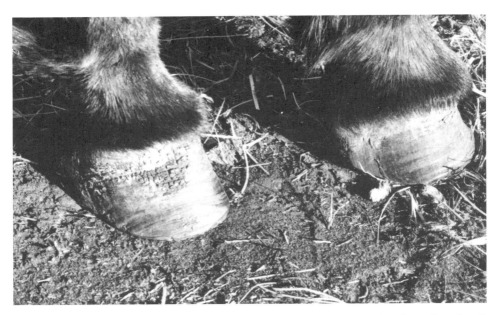

Although recently trimmed, these are the hooves of an animal who has been foundered. The right fore-hoof (left of photo) has scales and damage at the cormonary band, and the ridges can be seen from previous damage. The right hoof is upright, and typical of foundered hooves with rotation. The flared base and twists are visible.

ADMS Inspector's Checklist

It is the goal of the Society to encourage the registration and breeding of sound, healthy animals with few or no physical defects that might affect future generations. Note - any fault or combination of faults severe enough to exclude an animal from registration should also be a flag to exclude the animal from a breeding pool as well.

DENTAL: Bite of teeth
No more than 1/4" over or underbite is allowed. Bite may changed from milk teeth to adult teeth, so it should be noted and rechecked if the animal is immature at inspection.

REPRODUCTIVE (inspector must not take risks)
If male over 24 months, both testicles decended.
One or both testicles retained in male over 24 months old. (Cryptorchid/Monorchid - Disallowed in breeding stock. _____

CONFORMATIONAL DEFECTS OR BLEMISHES
Animals will not be penalized for defects caused by injury if it can be shown that they are not genetic.
Animals will be refused for registration only if conformation flaw are SEVERE, or there is a combination of severe flaws, or if there are obvious genetically transmitted flaws such as bad bite, dwarfism, or retained testicle in mature animals.

PROBLEMS FROM LACK OF CARE SHOULD NOT EXCLUDE AN ANIMAL FOR REGISTRATION PROVIDED THEY ARE BEING ADDRESSED BY OWNER. IF YOU ARE UNSURE OF HOW TO RATE THESE, PLEASE CALL FOR HELP.

OK: Is Animal in balance with good proportion of leg and neck to back and body.
OR: Faults: Indications of Disproportion (any or all: head oversized, neck too long, back and body too long, legs too short in proportion to body - no length of bone in legs-especially forelegs)

OK: Is Hair, skin in good condition.
OR Hair and skin in poor condition (fungal, lack or care, other?)

OK: Hooves in good condition, of proper shape
OR: Hooves in need of care - overgrown, heel underrun, foundered, clubfoot, other (severe founder not a fault, but upright or excessivly long pasterns can be inherited)

OK: Eyes clear and bright, no obvious vision problems
OR: Mattered/cloudy eyes or blindness(blindness due to injury should be noted - eye defects from birth that would be genetically trasmitted will excluded animals from registration.

OK: Ears, Nostrils, head Correct
OR: Ears broken, damaged (eartipes missing to frostbite should be noted but will not bar animal from regisitry) Mattered nostrils, deformed or misshapen nostrils, head overlarge for body (in Miniatures may be a sign of Dwarfism) , other._____

OK: Neck straight and firm (fat crest is allowed)
OR: Neck excessively short, excessively long, Ewed (underslung curve)(Please state degree) _____Crest broken, to which side? _____
(allowed but must be noted)

OK: Shoulder and withers in good slope and proportion
OR: Shoulder upright, wither problems, other _____

OK: Back in correct proportion, level or slightly dipped, loins strong
OR: Back too long in proportion, excessively dipped or swayed (not a fault in older

brood jennets unless very extreme), back roached, loins weak or dipped (common in larger animals, severe defect if excessive). Excessively weak loins with very small hips a disqualifying fault in breeding stock.

OK: Croup level and round (small fat pads allowed) tailset good.
OR: Croup severly angled or peaked on top (goose rump), too short or extremely narrow. Very shallow pelvic girdle a severe fault in breeding stock, especially jennets.

OK: Heartgirth and ribs full and well sprung. Belly line level (loose in brood jennets is allowed)
OR: Ribs too narrow or flat, body and chest too narrow for animal, distended belly on youngstock, other _____

OK: Hind limbs straight from side and rear
OR: Mildly cowhocked, moderate, severe (indicate degree, Mild allowed) _____
Hind feet point out mildly, moderate, severe Base wide or base narrow.

OK: Forelimbs straight from side and rear
OR: Feet point outward   Mild, moderate, severe, Age of animal may be a factor.
Feet point inward Mild, moderate, severe, base narrow, base wide, over at knees, back at knees, tied in, legs set extremely close in at chest.

Carefully note any other deformities or flaws that might affect the showing, breeding, or useability of an animal.

In viewing the overall animal, were there ANY SEVERE DEFECTS OR COMBINATIONS OF DEFECTS that you would feel would make an animal a poor breeding prospect or would not stand up to the show ring?

Were you able to view the parents of the animal? If so, and you detect faults or serious flaws, were they also observed on either or both of the parent animals? If so, you should consider that the flaws are inherited.

IF an animal fails inspection due to minor problems stemming from lack of care or other circumstances, do you think the animal should be passed over at this time and be reinspected at a later date?

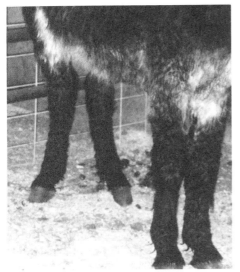

In looking at animals that may have possible inbreeding, the flaws are often genetic. This animal is severely cowhocked. Luckily, he is a gelding. In many instances like this, the animal may appear fine from the side, or standing in a field, but until you can get up close, observe the animal from all sides and watch their movement, you can't see faults like this. A good handler can pose a halter animal in a show stance for a picture where the legs are straight - if you are buying breeding stock, sight-unseen is not your best bet! Take along a knowledgeable friend to help you learn the basics.

(Taken from THE EMPIRE OF EQUUS by David P. Willoughby)

PERSONALITY

When you first go out to select a donkey several things will influence your choice. If you are looking for a breeding animal or a show animal looks will probably be your first concern. However if you want a pet, personality should be first choice. Actually no matter why you buy a certain animal, the personality of the donkey will turn out to be the most important thing in the day to day handling and training and using of it, so you must be very careful to choose a personality that suits yours.

There are several distinct types of donkey character that have been noted by several authorities and they can be defined as the following groups.

NERVOUS AND ACTIVE
PUSHY
TIMID
SPOILED
SULLEN
FRIENDLY AND TRUSTING
SLUGGISH
OUCHY

There are many combinations of these, but usually one character that will dominate the others.

NERVOUS AND ACTIVE

This animal is the easiest to train for an all around, versatile show and using donkey. Such an animal is alert, active, willing to work with a fund of nervous energy that is more horselike than donkeylike. This type is not the timid type referred to above, although it may indeed by shy and nervous before being trained as a youngster. It is a type that is usually ready to go, full of energy especially when being fed grain, and keeps its head up looking at things all the time.

The main fault of this type is nervousness, a tendency to shy while being ridden, being afraid of scary things for longer than the average young donkey and a more unforgiving nature about roughness and punishment than a donkey usually has. You must earn his trust and not frighten him or you will never get this fellow trained perfectly. Do not spank him much either or he will develop a very unattractive habit of nervously tucking his tail between his legs like a whipped dog. The best training place for any concentrated work with such an animal is familiar and "safe" ground where nothing will startle it and distract its attention. However the most necessary phase of training for this personality is lots of quiet work out in the countryside and on the road (well away from traffic) so that experience and age will calm any nervous fears it might have, and boredome will be avoided.

PUSHY

This is another good type of donkey for active work, but will be harder to train unless you make up your mind to be stronger minded than he is! This type is really bossy. Usually he is also a boss or demi-boss in the donkey herd too. Any sex can have this tendency. He thinks that everything should be done his way, not yours! He steps on your toes, barges past you through gates, refuses to stand still in show pose, comes in the house without invitation, eats your lunch and just generally wants his own way. This type of animal can be an adorable pet and excellent working animal when kept under proper control. It can be an unbearable pest without proper discipline.

Usually he has a nice sense of humor to go with his bossiness, but he must be disciplined like the precocious child he is. If kept under proper control he can make a good performance donkey because he will put all the zest he usually would use in keeping you in your place into action instead. He simply has to be shown that although he may possibly be "king" in the herd, you are his "king" and he your loyal subject. Whereas the timid or nervous type takes quite a lot of soft words, petting and encouraging, the pushy animal gets to know loud and impolite speech, jerking halters and shoulders in the face! He asks for them, and does not resent them as long as he knows there is love there with them. Discipline is not hatred, proper discipline is structured love and he must learn this.

The pushy type is an animal with more than his share of the usual "WHO ME?" donkey trait. All donkeys have this to some extent. He will "say" to you, "Are you ABSOLUTELY SURE you want me to, get into this trailer (or whatever) - do you REALLY mean for me to do this????" After this, unless you make him quite aware that you are positively more determined than he is to make him do whatever it is - he simply won't. Actually, however, once you persuade him with firm and sometimes slightly painful persuasion (albeit friendly), he will give in like a marshmallow and do whatever you ask. This is usually after he is trained for whatever the occasion is. Never expect an untrained animal to do what you want as he may not understand. Also never punish an animal for being afraid, you may make things terribly worse or spoil him for good for that thing he is afraid of. However this "who me" character trait is there in any donkey sometimes weak and sometimes strong and you must watch for it, learn to tell it from fear and cope with it. Don't overdo, use common sense, the donkey will!

TIMID

Timid donkeys when bought young and handled gently but firmly can mature into the friendly trusting type and be a pleasure to train. A very few remain forever shy but even these will come to trust and respect an owner who treats them well and gives them personal attention. Do not let them get away with mischief, but only stop them, do not punish them or frighten them. They can usually be made into well trained donkeys because they feel more secure with rules to follow in harness, or with bridle and saddle. However some will not take well to the confusion of the show ring, and brood jennies that are timid must have their foals handled early and often so they do not teach the foals to be shy of mankind.

SPOILED

A truly spoiled donkey is a pathetic thing because human beings have made him so. However he will usually kick or bite and only an experienced person should handle him. Unless he is a jack, a spoiled donkey will usually learn that an owner loves and cares for him and return the trust and respect of the owner but will probably be a one man animal even then and defensive toward strange people, and probably unsafe. If you get a jack like this and want to keep him as anything but a breeding jack, geld him, it will help him settle down and at least keep hormones from interfering with his neuroses! However, unless you want to retire a really spoiled donkey to a life of ease on green pastures (which humankind no doubt owes him), pass him by.

SULLEN

It is also very sad to see a sullen and broken spirited donkey. They have very patient natures and when one is truly sluggish and sullen, mistreatment and probably pain have made him so. Pass him up also unless you give him a good home as a pampered pet because he will not bring joy to your heart when you work him. He will probably do his work in an uncomplaining way but he will appear so miserable and depressed about it that you will feel guilty. However he may come round and make a good pet if you want him for this reason.

FRIENDLY AND TRUSTING

Obviously this is probably the ideal temperament for an amateur to train and use as a pleasure and show animal. He is a pleasure to be around, is eager to please, takes earned punishment in a proper spirit and learns quickly. If you get one of these donkeys you are truly blessed.

SLUGGISH

There are a few reasons for a donkey to be sluggish. One is bad health, especially malnutrition and worms and unkempt feet. Another is a large dose of some strains of

Mammoth Jackstock blood. Certain strains of this breed are of a decidedly sluggish nature, while others are not. Although sluggishness is attributed to the donkey by many authors on horses, those who deal with them know it is not their true nature and should be looked into as it probably shows such things as age or poor health.

OUCHY

Similar to the sullen temperament, he sulks, but every little thing tends to annoy him. *HE* doesn't like to trot, he doesn't like grooming, and is kind of a grouch. This may be a personality type based from physical problems as well as training, this kind of animal has often had leg or hoof problems and will never let you forget he is touchy and you are there to serve him in exactly the way *HE* wants.

In general, try to pick a donkey whose personality not only goes with your own, but with the work intended for it to do. If your brood jennet has some of these faults they may not be too serious, but handle her foals accordingly. The foals of a friendly-trusting type are usually that way themselves, but a shy and timid or sullen jenny tends to pass this on to her babies so handle them often and from a very young age.

For a pet, pick an animal that suits you the same way you ought to pick a spouse! For a pleasure or show animal pick an animal that has a lively and interested temperament, that likes to go and do and you can't go far wrong.

WHERE TO BUY DONKEYS

There is a certain amount of irony in this subject. Ask any breeder of miniature or standard donkeys and you are likely to hear that he is having a hard time selling his donkeys. Yet, from personal experience we know of many sincere, dedicated buyers who want high quality stock, both male and female that can't find what they want anywhere in the country at the time they want it! For this reason, we'll put our thoughts on buying and selling together in the hope that some help may come of it for both buyers and sellers.

Buying donkeys is a rather catchall title, since the man who wants a team of four matched paint jennies and the man who wants a miniature jack, not to mention the man who wants a whole carload of burros for a donkey basketball team, have very little in common. Of course the person who wants to buy one or two donkeys; of no particular quality, or training or color, for pets or just for fun is the person who will have the most luck closest to home. As with every other commodity the specialty or quality items are harder to come by. If you are looking for a pet and don't care for special qualities you can look in your local area. This is the first suggestion for those who are looking for something special as well. MANY AND MANY a show winner or prime breeding donkey, has been sold in the sale ring in between a Shetland and a broken down riding horse! The best thing about donkeys still, is that quality can be found anywhere at any price if you are smart enough to find it and know it when you see it, and brave enoh to take the gamble. One of the things that makes this a little easier is that the price for a "found donkey" will be so much lower than that of a good horse that it is much easier to gamble.

First of all, get a BREEDERS LISTING for a small fee (.50 per state at time of publication) from the AMERICAN DONKEY AND MULE SOCIETY. Also ask them for a list of the regional clubs, and contact the secretaries of each of these clubs that falls in the area you are willing to look in. Ask these hard working folks if they can recommend breeders, donkeys for sale or ads in their newsletter. Ask if you might take out a classified ad in their newsletter. These are very cheap and may bring you a bonanza.

The ADMS BREEDERS AND DEALERS LISTING is a very long list of people who have said that they have animals for sale. All different types are listed, and many of the people have probably run out, gone out of business or will refuse to answer your letters - but at least it is a good basis to work from. ADMS also has REGIONAL REPRESENTATIVE, INSPECTORS AND JUDGES who may be able to help you, since they have volunteered their services as donkey lovers. Also breeders may not have what you want, but have a good idea who has, so always ask your contacts if they have any ideas, even if they did not have the animal you wanted.

The next thing to think about is to put small advertisements in various magazines. WESTERN HORSEMAN, THE BRAYER, MULES AND MORE and other national or local horse or equine magazines are good choices. THE BRAYER and WESTERN HORSEMAN may bring you many answers from all over the country - or none - luck plays a big part here. There are many local and regional horse publications and there is bound to be one in your area - ask at your local tack shop, feed store, 4-H leader, vet or other equine person for the name of yours. Ads often appear in the newspapers, and you can look for them, and also put a wanted ad in the newspapers that cover rural areas nearby.

Try to find your local honest horse dealer and ask him to be on the lookout for what you want. The local farriers may well be able to put you in touch with someone with donkeys also. Try all the local horse auctions, grand bargains come into these sometimes because their owners, not being affiliated with clubs, have no idea where or how to sell them, and usually the auctioneer doesn't know their true value. Of course the best way to buy a donkey is from a reputable breeder who keeps his own herd and knows them well and can give you advice and help and hopefully has registered animals as well. If the animal you buy isn't registered you can get him registered upon inspection by an ADMS inspector or your vet and this is highly recommended, even if it is a gelding. Of course all breeders that are serious about their donkeys should register their animals and keep accurate records about all offspring.

Keep in mind when looking that a totally untrained donkey is not nearly so much of a handicap to the buyer as an untrained horse would be; most people including dealers are not aware of this. Tell the seller or horse trader (but not a donkey person) that you will take this untrained animal but pay a good deal less for it. You will easily be able to train it yourself, especially if it is a youngster and may save a good deal of money on a really good donkey in this way. Just remember that if you get a weanling or yearling you can't ride or drive him much until he is three, although you can put in a good deal of ground training, petting and handling before then.

HOW MUCH TO PAY

This is a thorny subject in any case, especially with inflation eating away at the dollar.

Keep in mind that the reputable donkey breeder has a GREAT DEAL of money in each foal, do not begrudge him the price he asks if the animal is obviously a good one, and well nourished with good antecedents. The breeder will probably be just barely making a profit! Only the seller of a well bred and/or well trained donkey can decide for himself what it is worth. Much depends on variables such as age, training, size, color, market, money already invested, etc.

In the past donkeys have sold at very low prices, even the valuable mammoth stock. It cannot be emphasized enough that this practice is very damaging to the breed and to its fanciers. People tend to think of the cheap donkey as worthless and only fit for dog food. We at ADMS. have spent years fighting for more prestige for the donkey and for higher prices for the good ones. People that pay a pittance for an animal frequently do not take proper care of it and keep it only as a toy. After all, for any animal, it is not the initial price that is the greatest expense, it is the upkeep. The upkeep on a good donkey is the same as on a poor one - and neither is very expensive to keep fat, healthy and sleek. It is much better to pay a reasonable price for a good animal and then to keep it properly than to pay almost nothing for a poor one and then try to keep it alive on thorns and thistles.

Although there is no clear "MARKET VALUE" on any of the donkey breeds, prices run about this way in 1998:

MINIATURE DONKEY - $800-$3000

STANDARD DONKEY (above 36" and less than 48") - $150 -$600 and up

LARGE STANDARD DONKEY (48" or taller) - $400 to $800 and up

MAMMOTH JACKSTOCK - $1,000 and up 54" for jennies, 56" for jacks, (minimum heights at 3-4 years. Do not count on 3-year old 48" animals putting on the required 8 inches)

Qualities such as fancy breeding from show winners, fancy colors, good training all add dollars, but can be more than worth it if this is what you need and/or want.

Of course, you may be lucky and find a bargain. They are prevalent everywhere, and you may be asked to pay considerably more than these figures for a fine animal. Just become knowledgeable enough to realize when you are being asked to pay a good deal for an animal that is NOT worth it. Naturally this will happen, and you should be aware of the possibility and be prepared for it. Never criticize the seller for this however, because this animal may be worth that price to him after all, it just isn't right for you. It is important to study the judging section and also to decide exactly what you want the animal for, before you go out and buy. A young, high-performance show donkey will cost more than the middle aged cutie you just want as a pet - but don't buy the fancy one if all you need is a loving family member. Don't be tempted to buy an animal that costs more than you can afford, if you don't really need and want such an animal!

BUYING BREEDING ANIMALS

If you are buying breeding stock there are some specific problems you need to watch for. Examine the jaws and teeth of the animal. **If there is more than a 1/4 inch over-bite or under-bite do not buy the animal for breeding purposes.** This is an inherited fault and these animals may not be registered. (Not only is it unsightly, but it can cause serious problems in the health of the donkey.) In addition, you should really have a vet examine the jack or jennet to make sure they have no reproductive tract infections. Such infections prevent good breeding performance and not only may make the animal worthless, but may spread to the whole herd causing untold damage and high veterinary bills. If you are buying a breeding jack of any type and are paying a good price for him, ask that not only a vet examine him for breeding soundness but a sperm count be taken to be checked by your vet. Remember, a jack that has been used for many mares may refuse jennets and vice versa, so make sure he will breed the way you want him to.

If you buy a bred jennet and it matters to you that she really is bred - make sure you have a guarantee of some sort (part of your money back if she isn't or something) or have her examined by a vet. Some of them look completely pregnant and ready to foal when they are barren, even experienced breeders are often fooled. A vet can do a pregnancy check in a few minutes and settle the problem. Of course your best bet if you want prime breeding stock is to buy registered stock from a reputable breeder. A jenny should have a foal at her side, should just have weaned one or should be pregnant, and if you are lucky you will be able to see her last foal - or the last foal or foals of the jack you are interested in. Your other best bet is to buy young, well bred animals that have never been bred. The normal young donkey should be a perfectly good breeder with maturity and proper health care.

We might add here, that if you want wild burros, adopted from a Government agency or humane group that they are usually in fairly good health, and will be in fine shape with some elementary worming, feeding and immunizations. Most of them have good strong conformation and good looks, contrary to the belief that they deteriorate in the wild. However, your choices will either be limited or none when it comes to picking out your animal and you will have to take what you get. Most wild burros are quite easy to tame if you are willing to put in the time, however **if you have absolutely NO equine experience** we wouldn't recommend getting one since you need a basic knowledge of working with equines to tame a, wild one. Most will become quite tame and usable in just a few months and quite trustworthy. Donkeys are like that, and if you can get one it may prove a bargain, as well as a humane act. Be sure you register your wild burro with the American Donkey and Mule Society when you get it, and be sure you include the brand markings that will be on it in your application for registration.

On the subject of branding. We do not advocate heat branding as it is considered to be inhumane, but if you can get your new donkey freeze branded or better yet, lip tattooed you will be much safer as he will be much easier to identify if he is ever lost or stolen. Electronic implants such as Avid or Home Again microchips are relatively inexpensive and are becoming invaluable in some cases of recovering stolen animals.

Some breed organizations are also requiring microchips (such as the French Poitou Studbook or the Canadian Livestock Board).

GETTING YOUR DONKEY OR DONKEYS HOME

If you have a good deal of experience in loading, own a nice trailer or have other good transportation and a trained donkey, you won't want to bother with this; otherwise here we go:

Short of tying a rope around the donkey's neck and leading him home, the new buyer will probably have a problem with transportation, and the farther away you and the donkey are the worse it will be.

There are reputable cross country horse and equine transportation firms that you can rely on to get your newly purchased donkey to you safely. They are expensive of course, but safe and convenient. You will find ads for them in any of the large horse magazines. We once sold a donkey and had her transported this way - and she enjoyed the company of fancy race horses all the way to her destination. Also the friend or friend of the friend who is going or coming that way may be prevailed upon - good luck with this one, it will be needed! Of course you can take you own, or rent a U-Haul horse trailer and go pick the donkey up yourself - which is probably the best way to do it most of the time.

The U-Haul trailer is quite a good idea for getting your donkey from closer areas too if you don't have your own. Or of course you can prevail on a friend of your farrier (maybe) or the local horse dealer's helper, etc., to pick up the donkey for you for a fee. Sometimes the seller can deliver - it never hurts to ask. He will charge a fee of course but you wouldn't expect him to do it for free would you? Also many a very small donkey has come home in a van, or if small, in a station wagon, and sometimes in the back of a car with the rear seat removed - but he had better be either placid or easy to control ! You should also check the laws in your area first before you get this extreme! If it is only a few miles a nice walk with a nice unhalter-trained donkey is guaranteed for weight loss and total frustration so try for a trailer if at all possible. Use your imagination for transport and people to transport for you, you probably aren't in as much trouble as you thought.

LOADING THE DONKEY OR DONKEYS

Whoops! Now we've said it! The chances that you will buy a trained donkey who jumps in a truck or trailer without turning a hair are probably rather small. It is not easy to tell a novice how to cope with the problem of a donkey who doesn't want a ride, although an experienced horseman should have no trouble with a smaller donkey. We hope we never even have to witness a man struggling with a Mammoth Jack that doesn't want to load! Even if the man doesn't cuss the donkey sure will!

Most of the time difficult loading occurs because the animal is young, unused to trailers or trucks or has had difficult rides in a trailer. Sometime YOU try standing in a stock truck or trailer without holding on while somebody drives the way most people do with animals behind. It will teach you a salutory lesson!

The first thing to remember about loading a donkey is that they are naturally very cautious, especially about where they put their feet. This is supremely logical even though frustrating to the human in charge. If your donkey refuses to load right away let him smell and examine the vehicle as much as he likes. When he is through he will let you know by either losing interest and trying to walk away, or by loading promptly. Only when he is truly through with examining the vehicle do you attempt your persuasion.

The second thing to remember about loading a donkey is DO NOT FRIGHTEN HIM. Having him respond to discipline is one thing, but if you truly get him scared out of his head, just forget it - besides you are training him to HATE trailers. The difference between an untrained and inexperienced donkey, and one that loads well but is "trying you on" is quite large. Beating the first one is totally wrong, but a couple of stiff switches on the back of the thighs of the second one will usually convince him that you are insisting he get in and he will load right up. If he does NOT get in with only very moderate spanking stop right there! If a donkey makes up his mind that he will not respond to physical discipline you can kill him in his tracks and not make him move -

so DO NOT OVERDO IT! Remember it is easier to TRAIN properly than to RETRAIN bad habits!

Here is a list of some of the methods that have been successfully used to load reluctant donkeys. Remember to keep your head, not to use violence and if you cuss, do it where non-cussers won't hear you.

1. Attach a good, strong, long rope to the (unbreakable) halter on the donkey. Run this rope from the halter to the front of the trailer and bring it around a strut or something strong at the front. If the trailer is enclosed make sure all windows are open so the interior will be well lighted, darkness and unknown places scare adult humans, much less donkeys! Bring the end of the rope back to you, where you stand beside the donkey - or better yet to a helper. Now, take hold of the donkey's tail firmly up near the root (supposed to keep him from kicking unless he is extremely wild) meanwhile keeping the rope taut and his head toward the vehicle. Do not get yourself or the donkey excited, but use the tail as a handle to push forward a few inches at a time. Try to apply enough irritation there to make him move away but not enough to hurt him and make him rebel and throw himself sideways or backwards. **Do not twist the tail** it can cause spinal damage. If someone can put the front feet one at a time on the ramp or floor of the vehicle it may help - but won't be easy. Many donkeys will go only so far and then stop. When this happens be sure to keep the rope tight to hold the ground you have gained. Then put your shoulder under the donkey's rump (unless he is very wild of course) and simply heave him up into the trailer - it helps to have as assistant pull on the front end of course. This works best when it is a total surprise to the animal.

2. Two people can hold both sides of a rope, put it around the donkey's thighs and then around a strong point in the trailer and heave him in this way, it is best to have a third person to put the animal's feet on the ramp or floor if this method is used.

3. Two strong people can simply link hands behind the donkey's rump and heave him in that way, we have seen many donkeys loaded by this method.

4. Some people get a long, strong, smooth pole like a fence post and use it to pry the animal ahead in the same logic as the rope trick, we know people who swear by this.

5. If the animal is gentle, place a bowl of its favorite treats in the trailer and move it away as it feeds. If you have a very greedy donkey, or one who does not really mind loading much this might work.

6. If the animal has loaded in the past at all, turn it around when it stops dead at the vehicle and walk it away. If it still stops turn it in small circles (not violently) until it signifies it would rather ride than spin.

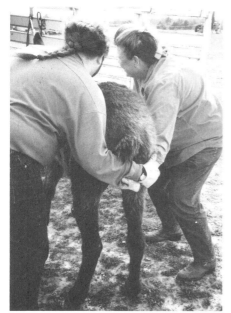

7. Some donkeys hate water and will load if you swish a wet broom, towel or a garden hose at them, or you can flap a jacket or umbrella at them (without panicking them) to influence them to move.

8. Some people report luck with blindfolding although great care must be taken and most animals don't respond well to it.

9. Have helpers holding fence sections, gates, etc., close in and see if the donkey will get in the trailer to escape them.

10. If there is a steep gradient to the ramp or the floor is high above the ground, back the trailer into a hole or against a bank so that it will be easier to walk in.

Loading the reluctant animal. Clasp hands with a partner and gently lift and encourage forward movement.

Take extreme care when you are having to load a reluctant animal. If the donkey is forced into the trailer and has balked, the hind legs can slide under the lip of the trailer and can be injured - sometimes just skinned up, sometimes badly! If it is possible to use a ramp, it is often much easier, or if the hind feet can be lifted and set up into the trailer. Many times a hind hoof set on the floor of the trailer and a gentle lift on the rump will cause the animal to step right in. Of course, buying a trained donkey or one that will follow a feed bucket in is much easier, but we have all had to deal with all kinds.

As Marjorie Dunkels has said, "Take things as slowly as you possibly can. If the donkey suspects that there is not time to be lost, it will invariably concoct all kinds of ruses to hold things up."
AFTER YOU FINALLY GET THE DONKEY LOADED, DO NOT SPOIL ALL YOUR EFFORTS BY GIVING HIM A BAD TRAILER RIDE WITH SHARP TURNS AND SUDDEN STOPS. The idea here is to show him that it will NOT HURT HIM to take a ride, not that you are going to force him into an unpleasant place and make it even more unpleasant for him after it starts moving!
ALWAYS CHECK THE VEHICLE BEFORE YOU LOAD THE DONKEY FOR GOOD TIRES, SOUND FLOORS AND SOUND CONSTRUCTION. ALSO MAKE SURE IT IS WELL AND PROPERLY HITCHED IF IT IS A TRAILER!

AMERICAN DONKEY REGISTRY   AMERICAN MULE REGISTRY
MINIATURE DONKEY REGISTRY

REGISTRATION RULES
1. INSPECTION. Donkey jacks and jennet must be INSPECTED. An inspector which has been appointed by ADMS will do this without charge unless mileage is necessary, and a list of these may be obtained from the registry office. If there is no inspector available INSPECTION MAY BE DONE BY YOUR LOCAL VETERINA-RIAN WHO TREATS HORSES. We can send you inspection forms for this purpose. You must realize however that this man is a professional and may charge for this service. MULES AND DONKEY GELDINGS DO NOT NEED TO BE INSPECTED.
2. ALL DONKEYS FOALED FROM ADR. REGISTERED PARENTS NEED NOT BE INSPECTED. Animals accepted with another registry with no glaring visual faults may be waived inspection. Correct bite and both testicles descended in mature males is still required.
3. Please include any possible pedigree (on separate sheet), all registration numbers from any other registries (mares, stallions or asses) and the name of that registry in full. Also if the animal is a specific breed such as Mammoth, Poitou, etc., please state the breed.
4. SIZES: MULES will be registered according to their sizes in inches. If the animal is young (mule or donkey) you may contact the registrar when it is 4 years old and change the size to the mature size. You may also state the type of mule on your application (pack, draft, miniature-saddle, etc.) IF ANIMAL IS A HINNY IT WILL BE REGISTERED AS SUCH.

DONKEY SIZES ARE AS FOLLOWS:

36 inches and less at the withers	MINIATURE
Over 36 inches and less than 48 inches	STANDARD
48 inches to 53 inches (jennets)	LARGE STANDARD
48 inches to 55 inches (jacks)	LARGE STANDARD
54 inches and up (jennets)	MAMMOTH
56 inches and up (jacks)	MAMMOTH

5. COLORS: Colors should be described from the ADMS color guidelines. Research is still ongoing as to the mechanisms of these colors, and some odd donkey colors seem to fall outside the range of descriptions. This is one reason clear color photos are needed, as well as stressing the importance of registering breeding stock -

much can be told from the colors and breeding history of the parents. See the color section for descriptions.

Mule colors may be given with any standard horse color description.

THE NORMAL MARKINGS OF WHITE UNDERPINNINGS AND MUZZLE WILL BE ASSUMED IN DONKEYS ALONG WITH THE CROSS. If they are lacking in donkeys or present in mules (stripe, leg stripes and/or cross) please indicate on color description.

6. SEX DESIGNATIONS: Male donkey, JACK; Female donkey, JENNET; Gelding donkey, GELDING. Male mule, HORSE MULE; Ungelded male mule, STALLION MULE; Female mule, MARE MULE. Male Hinny, HORSE HINNY; Female hinny, MARE HINNY.

7. AGE - Age is calculated from date of foaling. Put the date of foaling on application. If date is unknown put UNKNOWN on application and if possible year born, or approximate age.

8. PICTURES: Please send two color prints of the RIGHT SIDE, and two color prints of the LEFT SIDE. Polaroid will do if image is clear. THESE ARE FOR IDENTIFICATION AND FOR YOUR PROTECTION!

9. FEES: **Gelding** registration fee, $5.00. **Jennet** registration fee, $15.00. **Jack** $15.00. Mule registration fee, $10.00(Prices in 1999.) PLEASE INCLUDE FEES WITH APPLICATION.

10. TRANSFERS OF REGISTRATION: TRANSFER FEE IS $6.00. To transfer a mule or donkey registration send the registration certificate, along with the fee, and the name of the owner and the NEW OWNER with addresses to AMERICAN DONKEY AND MULE REGISTRY OFFICE. A new certificate will be issued to the new owner. OWNER DOES NOT HAVE TO BE AN ADMS MEMBER TO TRANSFER.

Contrary to popular belief, donkeys can gallop, and foals love to run and play. You will often see two jack foals galloping, bucking, and sparring all over the pasture. Donkeys can be trained to canter (lope) under saddle as well.

CHAPTER THREE

HEALTH

It is important that your prospective donkey either be in good health or is able to be brought into good health with a minimum of good care. When you first obtain your donkey, even if he seems in the best of health you should call your veterinarian to see him. Now, if you don't already have such a person on call, you must decide on one at this time. Be sure you choose a vet that normally treats large animals, especially equines if possible. If you call a small animal vet to see your donkey he is more likely to send those well known "little men in the white coats" than come himself! Ask around if you know some horse people and see what veterinarian is liked and trusted by them. If this is not possible just pick a large animal vet from the phone book - they are all professionals after all.

Even if your new animal seems in the best of health, do not fail to quarantine it from the rest of your herd for 10-14 days to avoid the possibility of infection!!! There are slow-developing diseases and parasites than can be transmitted and can devastate a breeding herd or show animals!

ARE THEY CURRENT?

When your veterinarian sees your donkey (you will save a travel charge if you can take the donkey to see him), ask him to give it the proper immunizations for equines in your area, take a test for Equine Infectious Anemia (Coggins) and not only give the donkey a thorough worming, but to set up a worming program (at least 4 times a year usually) that you can do by yourself. We happen not to be in favor of tube worming donkeys that are loving pets as we think it damages their trust in you and the vet, but sometimes it is necessary. If you are dealing with a wild equine, it might be the only way to make sure it is properly wormed.

Immunizations usually include tetanus, one for encephalitis and for whatever else might be endemic in your part of the country. There are no specific vaccinations just for donkeys. Your donkey or mule should receive the regular horse vaccinations The vet should do the first ones for you, after that, it is possible you may be able to purchase the serum at your feed store and do them yourself. If there are any other problems, such as external parasite infestation (lice, mites, etc.) thinness, obesity, overgrown hooves, etc., ask your vet to give you advice on treatment of these things also. Ask him to look at the teeth and make sure they are sound and do not need "floating" (filing down to even length) or do not need any other treatment. While he is there have him give the new donkey a good general check-up, this is worth its weight in gold to you in confidence and in caring for the animal later. We recommend this whether you are buying one single pet or a herd of breeding donkeys - nothing starts an animal off better with a new owner.

WHAT'S WRONG?

When examining a donkey for health, if you are considering buying him, there are some things you should do. Make yourself a checklist to take with you before your buy, or use the checklist on the previous pages.

If he is very thin, it is probably a lack of care combined with internal parasites. If you are spending much money on him you had batter have him examined for severe parasite infestation OR the dreaded **Equine Infectious Anemia.** The "**Coggins**" test is the easiest test run for this infection. This is becoming mandatory for many states. If at ALL possible the animal should have it **before** you buy him. Otherwise if he had the disease you might have to have him put down, which would be a terrible experience for a donkey owner. If you suspect he may have this and he hasn't had a test or if you are spending a lot of money, it is worthwhile to have him tested yourself before you buy him and at the same time the vet can look him over or other health problems. This is a common procedure for horses. The Coggins test should be given every year to animals that travel, show, breed or even go on local trail rides. There is no cure for EIA, and it is highly infectious. Some people may feel that the Coggins test is a waste of time, and there may be a slight basis in fact that it is not the best way to go. However, at this time, for most owners and equines, it is the ONLY way to go. An infected animal should really be put down. Not all animals die frrom EIA, although some do. An infected animal may be allowed to live - in flyproof quarantine, a minimum of 200 yards away from ANY OTHER equine, wearing a visible brand marking it as infected - for the rest of its life. It will also suffer the effects of the disease, anemia (poor blood count). Would you want this even for a beloved pet? A case in point came in 1997, when the BLM rounded up a herd of Mustangs. One year before, *one* of the 100+ herd had tested positive for EIA. A year later, 67 cases were positive in that herd. If the one infected animal had been put down, the cases might not have spread, or might not have been as great. That entire herd now faces possible euthanasia. Don't risk yours!!!

LOOKING SHABBY

Your new donkey will probably have worms and should be wormed from 2 to 4 times a year. The veterinarian should do the first worming and will probably set up a program which alternates different worming medicines which has proved to be the most effective type. Examination of manure samples can tell the type and count of parasites the animal is carrying. Most donkeys like the paste wormers you can buy in feed and tack stores. It comes in a plastic mouth syringe and you squirt it into his mouth. It is sticky like peanut butter and he can't spit it out. He may hate it, but it is surefire and he won't hold it against you like he would a tube worming. Wormers have become inexpensive to the point they cost less than a bag of oats in many places. There is really no excuse not to regularly worm your donkeys. Read the directions carefully. Breeding stock, show animals, or those who travel should be kept on strict schedules, as should animals on small pasture, where the chance or reinfection in higher.

If the new donkey looks "mangy" it is probably horse **lice**, which are fairly common in some areas and usually get into winter coats. Horse louse powder is easily bought at any ranch supply or feed store and will do the trick. Of course a more healthy "moth-eaten" appearance (no skin showing - just short hair) means he is just shedding his winter coat (donkeys shed 2 months later than horses in the same locality). If there are scabs, bare skin or other obvious problems it would be best not to buy him, but if you must have that animal, consult a vet. One skin problem you may find and is usually easily recognized occurs in animals with pink skin. Sores, scabs etc. form on this skin usually to sun allergy. It is best to keep animals that have this problem in at the daytime and turn them out to graze at night.

When the sores are cleared up sunscreen lotion such as red-haired humans use is a big help when you are using him in daylight. Sometimes these animals also suffer from a sensitivity to certain plants in pastures as well. Sometimes nettles can cause a severe rash.

You should pick up and examine the feet of your prospective donkey if he will let you. If he won't, find out just how aggressive he is about it! If your animal cannot be trained to pick up his feet for the farrier, you are in a lot of trouble. If he really fights hysterically just look for another donkey, if his resistance is less frantic and he is just protesting out of lack of interest or distaste then he can be trained. If he has feet that smell foul he may have **thrush**. This is a sort of foot rot which comes from standing in dirty wet places. Have a farrier come and look at him. Usually it can be cured fairly easily but it could be too far advanced. Never buy a donkey which is lame or which walks tenderly on its feet. There are too many serious complications that can keep a foundered or injured animal from ever walking properly again. An exception to this is if you want to give a pet a good retirement home - in this case go ahead, but keep in mind you may have some long-term vet and farrier bills.

If the donkey's droppings are loose and wet it can easily mean nerves at being in a strange place, riding in a trailer or being used for strange things. However it could be intestinal trouble, and only experience and luck can help you determine which by just looking. The safest thing is to have the animal "vetted", the next is to buy from reputable people and buy an animal that looks plump, sleek and well cared for. If he is at home, his droppings should be normal. You can see differences in the spring when the grass first comes in, the maure is looser and usually greener. If it smells really foul, then have a second thought! Manure usually has an odor, but a "farmy" smell, not rotten, or gassy or foul.

If you are forced to take chances - such as at an auction, examine the animal carefully. Make sure it has a bright, clear eye with **no discharge** at mouth, eyes or nostrils. Check genitals for discharges, pus or blood and examine loose or watery stools for black matter (dried blood), blood, worms or froth and bubbles. Bowel movements should not be odd colors (yellowy, rust-red, sticky black) or smell foul either.

If you are looking for breeding stock, do not buy animals who have poor conformation, and especially if the teeth do not meet evenly. Over-shot and under-shot jaws are usually inherited defects. Minor malocclusions are fine in the pet, but not in brood stock.

If the feet are overgrown it can usually be corrected fairly easily. If they are EXTREMELY overgrown it will be a long process and may never be perfect. Sometimes the animal can then only be used for a pet. The strain of extra weight on sore feet may exclude severely foundered jennets from breeding programs. If you cannot afford to hire or cannot find a good farrier do not buy an animal with really overgrown "Turkish slipper" hooves. These hooves will need special attention and care for the rest of the animal's life (remember we might be talking 35 years....).

There should be no swellings or open sores on the animal, especially under the jaw or on the face. Do not mistake "pones" of fat on the ribs or rump or the roll of fat on the neck for swellings - they are just "cellulite". The legs if you can see them should be clean and free of bumps, lumps or odd shapes. If you cannot see them, or even if you can, run your hand over them. If the animal objects really strenuously and is not a wild burro, or an unbroken colt - you might stop there and think of going on to the next one. If the legs or feet are deformed or twisted in any way do not buy except as a pet. If the deformation is clearly from an injury and the animal is sound it might make a breeding animal - but remember pregnancy adds a lot of weight to a jennet's leg and if she is lame she will be in pain. If she limps but is not in pain and the reason is an injury it should be all right. Rarely, in donkeys, the feet may be brittle or chipping away. This is a fairly unusual condition for the foot of the well nourished ass, and it may denote dietary deficiency or internal problems. Of course some chips or small cracks in the lower part of the foot are not abnormal, we are speaking here of severe dry and chipped hooves. If at all possible, examine the sole of the foot. Clean it out with your own hoof pick, brought along for the purpose if necessary. The sole should be solidly concave, not convex or bulging downward. If it looks this way, of if the animal steps tenderly "walking on eggs", do not buy him. He has probably been foundered, usually from obesity and it may be so serious as to keep him in pain and unusable for the rest of his life. Foundered donkeys can have hidden abcesses, and have hoof problems off and on as the seasons change.

After you have your donkey it may start to show signs of sickness, especially discharge from eyes and nostrils and a cough. THIS IS WHY YOU MUST QUARANTINE! Many equines pick up influenza or other diseases at shows, sales or any gathering of equines - CALL THE VET IMMEDIATELY. Your animal can die from this!!! (And if you have decided you don't have to quarantine, remember you have just exposed your entire herd to whatever this new animal is suffering from.) However if you call the vet as soon as you notice the symptoms he can probably lighten the sickness very much with treatment and make it change from frightening to minor - so call him! There is not a thing you can do to prevent this. However if you take your donkey where there are concentrations of equines in the winter months especially, have him given flu shots and other immunizations recommended by your vet first - it may save you big vet bills and much heartache.

LOOKING THE GIFT DONKEY IN THE MOUTH

The reasoning behind that old saying is based on the fact that you CAN guess an equine's age by looking that the teeth. A gift horse might have been 30 years old - not a really reliable prospect! If you would like to know your donkey's age and haven't a horsey friend who know how to tell, ask the vet to look for age at the same time as he examines teeth for problems when you first get your donkey.

On the nest page are some basic things you can look at to tell the age of an equine. The teeth have distinct angles and patterns of wear that change with the age. There are excellent Tooth Charts available, but shown on the chart are the basics which can let you make a good estimate. Buying from a reputable breeder will help, but even if you know the birth date of a mature animal, you can check the teeth against that date.

ROLLING

A word needs to be said about the marked tendency of donkeys to roll over and over in any suitable patch of dust, dirt, sand or if the weather is wet - mud. All equines roll this way, but in donkeys the tendency is much more marked than in mules. It is kindest to dump a load of sand (coarse) in the new donkey's pasture in the place you want to see bare - otherwise they will make it bare themselves and establish their own rolling places. The donkey will also scoop dust up with his tail to cover his belly. The newly cut gelding will need supervision to prevent this, or you will have an incision full of dirt.

When the donkey stands up after rolling, he will not, unlike the horse, shake his whole body. He will only shake his head and ears to remove excess dust. In his desert home this dust was needed. It is retained in the coat to protect the animal from both heat and cold and provides very good insulation. It is this characteristic which make donkeys almost always send up a huge cloud of dust when patted by the human hand. The same hand almost always comes away dirty! For this reason the donkey has to be bathed before shows or appearing in public. It is best to put a blanket on thm after a bath or else you will have a dirty donkey as soon as the hair dries enough not to feel uncomfortable when rolling. This rolling dries sweat and makes it go away also, if the donkey is hot. It is a healthy means of temperature control and skin maintenance and the donkey should always have a rock-free place to do his rolling since rocks can bruise the skin and cause infections and other trouble.

There is an excellent book called: How to Be Your Own Vet (Sometimes) and many other good equine Emergency Care manuals you can order from your local bookseller. If you are interested in breeding, you may want to order the Donkey Breeder's Handbook, by Ruth Harris, available from the Hee Haw Book Service. Meanwhile here is some basic information on diseases and emergency care. We are not vets, and the information here has been suggested and reviewed by vets, but this is not a Vet manual! IF IN DOUBT ABOUT ANY RECOMMENDATIONS, FROM ANY BOOK, LITERATURE OR VERBAL SOURCE, CONSULT WITH YOUR VET!

Historique of Wishing Star Farms, Leah's part-bred Poitou gelding, having a good roll!

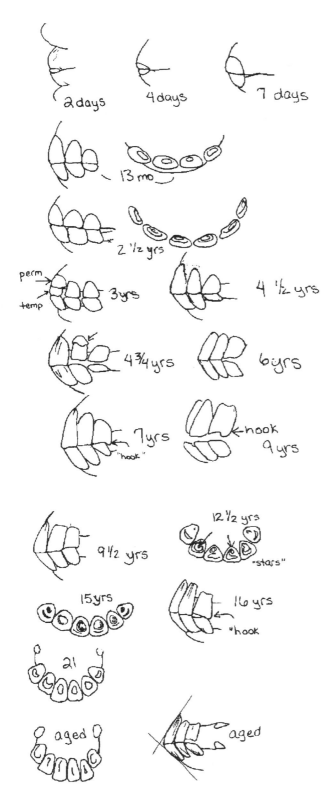

6-8 days - central baby teeth erupt.
6-8 weeks - intermediate baby teeth erupt.
6-8 months - corner baby teeth erupt.
1 year - Central and intermediate baby teeth in wear, upper and lower corners barely touching.
2 years - all baby teeth worn smooth
2 1/2 yrs - Permanent centrals erupt.
3 years - Permanent centrals in wear.
3 1/2 yrs - Permanent intermediate teeth erupt.
4 years - Permanent intermediate teeth in wear.
4 1/2 yrs - Permanent corners erupt.
5 years - Permanent corner teeth in wear.
6 years - cups dissapear from central teeth.
7 years - cups dissapear from intermediate teeth. Hook can be seen on corners.
8 years - cups dissapear from corners. Dental stars begin to appear.
9-12 years - angle becomes more acute (the term long in the tooth originates with the sharp angle seen in aged equines.) Dental starts move to the center of the teeth.
15-20 years, upper incisors appear longer. Table surfaces are more triangular as opposed to round.
25-30 years - teeth oval in shape, may be worn down. Gum may show between teeth when viewed as table (from above).

Aging by teeth can be fairly accurate, but after a certain age, it is nearly impossible to discern an exact age by viewing the condition of the teeth. Records and registration papers should be used for verification.

Disease	Outstanding symptoms	Treatment or Control
Equine Encephalitis (Sleeping Sickness)	Fever, Impaired vision, irregular gait, incoordination, yawning, grinding of teeth, drowsiness, inability to swallow, inability to rise when down, paralysis and death.	Annual vaccination (can be combined serum) is recommended in areas where the disease is prevalent. No specific agent is available for treating and treatment consists of supportive measures and good nursing. Consult your veterinarian.
Strangles (Distemper)	High temperature, increased respiration, depression, nasal discharge after 2nd or 3rd day, swelling of lymph nodes (under jaw) which usually abcess.	Antiserum and bacterin are available (including new intranasal injection). Provide complete rest. Avoid stresses of cold, drafts or moisture. Fresh drinking water should be available at all times. Consult your vet for systemic treatment and care of abcesses.
Tetanus (Lockjaw)	Follow infection of wounds, usually deep puncture wounds. Incubation period from 1 week to several months. First symptoms include stiffness and third eyelid may draw over eye when excited. Spasms occur after 24 hours of onset. Reflexes increase if animal is frightened or excited. Spasms of neck and back muscles cause distinct extension of head and neck.	Prevention in the form of regular Tetanus boosters (may be given in combined injections). Treatment of wounds, surgical procedures with an antitoxin immediately can help as prevention. Once contracted, this disease requires professional treatment. Disease is widespread. Vaccination of broodmares and pastured stock is essential.
Azoturia (Monday Morning Disease)	Occurs soon after being put to work: stiffness, sweating. Affected muscles swollen, tense, may assume "sitting dog" position. (Most commonly referred to in Draft animals who worked heavily all week then stood idle on Sunday, returning to work on Mondays "tied up".	Decrease grain feeding and allow exercise when animals are off work. Perform careful, slow warmup after long rests. Animals stopped immediately after beginning of symptoms have a good chance of recovery. Do not move the animal any distance. Blanket animal to keep it warm. Contact vet for systemic treatment.

Laminitis (Founder)	May be acute or chronic, follows feeding of excessive grain or lush pasture or other rich feed, fast work on hard roads, large amount of cold water while animal is hot, toxemia and/or fevers following infection or disease. Acute case shows inflammation of the sensitive laminae on one or more feet. Feet warm, sensitive to the touch, animal lame, pain on standing. Temperature elevated (over 106F), sweating. Chronic cases have hoof distortion, wall may be concave, sole drops, rings on outer wall, coffin bone rotation.	Acute case - stand animal in cool water or mud to ease fever and swelling in hooves. Call Vet. Chronic founder: Trim feet as needed, trim to protect sole. Prognosis not good. Founder will probably recur with seasonal changes, fresh grass. Abcesses common in chronic cases.
Hyperlipemia	Body's demand for energy exceeds supply, fat deposits broken down too fast for liver to process. Usually occurs after not eating for 3-8 days. Some cases may be caused by colic or parasitism. Liver & kidneys cease function. Donkey is lethargic, depressed, poor appetite. Pain in abdomen, increased temperature, respiratory rate. Progresses to incoordination, jaundice, edema. Severe nervous dysfunction as disease progresses, animal may become recumbent, abortion may occur in terminal phases.	Vet care essential if animal is to be saved. Therapy should be to treat primary stress, restore energy balance. Force feeding or IV fluids may be necessary. Frequent monitoring of blood values important. Antibiotics and vitamins may be beneficial. Insulin shows variable success Prevention of obesity and monitoring of stress levels in overweight or gravid animals may prevent onset.
Equine Protozoan Myelo-encephalitis (EPM) (Possum Fever	Primarily in USA, infection by parasite occur in brain & spinal cord. Brain: signs include head tilt, facial paralysis, disorientation, visual deficits. Spinal cord: stumbling, incoordination, lameness, inability to stand.	Onset may be sudden or gradual. Source of infection unknown by bird or oppossum dropping suspected. Diagnosis difficult, vet care required. Prevention includes parasite reduction program such as worming, clean environment. Prognosis unclear on known cases, but not good.
Vesicular Stomatitus	Characterized by fluid-filled blisters (vesicles) on tongue and mouth. Animal cannot eat or drink without pain, goes off feed. Weight loss, lethargy.	Highly contagious. Isolate infected cases. Call Vet. Restrict travel to and from states with active VS cases.

BASIC FIRST AID:

(Remember that some of this you can do before the vet arrives, but if EVER in doubt - do nothing and call the vet first!!! There are some cases where you might do more harm than good by attempting to treat the animal without Vet help.)

Deep Cuts: Do not panic when you see lots of blood. Donkeys have a good deal of this fluid and the only steps you need to take are to stop the flow as soon as possible. DO call the vet, and DO stay calm as if you get excited, the animal is likely to as well. Small wounds that have hit a vessel may bleed profusely while some wounds, especially in muscular areas may appear huge and not bleed much at all. Such huge gaping wounds do not mean your donkey is a lost cause. Donkeys heal well and you must always use good first aid and then call the vet - there might not even be a scar! In wounds where bleeding is profuse, especially those on the legs a pressure bandage is the best first aid but DO NOT USE A TOURNIQUET. A clean bandage can be used to wrap the leg and should be applied with even pressure above, over and below the wound. Special attention should be given to the pressure being evenly distributed. It is good where possible to bandage from the coronet band up to a point above the wound.

If circumstances permit, the wound can be cleaned with a mild soap and water or diluted hydrogen peroxide solution. However, it is more important to stop the bleeding and prevent further contamination. Do not change a blood soaked bandage for a fresh one, clotted blood is nature's way of bandaging a wound. A properly applied pressure bandage can be left as long as 24 hours with no serious problem developing. CALL THE VET. If there is a flap of skin hanging down clean it along with the wound and when bandaging put it in place. Don't attempt to remove the skin, and let the know there is a skin flap hanging. If there is a large wound, getting the skin black in place as soon as possible may result in a much smaller scar, with less granulation and proud flesh.

If there is any foreign object in the wound - a stick, wire, glass, etc - do not attempt to pull it out. It could be stopping major blood flow, or could cause more damage on the way out of the wound.

A Case history:
Leah Patton

A case in point, we had a Paint mare who went through a barbed wire fence, and tore a flap off of the point of her knee on her foreleg. She was missing for two days, and that time period was devastating to her leg. The bleeding was not bad, but the torn area puffed up bigger than a fist, and was hard and filled across the entire torn surface. The vet told us if we had been able to replace the flap where it belong, even without stitching it, the healing process would have been halved.

Since the tear was on her knee, the mare was placed on restricted movement (which meant special stall confinement) with twice-daily antibiotics and debreeding of the wound. We had to abrade the wound, spray with topical medicine, and re-apply a pressure bandage to reduce the size of the knee. It took several months for the pressure to slowly push the flap back to where it needed to be, and for the wound to close down to a ½" wide scar. During this time the mare was tied in a specially fitted stall (with an overhead runner and swivel for her tie, panic snaps, and a padded stall door where she could at least see and talk other horses). Her water had to be elevated, and her hay kept full, since she was not allowed to lower her head (so she could not chew on the bandage). She was not even supposed to walk from the stall to the wash rack, as even that little movement would break down the healing tissue. She lost over a hundred pounds (vet's orders and restricted diet) and could not lie down during all that time. To have placed that much strain on the knee would have opened the healing wound right back up instantly.

Secondary infection set in under the original gash and setback the process again. This was die to the delayed start on the treatment, allowing infection to settle deeper into the tissue. She finally healed up, but it was wearing on horse and owner.

The moral - call the vet as soon as you can - take all emergency precautions you can to prevent setbacks and longer-term healing!!!

For wounds that cannot be bandaged, pressure can be applied by holding thick, clean cloths over the wound. Most will stop of their own accord fairly soon and no medicine that will interfere with blood clotting should be used. Use good common sense and keep the donkey warm, dry and protected from the elements as much as possible.

Chest or abdominal wounds must be bandaged with a large firm bandage wrapped completely around the body and any protruding intestines must be kept in. If dirty they may be washed off with a warm salt water solution - intestine must be kept moist! Keep around the barn a sterile solution of boiled water with 1 tsp. per pint of salt in it.

Eye Injuries: Call vet, reduce sunlight, remove foreign body if that is EASILY done. If not leave it for vet. Do not wash eye or medicate! Castor oil may be used to wash an eye for first aid purposes. Never use any medication containing cortisone. Cover the eye only if instructed by a vet.

Saddle Sores: Cold packs, keep area most, correct the cause.

Bruises: Cold water, cold bandages, cold packs.

Broken Leg: Very serious, keep immobile if possible, protect wound from contamination with bandage. A splint may be made with a pillow and stock or rod. Pillow must be taped to leg as tightly as possibly and stiffened with broom handle or something similar. Even a crop and vetwrap can be used. CALL VET IMMEDIATELY!

Digestive Problems: Twisted gut can kill in great agony. If the donkey shows any of the following symptoms call the vet immediately.
1. Turning the head to look at his side, obviously distressed.
2. Pawing the ground, sweating, combined with above.
3. Lie down as if to rest, look at side, roll, rolling is different from usual. Donkey rolling, sort of violent as if he wants to ease the pain.

Walk the donkey but do not exhaust him, and call the vet. If the symptoms are light, watch him for 10 or 15 minutes before you call the vet. He may tell you to walk him for half an hour and call again, but if he is violently ill he may have a twisted intestine, get the vet immediately.

Gut sounds: If you have ever put your ear to the side of an equine, his tummy is almost always gurgling. This is GOOD! It doesn't mean he's hungry, it means the gut is functioning normally. If you suspect colic, listen for gut sounds. If you DON'T hear gut sounds, this is a good indication of something wrong. Be sure to tell the vet.

Do not administer any medicine to the animal unless your vet directs you to do so. Keep mineral oil on hand in your barn, as this is probably the only medicine you will be able to give - most other colic medicine are injections that the vet will give.

RESTRAINING THE INJURED ANIMAL

First, make sure the animal is restrained with a halter and lead. However, if you must chase the injured animal all over the field to halter it - just wait! Consult with the vet in case you could cause more damage by exciting the animal or risking more trauma by the struggles. If your haltered animal is excited a blindfold may help.

If the animal is already down, you can restrain by sitting on the neck in large animals. Sit up near the junction of the head and neck. Face away from the legs - if the animal manages to shake you off, you will not be under the feet.

For smaller animal, kneel on the neck at the head. Face the same direction as the legs - you can stand up and be clear of the animal if it struggles.

Do not attempt to truss up the legs unless the vet instructs you to do so - you are very likely to get hit by flailing hooves, and might possibly cause more injury to the animal.

Tie only with a halter and lead, and don't tie with the stud chain. If your animal must have a stud chain for handling, use a second lead attached to the halter to tie with. A lip twitch (there are numerous kinds from the humane clamp to the old broomstick-and-cord) can be used if you can safely get near the head and apply the twitch. If you are able to restrain the animal in the barn aisle or at a sturdy fence rail, use a quick-release knot, or keep ropes with regular snaps on one end and "panic" snaps on the other available for emergencies.

If the animal is bridled, be sure to get a halter on as soon as possible, especially if the animal is to be tied. The reins are not made for tying, and will break easier than a lead rope. If the animal pulls back against the tied bridle, the bit may twist or slip and injure the mouth as well. If you can't safely remove the bridle and replace it with the halter, put the halter on OVER the bridle, and use the lead rope for tying.

Let the reins go up into the halter, to help keep them out of the way. The throatlatch of the halter will hold them looped up away from the snap of the lead rope. Attach the lead rope to the halther and not to the bridle or bit.

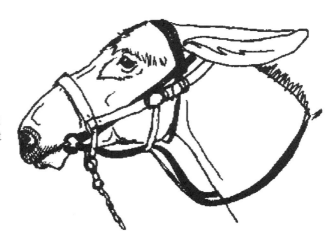

EXTERNAL PARASITES

Have you ever been aggravated by swarms of mosquitoes, irritated by ticks and chiggers, or agitated by fleas? These discomforts and many more are experienced by some horses for extended periods of time because of external parasites.

A parasite is defined as "a plant or animal living on, in, or with another living organism (its host) at whose expense it derives food and shelter". External parasites of horses/donkeys/mules usually bite (with the exception of certain flies) and/or suck blood for food, and use body temperature and the hair of the host for comfort and shelter.

Foals and young growing donkeys are especially susceptible to all types of parasites, which may result in temporary or permanent lack of development.

External parasites are a problem to many donkeys. They are often associated with improper nutrition, mild forms of disease, stress, and sometimes conditions of general neglect. External parasites are easier to eradicate or control than internal parasites, but response to treatment may be disappointing unless a total health program is practiced.

The most common external parasites are (1) flies, (2) lice, (3) mites, (4) ticks, and (5) a fungus causing ringworm. Both ringworm and mange mites are communicable from the animal to man.

FLIES

Flies are a constant source of annoyance to equines, making them restless and ill at ease. The **house fly** and **face fly** feed on skin, nasal and eye secretions, or debris, but do not bite. The tenaciousness of the feeding face fly makes its presence particularly annoying to horses. They are commonly found in the northern half of the United States. **Horn flies, stable flies,** and **deer** and **horse flies** are biting insects that suck blood.

Since they show a preference, some horses or donkeys are severely harassed by these pests. Biting flies can be vectors of serious diseases such as encephalomyelitis.

Blow flies are common to large areas of the United States, and effect damage by laying eggs in wounds. One type hatches into **maggots** which feed on dead tissue, retarding healing and enlarging the wound. The other type hatches into **screw worms**, which feed on live tissue, causing severe damage and sometimes death. Both types are easily eradicated by cleaning the wound and applying a proper medicant.

Control

Fly control is best effected by removal of waste and decaying vegetable material. Manure should be stored in covered containers or spread thinly (for rapid drying) on fields not used by horses.

Remove moist hay, straw, garbage, and grain frequently during warm weather. Use screens when practical.

Fly predators can sometime be beneficial, although their use is not approved in all areas. You must time the release of fly predators with the life cycles of both insects as well.

Life Cycle

The four stages of the life cycle are the egg, the larva, the pupa, the adult. House, stable, and horn flies commonly lay their eggs in manure or occasionally in decaying vegetation or any moist collection of spilled grain. Face flies lay their eggs in fresh manure on pastures. Horse and deer flies deposit eggs in the mud of swamps, salt marshes, or on vegetation near water.

Treatment

Successful treatment of flies varies from one part of the country to another and will be influenced by the degree of immunity they have established for a specific product. For this reason a qualified person should be consulted for recommendation in a given area. Regardless of the area, pesticides should be considered poisonous and should be regarded with extreme caution. Read the directions carefully and follow them closely. Do not permit sprays to contaminate feed or surfaces that horses will lick. Do not store them where they may accidentally get into feed. Baits are effective but poisonous and should be placed out of reach of horses because many contain enough sugar to induce their consumption. Strands or cords treated with insecticide and hung in stables are often effective. Daily sponging or spraying may be necessary to give protection from horse flies and face flies. For those insecticides commonly used and recommended for your area, contact your local county agent or veterinarian.

Use only fly sprays that are approved for horses. Do not use cattle dips or sprays on equines, as many of these products may be toxic to horses, donkeys and mules.

LICE

Lice that infest equines are of both the biting and sucking kind. Long hair is conducive to maximum reproduction and spread of lice, thus they are often observed in poorly groomed and poorly housed horses and on donkeys, especially in early spring. Symptoms include rubbing, biting, general unthriftiness, and patches of skin denuded of hair. The longer, coarser hair of a donkey is a perfect host environment for lice.

Life Cycle

The adult lice attach their eggs to the hair, usually close to the skin (the so called nits). Here they hatch in from 11 to 20 days. The young lice reach maturity and the female begins laying eggs when she is 11 to 12 days of age. Lice live their entire lives on the host, and can exist only about three days when off the host animal.

Prevention

Proper feeding, grooming, and clean stabling will do much to prevent louse infestations. Lice may be carried from one animal to another on harness, saddles, blankets, brushes, or curry combs moved directly from a lousy animal to one free from lice. Use nylon grooming brushes on the infected animal, and wash thoroughly after use. Do not use brushes from the infected animal on other stock.

Treatment

Donkeys may be dipped, sprayed, sponged, or dusted thoroughly for lice control. The treatment should be repeated in two to three weeks in order to destroy the lice hatching from eggs not destroyed by the first application. Contact your county agent or veterinarian for the recommended insecticides most commonly used in your area under prevailing regulations.

MITES

Mites are microscopic creatures that cause horse mange. Positive identity is difficult because skin scrapings must be examined carefully under a microscope. Three genera exist - Sarcoptes, Psoroptes, or Chorioptes. **Sarcoptic mites** burrow under the skin scurf where they lay eggs and reproduce. **Chorioptic type** may cause foot mange resembling scratches, although all three may cause mange on any part of the body.

Symptoms include irritation, itching, inflammation, loss of hair, crusty scab formation, and folding of the skin.

Life Cycle

Female mites lay from 10 to 25 eggs during the laying period, which lasts from 12 to 15 days. After this period the female dies in the burrow. Eggs hatch in 8 to 10 days into young mites. After passing through several molts, they reach maturity and are ready to begin egg laying again in from 10 to 12 days.

Treatment

Mange is difficult to eradicate in any species of animal. Experience indicates that infested animals should be re-treated every 7 days in order to gain control. Dusts are not effective. Spraying or thorough wetting with a brush-washing technique is necessary to reach the well-hidden mites. Your county agent of veterinarian are your best sources for information regarding the prevailing regulations for the kinds and use of insecticides.

TICKS

Ticks are a problem to horses in many parts of the country. Like other biting insects, they are vectors of some serious diseases. Piroplasmosis recently infected over one hundred horses in the southeastern part of the United States. In 1960, the **red tick,** carrier of African horse fever, was identified for the first time in this country, in zoo animals in Florida. Lyme disease, carried by the tiny **Deer ticks,** can be transmitted to human and equine alike.

Life Cycle

The four stages include the egg, the six-legged larva or **seed tick**, the eight-legged nymph, and the adult. Transition from one stage to the next occurs by molting. The number of generations produced annually varies from one every two or more years up to four or five per year, depending on the species. All ticks attach to the host by biting and feed on blood.

Treatment

In areas where ticks are a serious problem, dipping entire animals must be resorted to. If only a few ticks are found, swab them with cotton dipped in alcohol or chloroform. Since ticks breathe by means of spiracles or holes found on the abdomen, this tends to anesthetize or suffocate them. Pulling ticks off can result in mouth parts being left under the skin and causing an infection at the site. Several insecticides are available. Follow the recommendations of your county agent or veterinarian regarding their use.

RINGWORM

Ringworm is caused by various species of fungi, arranged in circles on the skin. If penetration is deep enough, severe itching results; and secondary infection may lead to abscesses. The lesions are usually covered with greyish crusts through which short hairs protrude.

Treatment

If only a few lesions are present, soften crusts with warm soap and water and remove, dry the area, and paint with tincture of iodine daily for one to two weeks. If lesions are extensive, contact your veterinarian, since there are many new fungicides more effective than iodine. When treating or handling infected horses, use rubber gloves and wash hands thoroughly after treatment. All scraping should be carefully disposed of. Children are particularly prone to ringworm infections.

Under the best management conditions donkeys harbor some parasites. Their effect is not spectacular or may be unnoticed, but they decrease work efficiency and cause discomfort. Heavy infestations render horses useless and may cause death or permanent damage. For these reasons a total health program should be effected.

Horse Fly

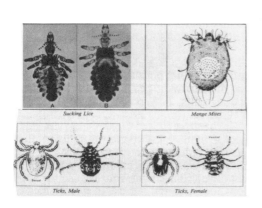

Sucking Lice

Mange Mites

Ticks, Male

Ticks, Female

Stable Fly

Horse fly approximately 1.5 times actual size. Other photos enlarged to show detail.

SPRAYING THE PET DONKEY FOR FLIES

When donkeys are out in pasture in the summer, especially if clipped, biting flies are a terrible pest for them. There are as many ways of applying fly repellants as there are folks who apply them, but here is the way we have developed for our many animals over the years.

In the first place, you must use a fly preparation that is made exclusively for equines. Never use cattle insecticide as it will cause terrible skin problems on horses and donkeys. Of the different types that are offered, the oil base ones last the longest, the types that are thick like petroleum jelly are good for the odd place like around the eyes, around wounds etc., since they last a long time. The types that come in a spray bottle already are the most convenient, and the water based type that the donkey owner dilutes himself with water is the most economical.

The type we use, selected on the basis of economics is the water based type. We buy the container then obtain a really good plastic spray bottle. We prefer the ones we get from our Amway dealer, because the quality is excellent, and they have all the markings and dilutions (for instance 7:1 is shown, as are other dilutions). This makes the preparing of your fly spray exact which is nice, and much safer. Pet-supply stores such as the PetsMart, Petco, or other large stores are now beginning to carry equine supplies as well, or you can get gardening spray bottles (again, marked nicely for measuring) in the garden-supply section of Hardware stores, Wal-Mart, or your local grocery or feed store.

We make up the spray in this bottle fresh each day. Then we spray each donkey once every day or two. We concentrate especially on the cannon bones since in our area flies eat the donkeys unmercifully on this area. If special work is needed around eyes, we have a stick insecticide made especially for this purpose and use that.

At first the donkeys do not like the spray, so we tie them up. After a few times they decide it feels good and we only have to bribe them with a crust of bread or a carrot to keep them still - and some just stand still because they seem to like it.

This spray bottle method takes only about 5 minutes for four animals and they are fine for a day or two unless they get rained on, which immediately washes any type of fly spray off.

INTERNAL PARASITES

According to Webster's Dictionary, a parasite is a plant or animal living in, on, or with another living organism (its host), at whose expense it obtains food and shelter. More than 150 different kinds of parasites have been found to infest horses. Almost all horses harbor some parasites. External types include lice, flies, ticks, mange, and ringworm. The internal types, which we will deal with include strongyles or blood worms, ascarids, stomach worms, pinworms, and bots.

Every horse owner should have his animal on a parasite prevention and control program. In order to draw up such a program, it is important to know the life cycle of the various worms so that proper preventive and treatment procedures can be followed.

ECONOMIC IMPORTANCE

The effect of the presence of **worm parasites** are not usually spectacular. However, they do cause decreased work efficiency, poor utilization of food, are one of the causes of colic, may be the cause of intermittent lameness, may cause a chronic cough and bronchitis, and occasionally death due to blood clot. Some adult worms produce toxins that destroy red blood cells, leading to an unthrifty anemic condition. Immature worms migrating through body tissues open the way for bacteria and fungi to enter, causing other serious diseases.

PREVENTION OF PARASITISM

Internal parasites gain entry to the animal body in the form of eggs, larvae, or adults. This may be largely prevented by various forms of management which break the life cycle of the parasite. Those worms already present will have to be killed by drugs, depending on the kind of parasite present. The following practices have been found to be effective in reducing parasite numbers:

1. Do not feed hay or grain on the ground . This prevents contamination of feeds with manure, which may contain large numbers of parasite eggs or larvae.
2. Do not allow equines to obtain water from barnyard pools or water holes on pasture, since manure drainage into these areas makes them a source of internal parasites.
3. Clean stalls and rebed as often as possible so that there will be less chance of internal parasites getting on feeds from fecal material.
4. If the stall floor is of earth, remove ten to twelve inches once or twice yearly and replace with clean soil.
5. Remove manure from premises daily and either spread on a field where horses will not graze for a year or where the field will be plowed and reseeded before equines have contact with it.
6. If manure must be left near the barn, keep in a covered pit where it can heat and thus kill parasite eggs and larvae. This will also prevent fly breeding.
7. Small, heavily used pastures tend to build up a heavy parasite load. Small exercise yards should not contain pasture grasses which encourage animals to eat contaminated material. It is best to have them covered with sand or bark footing.
8. Rotate pasture plots as frequently as possible to break the life cycle of the parasites.
9. Flies should be prevented from breeding by keeping surroundings free from manure, wet straw, and bedding.
10. Grain should be kept in covered containers away from flies, birds, and rodents, which may carry parasites from farm to farm.

TREATMENT

Treatment is a necessary but small part of the total parasite control program. Major emphasis should be on prevention. Even though adult worms are eliminated from the animal, damage has already been done by larval migration through body tissue. All drugs used for worming are dangerous to a degree and must be used with extreme care. In most cases, it would be best to have your veterinarian perform this service.

A regular program for worming horses should be adopted in cooperation with your veterinarian. Horses should be wormed in the fall after the first killing frost, and again in the spring before they go out to pasture. If strongyles are a particular problem, continuous low. level feeding of phenothiazine should be considered some areas, worm control programs are organized on a community or county basis. Since some of these parasites are transmitted by insect vectors, area action tends to reduce the possibility of this type of transfer. Such projects should be considered with your veterinarian, your county agent, or your 4-H club leader.

Management practices for maximum parasite control should include (1) composting manure for at least one year, (2) use of clean, dry stall or paddocks, (3) dragging and clipping of pastures, and (4) pasture rotation. The worming program itself should include, (1) use of an economical and effective routine suited to the conditions of husbandry, (2) treatment of all donkeys on the farm, (3) quarantine and treatment of new donkeys before being introduced into the herd, and (4) fecal egg counts to determine the intervals between wormings, taking into account effectiveness of the drug against the species of parasites found. Under farm conditions it is not possible for all parasites to be removed from donkeys, and it is the adult animals that serve as a reservoir of infection for foals. Therefore by judicious use of drugs and management practices, a control program can aim to keep the parasite burden of the donkeys as low as feasible. Always follow your vet's recommended regimen for the worming of stock, both foal and adult, and especially for breeding and show animals that may contact outside populations.

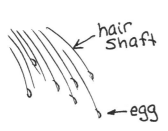

Bot Fly

The eggs of the bot fly (shown right enlarged 4x) are "cemented" on the hairs of the animal, usually on the legs. They resemble tiny yellow beads or the heads of pins. Photo enlarged approx 5x)

BOT FLIES

There are at least three species of horse **bot flies**. The are often mistaken for bees and are similar in color and size, although their body shape differs. It is their habit to hover about the horse, and then quickly darting toward the animal they glue individual eggs to the hair in a matter of seconds. The female of the common bot usually lays up to 500 eggs. Eggs are usually deposited on the hair of the forelegs, although they may be deposited on the mane, shoulders, belly, chin, and occasionally the flanks. The eggs look like tiny yellow beads on the end of each hair.

The donkey or horse tends to lick or bite itself where the eggs are attached, thus stimulating hatching, and the newly-hatched larvae are taken into the animal's mouth in this manner. Some larvae burrow into the tongue and migrate through the body tissues until they finally arrive in the stomach where they attach to the stomach wall. They arrive in the stomach in from three to four weeks. They mature in the stomach in from ten to eleven months, at which time they release their hold on the stomach wall and pass out with the animal's feces. Mature larvae burrow into the ground and change into pupa stage. In from fifteen to seventeen days the mature bot fly emerges from the pupa case and mates to begin the cycle again.

Bot eggs can only be removed from the hairs by shaving them off - not by removing the hair, but by using a disposable razor stroked downward on the hairs, or by a bot removal stone. This is usually a pumice-type block than will rake the eggs off. They are FIRMLY glued on and cannot be picked off by hand or just by a grooming brush. Don't attempt to pluck them off, as you will probably end up plucking the hair also, much to the annoyance of your animal.

STOMACH WORMS

There are at least ten different types of stomach worms, four of which are known to cause lesions, resulting in an inflammation to the stomach wall. The larval forms of the larger stomach worms are thought to be responsible for a skin disease of horses called "**summer sores**". The larger stomach worms are approximately and inch to an inch and a half in length. Adult worms in the horse's stomach lay eggs which are passed out with the manure and picked up by maggots (larval forms) of the house fly or small stable fly. The stomach worm eggs hatch in the head region of the adult fly where they had come to rest as the fly matured. Horses probably swallow infested flies accidentally, or larval worms may leave the flies while they are feeding on the moisture around the horse's lips. Once in the horse's mouth, they are readily swallowed and mature into adult worms in the horse's stomach to repeat the cycle.

ASCARIDS (INTESTINAL WORMS)
Adult worms in the small intestines deposit eggs which pass out with the manure. During warm weather, embryos develop within the eggs and are infective in about two weeks. Embryonating eggs are swallowed by grazing horses, the embryos are liberated in the small intestine, penetrate the gut wall, and are taken by the blood stream to the heart and lungs. After about one week's period, the larvae escape from the lungs, migrate up the trachea to the throat region where they are once again swallowed and the worms develop to maturity in the small intestine. Adults are approximately nine to twelve inches in length.

STRONGYLES [BLOOD WORMS, PALISADE WORMS]
The horse strongyles are a large group of approximately forty species infesting horses. Most of them are less than an inch in length and scarcely visible to the unaided eye. They are usually found firmly attached within the host, sucking blood. Female worms deposit large numbers of eggs which leave the horse with the manure. After the eggs hatch, the larvae molt twice before becoming infective. Infective larvae climb to the upper portions of pasture grasses and are usually swallowed by horses during grazing. Larvae migrate to various organs within the body, depending somewhat upon the species. Those that favor the walls of the arteries are responsible for certain types of lameness and even death due to embolism by restricting or blocking blood flow in the arteries.

PINWORMS
Pinworms are approximately two- to three-inch-long white-appearing worms with long slender tails. They are frequently seen in the feces of infected animals. The worms mature in the large intestines, and females full of eggs proceed outward through the small colon and the rectum, sometimes crawling out of the anal opening. The irritation causes infested animals to rub themselves against posts and other objects. Adult worms in this manner are crushed, at times leaving the eggs glued to the anal region. Normally, however, the eggs develop in manure and are picked up during grazing or feeding by horses to repeat the cycle. The vigorous rubbing of the posterior parts results in the loss of hair and occasionally injury may result in secondary infection. Fourth stage larvae are also found attached to the mucosa of the colon and are voracious feeders.

LUNGWORM
Sometimes horse owners cause trouble over a prejudice that "donkeys give horses a parasite called lungworm". They will sometimes refuse to let a donkey near their horses. This is totally unfounded, but you may hear very odd explanations of it from people who do not know. This parasite is not considered at all important in most sections of the United States and you will rarely find it mentioned in most books for horse health for laymen.

Here is a cogent explanation from the book KEEPING A DONKEY by Dorothy Morris, which is published in England.

..... The eggs of these worms are laid in the donkey's lungs and may be coughed up, but they are more often swallowed and evacuated with the dung on to the pasture. There they eventually become infective larvae, are swallowed by the donkey and carried to the intestines. They penetrate the intestinal wall and migrate through the bloodstream to the lungs. On the pasture the larvae are killed by drought but can withstand fairly low temperatures and keep alive in most conditions for several months.

Donkeys are accused of infecting horses and ponies with lungworm because they can carry a certain number without displaying any symptoms. If a horse or pony is even slightly infected it will probably cough and then be treated, but donkeys seldom cough unless the infection is severe.

It is therefore wise (if you live in a lungworm area) to have your donkey's dung examined for lungworm or to treat him twice a year with a preparation recommended by your veterinarian. One drug of choice is Ivermectin ."

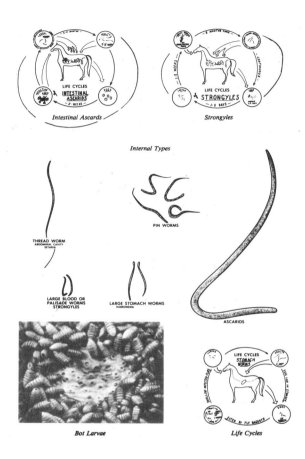

Intestinal Ascards   *Strongyles*

Internal Types

THREAD WORM
ABDOMINAL CAVITY
SETARIA

PIN WORMS

LARGE BLOOD OR
PALISADE WORMS
STRONGYLES

LARGE STOMACH WORMS
HABRONEMA

ASCARIDS

Bot Larvae   *Life Cycles*

JACK SORES

A jack sore is a term applied to localized, chronic irritations which seem to be peculiar to jacks and jennets, most especially large, heavy Mammoth stock. The irritation may develop on any part of the body, but most often on the legs around the joints. It may vary in size from minute to involvement of the entire joint. The following factors seem to have bearing on this problem.

1. Temperament: very sluggish, lack of sufficient exercise to induce blood flow
2. Too rich feed, overfeeding, obesity, lack of green feed in hot months
3. Temperature, very hot, humid weather

(Ed. Note. luckily nowadays if signs are seen of this disorder modern antibiotic treatment can usually clear it up immediately - however, it must not be allowed to get established as secondary infections and even gangrene can set in and the infection will never be healed)

FOUNDER (LAMINITIS) IN DONKEYS AND MULES AND GIVING MEDICATION
by Betsy Hutchins (Revised from 1981)

First of all, let me say that even the title of this article is pure heresy, we would all like to believe that rather than being rare in our animals - laminitis is unknown. Don't send me poison pen letters however, I will just give them to my poor jennet to read. She can't walk or eat anything but a little dry hay and she could use the entertainment.

Yes, one of our donkeys grass foundered again this year. Founder is the common name for a condition called "LAMINITIS". It is defined as: Inflammation of the sensitive inside structures of the hoof (laminae) for unknown reasons, but thought to be a metabolic or allergic reaction to: too much rich grass all at once; too much grain; drinking water while hot; too much hard work on paved roads causing mechanical irritation; retention of fetal membranes for too long after birth. In donkesy, it can be from too rich a protein, such as dog food. To get an idea what it feels like to your donkey, imagine a swollen, infected boil UNDER your fingernail where it cannot get relief from the swelling but is trapped by the hard nail. PAINFUL in the EXTREME.

If you are experienced with this problem, then go on to another article, this one is written for people who have never had it happen to their animals, and who need to know more about it than you can find in most reference books. We must have 20 books that mention it, but none of them carry it beyond a paragraph or at the most two - to give the inexperienced any idea of how to handle it in a modern way.

As far as causes of it go, donkeys and mules are the least susceptible to the version which is caused by drinking too much water while hot. If however you come in from a ride or drive with your animal wet with sweat and lathered up - cool him out before you allow him to drink. On the other hand, moderate body heat won't hurt them because they have a mechanism that allows them to drink only what they need to replace lost body tissue water and then they stop. However it doesn't hurt to use decent common sense. (Just as a comparison, think about mowing the lawn in 100+ temperatures, then coming in to air-conditioning and drinking a gallon of ice-cold water. Those of you who have experienced this kind of body shock would NEVER want to risk letting your animals repeat the feeling, would you???)

Any animal will founder or get colic or both if allowed to get into a grain store. Don't believe that donkey and mules won't eat themselves to death. If they do get into one they will almost certainly eat less than a horse in the same situation - but an unbalance of grain in the body system can and will cause digestive and metabolic disturbances (colic and laminitis) and is dangerous even though not as much as might be ingested by a horse. A third cause, and what happened to us, is eating too much spring grass, especially when it first comes in, too fast. This is much aggravated if the donkey or mule is too fat. Our jennet was too fat and foundered on eating grass that was long and had been out for a couple of months, so it isn't just the fresh grass that is dangerous. However, young, fresh grass has a very high protein content which can trigger the allergic/metabolic disturbance quicker than older grass. Be very careful with spring grass. Try to bring your animal in at night (or during the day if flies are bad) at least to a dry lot. Try fencing off a corner of your pasture securely if you don't have a separate lot. He must be restrained from munching down on that fresh grass 24 hours a day! If he is obese he is in acute danger. If he is thin or moderately in condition he is in less danger, but new grass is always dangerous, especially if mixed with clover, or alfalfa,

The birth problem is different, but should be looked into by a vet immediately - it is very dangerous for the female animal not to pass the complete foal membranes after she has foaled! As far as working too fast and too long on pavement - I hope no ADMS member would do such a thing to his animal - and a modicum of common sense will prevent the problem.

Diagnosis is not too difficult once the problem becomes acute - BUT it should be diagnosed right away before it gets really bad. This is not easy. Since this jennet was subject to a periodic problem with a strained muscle in her left leg - we left the condition alone for five days because we thought it was that. Lameness was very mild and seemed to be in the front. Actually it obviously started in the front and progressed to all four feet. Two feet at a time seem to be affected for some reason. An animal may founder in front, in the rear or in all four feet. Because of our lack of experience with this condition years ago, we allowed it to progress to all four feet, so be careful - assess any lameness, but especially under the conditions mentioned below very carefully and immediately!

If we had taken her off grass completely before the condition became acute it probably would have gone away without becoming serious - and you wouldn't be reading this article. If an animal is suspected to be in an acute stage of founder, there are several common ways of diagnosing it. First of all is the lameness. This can be slight when it is starting or almost completely crippling in later states until the attack wears off. The hoof will have heat in it. This symptom may well be absent in early stages so do not rely on it. Under the conditions mentioned above assume that any lameness if founder and treat it as such which won't hurt if it is due to something else - check for other things too of course. When the inflammation progresses you will be able to feel heat. Remember that the usual hoof is quite cool to the touch. The place where you feel for the heat is the coronary band, just below where the hair meets the hoof. If your hands aren't tender skinned, place your thumb and forefinger around this area, so that the web of skin between them is pressed against the hoof at this spot, this is a tender part of the hand and should be able to feel a difference. If you don't feel it one time, try again a few hours later because the inflammation, once it has a good hold, progresses rapidly.

Next, look at the way an animal is standing. There is a typical (and pitiful) stance in founder. The donkey or mule stands with its hind feet tucked well up under its body in order to rest as much weight as possible on the less sensitive heel of the foot. If the front feet are painful it may try to shove them as far forward as possible in order to rest on the front heels. Often the animal will spend most of its time lying down to take off the pressure - but that is individual preference and not necessarily diagnostic. Also the animal, when it walks, tries to walk as slowly and gently as possible, like it was walking on eggs. It is a really pitiful sight.

This jennet is chronically foundered. She no longers shows the severe rocked-back stance of the founder animal, but she will not stand square. Note the badly broken crest and pones of fat over the hips. She must be restricted from free-choice green grass in the spring and summer months, but still becomes lame again at that time each year.

Treatment is both nursing and medical in nature. If you even suspect your animal is foundered CALL THE VET RIGHT AWAY! Because we were willing to give our jennet shots and pills ourselves our vet bill was kept low. Of course it can be more -but you see it is not necessarily going to cost you more than the animal is worth.

Nursing care consists of taking the animal off the grass immediately. If it has had too much grain this is more serious and the vet will probably treat the animal for colic or to prevent colic. Give the donkey or mule dry hay and water to eat and drink and not too much of that. Don't give alfalfa or clover hay - go to whatever trouble you need to go to give him grass hay. Don't give straw with no nourishment - but good nourishing GRASS HAY. Alfalfa has a DANGEROUS concentration of protein for this condition. If you have trouble with this ask your vet for a diet. Sometimes in certain areas of the country alfalfa or mixed hays are all that can be gotten. In this case, vets have worked out proper diets given what is available in their area.

Now, the old treatment was to stand the animal in mud or water - but what type of mud or water is still disagreed on from horseman to horseman. The actual and only real good this did was to support the hoof tissues with less discomfort to the animal and keep the hoof moist. The animal should properly stand in soft but not runny, mud OR moist, deep bedding, not soaking wet. Standing an animal in a cold, running stream with a hard bottom is worse than not doing it at all. Standing it in a frigid mountain stream is just plain cruel - try doing that yourself for hours at a time someday - it does NOT help the blood circulation, which is what you are trying to do! Actually warm moist mud would be better, but few of us have a mud-warmer except in mid-summer! The animal does not have to be in mud every minute of the day, but if his area can be kept under these conditions for a week or so it will ease the pain, help the circulation and probably make you feel like you are really doing something active for your animal. If mud is impossible, and it often is, bed the animal's area down thickly with hay, straw, shavings or other bedding so he is standing or lying on a nice soft cushion.

Although some people believe in paring down the patient's hoof sole to allow for more moisture to get in - this is not considered good practice for donkeys and mules according to our farrier, who understands them. The hoofs should be trimmed properly so that the wall does not stick out far beyond the sole, but then left alone! Properly trimmed hoofs make a LOT of difference in a good recovery. If your animal is foundered and need its hoofs trimmed, consult with the farrier RIGHT AWAY, but do not allow him to pare back the sole any more than he normally would (not much for donkeys and mules at ALL) just do a normal trim. The animal may have to be trimmed lying down, as if the pain is bad he may fall to his knees when asked to support his weight on three legs. If the feet are properly cared for, the animal is on soft bedding, and his diet is much reduced and the obesity is being taken care of (get that animal in condition again- right NOW) then your nursing care is done. Now for the vet part of it. The accepted treatment for laminitis unless extremely severe (in which cases more heroic measures are taken and the vet has to do it himself) are antihistamine (like you might take for a hay fever attack) and the painkiller "bute". We can only tell you what we and our vet did - each vet is different no doubt. Other treatments may be used now.

Our vet prescribed an injectable antihistamine, 10 cc's twice a day, and a large white tablet of Butazolidin (Bute) twice a day. This prescribing is done by weight - so will be different for each animal. We used to have to give the medicine as we could not afford a vet visit twice a day. Over the years, we have become experts at worming and basic medicating! This is the way to do it, if you must inject your donkey with any medicine. Go about this operation gently and quietly, try to get or keep him calm. If he is well and truly foundered he will be in so much pain at first that he will probably be unable or unwilling to fight you. You can at least get started in calm circumstances. Speak reassuringly to him, keep him confident if you can. I hope your donkey or mule is a pet and that he loves you - but if he is wild you may have problems. If you can get him into a chute or some restraint that will help. If not, and he is very jumpy put a twitch on him. Ours take the shots calmly since they don't hurt,but we give mouth medicine first and that keeps her occupied.

These are normal donkey hooves, a little more upright than a horse. Some cracks at the bottom edge are normal, but have your farrier keep an eye on any rings or cracks.

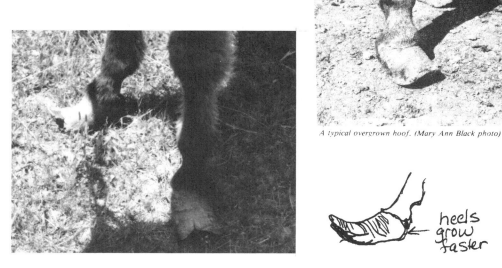

A typical overgrown hoof. (Mary Ann Black photo)

heels grow faster

The hooves of this small Standard donkey are terribly overgrown - no animal should ever get to this stage of neglect. In addition to not having any trims at all, he had foundered from eating free-choice cattle cake.

GIVING SHOTS and MEDICATION

Although donkeys and horses and mules have tougher skin and muscle than people, a sharp needle will enter the skin easily and should not be JABBED in as though you are trying to go through to the other side. The best areas to give a shot are the hind leg muscle below the point of the hip and before you get near the hamstring - any of that nice muscle back there. OR, the neck, just below the area of round muscle and gristle below the mane and above the midline and in front of the shoulder blade, in a triangle of muscle there in the neck. Don't go too far forward as you may run into vertebrae, or too far down as you may damage an important nerve.

To fill the syringe put the disposable needle on using the plastic needle cover to handle it. If it is a twist-on needle, make sure it has set down on the threads! If it just pops on, make sure it is as far down as possible! Pull off the needle cover and turn the bottle of medicine upside down. Insert the needle into the bottle and syringe upside down and draw into the syringe the amount of medicine prescribed. (You may actually pull the plunger back slightly further than the fill mark. If the medicine is low in the bottle, you may need to inject a tiny bit of air into the bottle to allow it to come out better.) Pull it carefully out of the bottle and set the bottle aside. Still holding the syringe pointing upward, tap the side of the syringe with your finger, (you will see the bubbles rise) then carefully push in the plunger to get rid of that dangerous air bubble that will be in the medicine. When a little of the medicine beads up through the tip or squirts out of the needle the air bubble will be squirted out with it. Now carefully replace the needle cover keeping things ABSOLUTELY STERILE (especially that needle).

Now have an assistant tie up your animal to a STOUT post, fence etc. VERY STOUT. Have him stand by the head of the animal, and if possible, give it the mouth medicine first. Hold the syringe between your first and second fingers and rest in on your third finger, the same as holding a pencil. Now you may do a number of things. Some people tap or lightly pound on the animal three times and insert the needle the fourth time, our vet takes up a fold of skin and lightly pinches and twists it, so that the animal doesn't realize that something else is happening. You can rub the injection site with the covered needle, then after a moment slip off the cover and prick with the needle. We take a few hairs and pull them a little bit so the animal thinks the needle is just part of that minor irritation. The needle should slip in nicely with just a moderate amount of force. If you need to practice first, a grapefruit is good - use an old and unsterile needle on the grapefruit.

Our vet says that the only really sensitive part of the animal is the actual skin and that after the needle is in they feel no pain, so be sure the needle is a fresh disposable one and is sharp. Some people put the needle in first and then attach the syringe, but we personally find it easier to do it with the two together. Once the needle is in, pull back slightly on the plunger to make sure no blood is drawn back into the syringe. If blood shows, remove the needle and try elsewhere (later if necessary). If you inject intramuscular medicine into the bloodstream you are just begging for a terrible abscess if not worse. If no blood shows, inject the medicine at moderate speed (the viscosity and amount determine the speed for you really) and pull the needle out in one swift pull. If you are dexterous the animal will have felt no pain except maybe a fly sting, and if you caused a little irritation there first, he won't have noticed the needle.

As he gets better and as he has several shots he may get tired of this, and you may need to use that twitch after all. But during all this STAY CALM and confident or you will surely frighten him and make him act up terribly. Be sure and ask your vet for his advice also.

You may find some vets who still use the old "slap and stick" technique, where they slap, slap, slap, then pop with the needle into the haunches or neck. All the experience we have had is that the animal flinches with the slapping, and sometimes kicks on the "stick" part. (We have even seen needles bent when an old mare got mad and started firing with both hind feet when the needle sank into her rump...). Irritating the spot of the injection gently - such as with the cap of the needle, then gentling sliding it in deep seems to work best. We have used it quite successfully on newborns, who turned their big gentle eyes to watch, and never even flinched. They never learned to be afraid of medicine or needles.

Now about those huge white pills!!!

The best way we have found to give medicine by mouth to a donkey or mule is by taking a leaf from the book of the worm medicine manufacturers and giving it by oral syringe. First of all you must obtain the syringe (no needle of course). The easiest and best may be to save the one your worm medicine comes in if you use that kind. Next is to buy one specially made for the purpose from a vet and animal supply store or through a catalog. If this is not possible ask your vet for a 30 or 50 cc syringe for this purpose. He will sell you one and they are not expensive. You may have to enlarge the hole a bit, but they are relatively soft plastic and it is not hard.

Next, crush the pills in a cup with something (we use a wooden spoon). Next add something that is sticky, viscous and tastes yummy. The Donkey Sanctuary has had success mixing crushed pills with the ready-made vanilla frosting, and offering it in a syringe - apparently the old racehorse was waiting with his mouth open for the next dose! Any stockman will tell you that molasses is good enough for any livestock - but our donkeys are family members and we use honey. Cane syrup or pancake syrup are not thick enough. You need something that will stick in the animal's mouth and that he can't easily spit out. These pills are painkillers and you want him to get as much as possible to relieve that terrible pain, as he may not eat or drink while he hurts so badly. Not to mention that you don't want him to suffer. We use honey because it tastes so good, that after a few doses most animals look forward to getting their dose of medicine by mouth - which is MUCH easier than fighting them every time over it! Anyway crush the pill, mix it with a couple of tablespoons of honey or molasses (making sure not to contaminate your honey with the medicine - then you can't also use it on your own pancakes). Take the plunger out of the syringe, cover the hole in the front with your fingers or with the special cover that came with it (if you are lucky) and carefully spoon the sticky mixture in, trying to waste as little as possible. After you have done this, put in the plunger, turn the syringe upside down and let the medicine slide down to the syringe. Adjust for convenience and you are ready.

To give the medicine have the animal tied secure and short to a sturdy post. Approach from the usual side and pet the head. Try to insert the syringe in the corner of the mouth (you are now facing the head) if he resists put your other hand GENTLY in the other side of his mouth, pressing with your finger on the bars where you press if you have to get him to open his mouth to take the bit. BE CAREFUL NOT TO BE BITTEN. Insert the syringe in the corner of the mouth and quickly squirt the medicine as far into the mouth as possible. He will make horrible faces but as soon as he finds out it is honey he will settle down quickly. While he is enjoying the honey, give the shot. If he is a wild and unhandled animal you will have to use more restraint - but maybe you will learn to handle your animals sooner and more!

Now he has had all his medicine, stand him back in his mud or bedding (I hope you didn't make him walk far if he was in pain) and make sure he has his grass hay and his water in reach and leave him in peace. If he is used to having company, by all means give him company - the LAST thing you need is to have him braying, fretting and restless because his friends or special chum is separated from him. This can seriously hinder his convalescence so make sure he is as happy and contented as possible.

IT TAKES TIME!!!

Getting better is a slow process. A moderate case with the above treatment can be much better in 5 days, BUT, the inflammation takes quite a while to go away completely, and you should not ride or work the animal for at least 6 weeks without complete veterinary exam and permission. Then it should not be hard work for several weeks longer. If the animal was obese he had better not be any more. Also once an animal has had a case of founder he is more susceptible to it forever more - so you must watch that obesity and limit that grass and high protein intake ever after (probably much to his own good).

Severe founder can result in permanent crippling with infection, "dropping" of the bones of the foot, misshapen feet, "founder rings" in the hoof and other very unpleasant things. ALWAYS GET VETERINARY CARE FOR LAMINITIS. You may save your animal's life!

Both this small Standard gelding *Bad Burro Bob* (and anonymous owner) could benefit from diet and excercise. This it the same donkey who's hooves are shown previously as long "slippers", immediately following that first trim. It took many months of corrective trimming for *Bob* to have fairly normal hooves again. He had foundered after eating free-choice high-protein cattle chow daily.

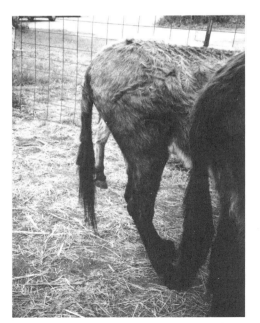

This is the extreme degree of a founder stance, the animal rocked so far back the leg angles are almost 45 degrees under the body. This is to attempt to take the weight off the hind feet and lessen the pain in the feet.

ASPECTS OF DONKEY NUTRITION

FEEDING:

If you buy a wild burro or a thin donkey and want to fatten it up, DO NOT immediately start cramming it full of rich sweet feed and alfalfa!!! If you have a wild burro it almost certainly will not know how to eat either grain or hay. You will have to start it with the weediest grass hay you can beg, borrow or pick at the side of the road. Do not give it moldy or dusty hay - but it is used to scrubby desert plants, and you can only mix good hay with its poor feed slowly and in small quantities at first until it realizes that this is food too. When it is eating hay well try to introduce grain - sweet feed may be the easiest since it is quite delicious (sort of donkey granola). With a more domesticated donkey you still start slowly with more hay than grain. Give it all the good, clean grass hay it wants to eat at first. Feed a small amount of grain 9 or 10 percent protein, about 1 cup at first, oats is probably best to start with in this type of situation. When the donkey is eating small amounts well and seems healthy you can start to mix 1/3 sweet feed with 2/3 oats and feed him that ration, increasing a very little at a time until he starts to fill out. After he is doing well on that, if it is more convenient to switch to straight sweet feed or straight oats you can do that. Remember, that with a very thin animal, fat has to form around the kidneys and internal organs before he will start putting it on his ribs, and that takes time, and PATIENCE! A moderate vitamin and mineral supplement may be used and corn oil may be added to his ration, about 2 tablespoons per day, to sleek out is coat. Don't overdo this ration! If he is getting a good healthy ration as described above he will fatten up and slick out. Amounts are difficult to give since animals vary so much - but the usual for fattening up, nursing or hard work is 1/3 lb. grain for every 100 lbs. weight. (Donkeys need about ¼ to 1/3 of what a horse would eat.) Be especially careful with young donkeys, weanling to two years old. If the donkey is young, too much rich food and too many supplements may PERMANENTLY DAMAGE his bone structure. Stick to a common sense moderate diet, with grass hay if possible and not too rich a grain mixture with a minimum adequate amount of supplement with young and very thin animals. For more details on feeding see the chapter section on feeding donkeys.

FEEDING THE DONKEY : FEED THE INDIVIDUAL

Feeding management of donkeys is as important as it is with horses or mules, regardless of the amount of feed. The donkey must be fed as an individual to feed it well. The individuality of the donkey must always be considered because the feeding of equines is an art, and not fully a science.

REGULAR TIMES

Always try to feed donkeys at regular times. A feeding program of regular intervals helps to prevent digestive upsets. Since donkeys are creatures of habit, they appreciate being fed at regular times.

CHANGE FEED GRADUALLY

Changes in type of feed should be made gradually. Colic, off-feed or diarrhea are the conditions often associated with feed changes. Donkeys do not respond well to high protein or high energy feeds, but some high energy feeds may be necessary under some conditions. Changes from a low energy to a high energy diet can cause problems very readily.

CLEANLINESS

Feed containers, water containers etc. should be kept clean at all times. A clean food container will decrease waste and help prevent diseases and upsets. If the manger of buckets are not clean mold may develop. Botulism has been known to develop in wet grain left in the corners of feed containers.

Moldy feed should be strictly avoided. Donkeys are quite susceptible to moldy feed toxicosis. Mold is frequently encountered in hay, and grain left to sit too long in damp areas.

WATER

A source of fresh, clean drinking water is essential for donkeys at all times. Daily consumption may average 8-10 gallons, and nursing jennets require more water than other donkeys. Higher consumption will be found in hot weather or after hard work. Donkeys have an interesting and life saving water mechanism. Their metabolism is so regulated that they will drink only the amount of water the body has lost and then stop. Therefore they are not as susceptible to water founder as horses, but it is a wise precaution to cool a very hot donkey before allowing it to drink anyway. A lack of fresh clean water may cause donkeys not to drink because the water is dirty, hard to get or non-existent (such as being ice in cold weather). Impaction is a common and rather serious problem resulting from infrequent drinking. In very hot weather, frequent drinks refresh the animal and reduce the chance of heat exhaustion. Donkeys usually love heat and thrive in it, but hard work may cause stress which may be relieved by frequent drinks of cool water.

Animals that have just changed locations may seem reluctant to drink from a new water source. If you know in advance you have an animal that might be this way, work out with the seller to add a flavor to the water a few days before you pick him/her up, such as cherry or cider. Continue this for a few days after you get the new animal and it is in quarantine. This also can be used on show animals that must travel but prefer home water.

If an animal seems to be droopy and off it's feed a little in cold weather, you might try offering slightly warmed water instead of cold.

DENTAL CARE

Routine dental care, though usually neglected for donkeys, is really essential for a truly good feeding program. Teeth that are not functioning properly can result in decreased utilization of feed. Donkeys of all ages are subject to dental problems, the most common being, caries, floating points, wolf teeth and caps (deciduous premolars). Head shaking and being off-feed as well as slobbering or dribbling grain are common symptoms of tooth problems but these problems can exist with no obvious symptoms.

PARASITES

One of the most common causes of undernourished donkeys is parasites. In order to have a good feeding program there must first be a good parasite control program. To reduce the potential of worm populations to subclinical levels, a sustained schedule of treatments is required and the treatment must be continued if the potential is to be held to a low level.

This jennet isn't pregnant - she's a little too well fed!

FORMULATING RATIONS

Determining the amount and source of energy is the first step in formulating rations. Many owners enjoy feeding their donkeys and therefore may receive too much energy. What many owners do not consider is that overfeeding is extremely costly and can be detrimental to the donkey's performance and health.

IDLE OR WORKING?

Many animals are not exercised adequately but are still fed as though they were pulling a plough. Exercise is essential to maintain health. Abundant exercise is of special importance to pregnant jennets. Animals should be given plenty of room to exercise themselves and as much work as you can manage within reason.

Many donkeys are overfed and the impetus for this comes from many facets of the industry. Jennets are often overfed during pregnancy because the owner feels he has to provide for two individuals. Sale standards and show standards also foster overfeeding. Rapid growth by overfeeding of young show or sale stock may result in abnormal limb angulation due to a defect in the epiphyseal growth plate. In these young individuals the condition is termed epihysitis or epiphyseal compression, commonly called "big knees", "Open knees", "Knock knees", and "knobby fetlocks". Remember also that malnutrition causes severe bone deformity in young donkeys also!

The best course in feeding donkeys especially young stock is a sensible and moderate middle course. Malnutrition also favors infection and infection can convert a borderline case into an acute deficiency disease. In the malnutrition process a vicious cycle occurs which results in a loss of body weight, a negative protein balance, a negative energy balance, and a decreased host defense capability. A basic point always to remember is that protein deficiency interferes with antibody formation and phagocyte (destructive cells in the body) formation therefore protein-calorie malnutrition has been associated with a decreased immune function. In breaking the physiological cycle and preventing wasting associated with malnutrition, controlled nutritional management is of primary importance. Remember that before the thin donkey can gain weight on its body it has to refurnish that fat around the internal organs, so with a really thin animal patience is essential, and much time is required.

GRAINING

When balancing the donkey's diet any grain can be used for energy sources if the characteristics of the grain are considered. Grains are high energy feeds used with hay to regulate energy intake of the animal commensurate with work performance, growth made and/or reproductive performance. The energy content of equine feeds is usually measured in terms of Total Digestible Nutrients (TDN), kilocalories of digestible energy. Grain usually contains 65-85% TDN, whereas hay usually contains 50% or less.

The grain most preferred for donkeys is oats. It is an excellent donkey feed but usually more expensive per unit of energy than corn. Because of their bulky nature, oats permit donkey owners maximum liberty in their use with minimum danger of digestive disorders. Oats are higher in protein than most grains, which makes them useful with low protein grass hays, which are the best for donkey consumption. Oats have the lowest digestible energy (DE) and the lowest weight per volume. For example, there may be twice as muh energy in a quart of shelled corn as there is in a quart of oats. While oats are an excellent donkey feed, the quality may vary considerably. There is a good deal of variation in the energy content of oats. Another problem with oats is that unless they are properly cleaned they contain excessive foreign material and dust. Oats do not have to be processed for donkeys with sound mouths, but for aged stock and for weanlings they should be crimped or rolled.

Corn is the most economical grain for feeding equines in some parts of the United States. Corn contains around 80% TDN and can be fed whole, cracked, or as ear corn. In terms of energy value, approximately 15% less corn would equal a given weight of oats. For this reason, corn is a good buy on an energy basis and is especially useful for improving and maintaining condition on individuals at hard work. Because corn has a high digestible energy content and low fiber content it must be fed with more care than oats. Many jack men classify corn as "hot" food and feel that animals do not perform as well on it. Straight corn is usually reserved as a winter feed, but care should be taken in feeding it straight to donkeys. Corn MIXED with oats in equal parts can make an excellent grain ration. Sweet feed (mixed grains including corn) is usually the best ration for donkeys if it has a balanced vitamin and mineral content.

Barley has been used as an equine feed for many years and is an excellent feed. It is commonly fed in the western U.S. and has a TDN of 75%. Barley should be processed by crimping or rolling. 15% wheat bran or 25% oats fed with barley almost eliminates the risk of digestive disturbances.

Milo has a TDN of about 70%. Milo must be ground, crimped or rolled because the small, hard kernels cannot be efficiently digested. Some varieties of milo contain a high level of tannic acid and are not palatable.

Rye is not palatable to equines and should not be included as more than 1/5 of the grain mixture. Rye is seldom fed to equines as they do not like it. (Rye is also highly susceptible to the Ergot fungus infection. Rye infected with ergot has been known to cause abortions in human and animal alike, as well as other serious side effects!!!)

BRANDS AND CONTENT

Almost all feed stores, even some tack shops and other stores will carry equine feed. There are national brands (like Purina), Local brands (like Bluebonnet) and your feed store may even make its own mixes. Local brands and in-store mix are usually the same content as the National brand, but far less expensive!!! Look at the labels sewn onto each bag and see how your local 10% Horse and Mule compares to the national brand! Occasionally, you may find a pelleted cattle feed meets the requirements, but make sure that any cattle feed you may use or mix in DOES NOT CONTAIN UREA! It is harmful to equines, while found commonly in cattle chow.

12% Creep
- PURPOSE -

To be fed as a suppliment to nursing beef calves from birth to weaning and to weaned growing beef calves on pasture

- GUARANTEED ANALYSIS -

Crude Protein	not less than 12.00%
Crude Fat	not less than 3.60 %
Crude Fiber	not more than 15.00 %
Calcium	not less than 1.00 %
Calcium	not more than 1.50 %
Phosphorus	not less than 0.55%
Salt	not less than 1.00 %
Salt	not more that 2.00%
Potassium	not less than 0.80 %
Vitamin A	not less than 7,000 IU/LB

-Ingredients -

Processed Grain By-products, Grain Products, Roughage Products (30%), Plant Protein Products, Forage Products, Cane Molasses, Calcium Carbonate, Salt, Vitamin A Acetate.

10 % HORSE & MULE
for Mature Horses, Mules & Cattle

GUARANTEED ANALYSIS

Crude Protein, Min	10.00 %
Crude Fat, Min.	2.00%
Crude Fiber, Max	19.00%
Calcium, Min	0.20%
Calcium, Max	0.50%
Phosphorus, Min	0.30%
Salt, Min	0.50%
Salt, Max	1.00%
Potassium, Min	0.70%
Selenium, Min (ppm)	0.10
Vitamin A, IU/lb, Min	2000

INGREDIENTS

Grain products, processed grain by-products, forage products, roughage products (20%), cane molasses, calcium carbonate, dicalcium phosphate, monocalcium phosphate, salt, manganese sulfate, ferrous sulfate, copper sulfate, zinc sulfate, vitamin A supplement, vitamin D3 supplement, vitamin E supplement, riboflavin, niacin, biotin, thiamine, pantothenic acic, pyridosine, hydrocloride, vitamin B12 supplement, ethylene diamine dihydriodid and sodium selenate.

FEEDING DIRECTIONS
Feed as a maintenance diet to mature horses and cattle. Usual amounts are 0.5 to 1.5% of body weight daily. Provide good quality roughage and fresh water at all times.

PROTEINS, MINERALS, VITAMINS

Donkeys do not usually thrive well on a high protein ration. However they should have an adequate amount, more if they are in hard work or are growing. Pasture of good quality can supply protein as can good hay harvested young. An excellent protein source and the most economical is soybean meal.

Donkeys of all ages require minerals. The requirement for minerals can usually be met by using good quality grain and hay and by feeding trace mineralized salt free choice. Pregnant and lactating jennets and growing stock need plenty of calcium and phosphorus. They require at least 0.6% calcium and 0.4% phosphorus in the diet. Ground limestone, steamed bone meal, oyster shell and deflourinated phosphate are commonly used as formulated mineral mixtures, they may be fed free choice separate from the salt supply. Salt is absolutely necessary and can be fed in a block or free choice as ground up salt. If you use a salt block, there are several types. One is the plain white salt block. The second is a red salt block with trace minerals. If you buy the red one, make sure you specify the red SALT block and not just a Mineral block. There is a cattle mineral block which is closer to compressed sweet feed in makeup (crumbly like a granola bar). Horses, donkeys and mules will think you have given them a big candybar, and will gobble it up in chunks in a matter of minutes!!!

In certain places selenium is deficient. This is a poisonous mineral and your county agent can tell you whether it is deficient in the soil in your area. If it is, linseed meal and wheat bran are good sources for it.

Donkeys with access to good pasture if only for a brief time, and those receiving good quality hay, especially if half legume will probably need no vitamin supplements. Deficiencies will occur in donkeys kept in confinement for long periods of time on poor quality roughage. This can be common for some donkey herds, kept in bare lots with low quality roughage for their main feed. These animals should have a vitamin as well as a mineral supplement. A rule of thumb when considering vitamin supplementation: stuffing an animal many times beyond him known requirement increases expense and contributes nothing to its health.

Feed grain and hay by weight, not by volume. There are considerable differences in density among feeds. For instance, one quart of corn may provide twice as much digestible energy as one quart of oats because the same volume of corn weighs more and is more digestible. Alfalfa flakes of hay are smaller and heavier than a grass-hay flake.

HAY TYPES

The key to simplified donkey feeding is good quality hay! Every donkey owner should make an effort to learn to evaluate hay. Any of the common hays can be fed to donkeys. When evaluating hay the important factor is not the species of hay, but rather the nutritive value in relation to cost. High quality hay that costs more per ton is often a better buy than cheaper, poor quality hay. The most important factor when evaluating hay is age at harvesting, which is the most important factor affecting the nutritive content. Young plants contain more digestible energy and nutrients per pound than older plants. A general rule of thumb is: as hay matures, the higher the fiber content the lower the concentration of protein and digestible energy. Other criteria of good hay are (1) freedom from mold, (2) freedom from dust, weeds and foreign matter such as cow manure, (3) lack of excessive weathering, (4) leafiness and lack of stems, (5) color.

There are two general classes of hay, legume and grass. Legume hays (alfalfa, clover, lespedeza) are higher in digestible energy, protein, calcium, minerals and Vitamin A activity than grass hays (Timothy, Bermuda, prairie, bromegrass, orchard-grass, oat etc.) harvested at the same stage of maturity.

The legume hays make an excellent horse feed, but donkeys should have them mixed with grass hays. Straight alfalfa is too rich for donkeys. Contrary to popular belief alfalfa does not harm the kidneys. However, given choice between a pile of alfalfa, and a pile of grass hay, most equines will choose the rich alfalfa and ignore the grass hay. If legumes or alfalfa are the only available hay source, they must be fed sparingly, and grain should be restricted.

A general rule is that a mature equine requires about 3/4 of a pound of TDN per 100 pounds of body weight. This can be supplied by hay. The amount of hay needed depends on several factors, such as quality of hay, temperament of the donkey and climate. For example, cold weather increases energy requirements.

If you wish to properly evaluate your feeding program weighing the donkeys monthly is a big help. If scales are not available tapes can be placed about the height of the girth to estimate the weight. These tapes are available from many feed manufacturers. The donkey will typically weigh about 10-15% less than shows on the tape than a horse.

HAY SUBSTITUTES

Even for the one donkey pet owner, hay may be your biggest concern, headache, problem and lifesaver! Donkeys do well on hay, most mature donkeys need nothing else basically to eat but hay or grass, and it is by far cheapest feed - but handling it, obtaining it, storing it and paying for a large amount of it all at once are not easy!

There are some substitutes for hay. They have limited usage, but various circumstances arise where they are necessary - especially a hay shortage such as we have in my area as we work on this book. One of the best is ALFALFA CUBES. These are just small blocks of alfalfa hay, made right in the field at harvesting time, and they look sort of like little miniature hay bales. They are hay in fact. They come in 50 lb. paper bags, just like feed. Compared to other feeds they aren't too expensive, but compared to bulk hay they are. However they take some time for the animal to eat, and provide good nourishment and roughage and are a good choice for a substitute.

Complete feed pellets are another substitute, and to our minds the least suitable complete diet for donkeys. They are grain and hay in one pellet, and look a bit like rabbit food, of the pelleted variety. They are eaten quickly and don't give the donkey the pleasure and time using facility that eating regular hay does, but if roughage is impossible to get, they are there for your use. If you are having an extreme hay shortage (like the Texas summer of 1998) then go with pellets, otherwise, try to make hay the majority of your feed.

The four main problems with you main donkey food supply are OBTAINING HAY; STORING HAY; PAYING FOR HAY; and THE MESS HAY MAKES. Add to that transporting hay and you just about have it all.

OBTAINING HAY

For many years we had the ideal situation. We knew a friendly farmer, only a couple of miles away who raised hay and kept it in his hay barn all year round. He was kind enough to allow us to come and pick up 10 bales at a time (the amount that will conveniently fit in the average pick-up truck) as we needed it and pay him for them so that we only spent a small amount of money at a time. This made storage and payment and even transportation much easier. If you can make this arrangement with someone it is by far the best one for the person who owns only one or two donkeys.

Most people however find they have to buy their hay all at once. We use "Grass" hay (that is, any hay that is not legume) and find that about 300 bales per year is all we need for 3 standard donkeys with some pasturage in spring and fall for each donkey. I would imagine that alfalfa being richer would be somewhat less per animal.

The thing that is usually done is to check in newspapers in rural or semi-rural areas or even in big cities and look under the livestock or feed and grain section. In early and late summer, when farmers make hay, you will find ads for their hay. Look for "horse hay" not cattle hay. In the south it is usually coastal Bermuda grass, out west they seem to use almost entirely alfalfa, and in other parts it is other types of grass hay. Do not get Johnson grass hay or sorghum hay. If you are unsure ask the seller if it is horse hay. You have every right to check out the hay bales before you buy them. If they are full of weeds, find another place. If they are weather-beaten, moldy or dusty, get away as fast as you can - never buy hay of this sort! All over the country there is good, green, clean hay so don't buy bad hay. If you cannot find newspaper ads in early and late summer, ask around your area where there are horse people. Where there are horses, there are hay suppliers. Check a few prices though, and if a price seems almost too good check the hay carefully. Hay will be quoted at a certain price by people you meet, but it actually varies quite a bit and you may find perfectly good hay at reasonable prices when other hay is high.

Donkeys do not have to have extra fine, race horse quality hay. They enjoy roughage and if the hay is clean and good quality it doesn't have to be super-special. Look at, smell, examine the hay. If it is dusty, moldy, full of sticks and weeds, or comes from a county with a blister beetle infestation - just don't risk it!!!

Transporting hay is not easy. Sometimes, if you buy enough, or if he is a nice fellow the supplier will deliver a truckload. Sometimes you can get a local horseman to pick it up for you for a fee - or to pick up extra - the extra being yours. You can borrow or even rent a truck. Hay bought in the field, before it has been taken into the storage barn is quite a bit cheaper, so if you can find a hay supplier and buy your hay and load it yourself you will save quite a bit of money - but hay is heavy so be careful if you are not used to it.

Storing hay will possibly be a problem. If you plan to keep having donkeys into the future it would pay you to build a hay storage shed, sheet metal and 2 x 4"s will do, but it needs to be waterproof and water should not blow in the front or come into the bottom. Hay in the bottom tier should be put on something (old tires or wooden pallets will do nicely) that is raised from the ground, or the ground will rot the bottom layer of the lower bales. You can always cover hay with a tarp or something of the sort, but you will find that it will not be satisfactory unless you live where it doesn't rain much. Rain and sun are the biggest enemies of stored hay and it should be protected from both. If you only have one donkey and a part of your garage free, quite a few bales can be stored in part of a 2 car garage. It will make a mess, but it can be raked up and kept neat and the rakings can be fed to the donkey also.

Feeding hay should be done off of the ground. The donkey ought to have a nice hay rack of some sort built in his barn or corral. Failing that, feed your hay in a "hay net" or "hay bag". This is a very wide mesh bag, made out of plastic or rope, it has a draw top like a laundry bag. You stuff the hay in, draw the top and tie the bag to something with the resulting cord "handle". Tie the bag so high that the animal can eat hay, but even if he rears up he will not get his legs caught in it. Rope nets are easier and safer because they will break if an animal struggles. A plastic hay net is a real trap, and although it reduces waste by about 30%, and gives the animal longer to nibble on his hay, it must be used with caution and respect for it's leg trapping qualities.

Some people will tell you to feed your donkey on the ground as that will prevent the roll of fat on its neck. Oh that it would!!! That roll of fat is just that - fat, and only reducing total body weight will get rid of it! Some donkeys get a fat roll as soon as they mature and never lose it, even if they are kept in good condition, and others never get a big roll of fat. This seems to be genetically determined, and if you are raising donkeys for show or looks you should pick breeding stock that does not have exaggerated fat rolls so as not to have your foals inherit the tendency.

Feeding at ground level is usually done because this is the normal grazing position of the animal. If you want to feed the grain out of a flat pan, there are rubber horse pans that look like big black pie plates. These are fine for grain but not for hay. Some people feed out of old bathtubs, which keeps the head-down position, but here too are drawbacks. The bathtub must be set where the sharp edges (the corners that don't face the outside of the tub when in your bathroom are sharp!) can't injure the animal. The drain plug must be taken out, and a tiny slope added, or feed can get wet (and they may not want to stand by a watery tub in the rain to eat). Some animals will also put their front feet in it, others may kick it because they like the sound it makes. In extreme cases, some young animal have been known to get all four feet in the tub, fall down and get stuck inside!

This of course has little to do with hay except that too much of it makes for a fat donkey.

The other option on hay bales is Round bales. These (again depending on the type and quality of the hay) can weigh about 500-1000 pounds. They have advantages and drawbacks. The most common drawback is waste. If you don't have a metal "hay ring" to put around the bale, the animals will eat at it and spread it out further and further. Quite a lot can become trampled and too dirty for them to eat. It's great if you have a ring, and a number of animals must share bales. On the other hand, small animals (Minis, and foals) may get INSIDE the ring - some do it just for fun - and eat hay from there too!!!

On either type of bale - take off any strings you can. Wires and nylon baling string will both eventually wind up wrapped around your boot, the mower, the axle of your truck, your pet cow's horns, or your donkey's leg if it remains in the pasture. If you see loose string, cut it off and take it out of the pasture RIGHT THEN. Otherwise you will find yourself flat on your face, hung up in a half-buried and long-forgotted string at the most inopportune moments!

You may also have heard that fresh hay brought in from the fields and stacked tight will catch on fire - Not an Old Wives Tale - it is true. Hay should be left to "cool" in the field for a few days before being stacked. Fresh hay, baked in the sun and then raked, can build up internal heat. Close-pack 200 bales in a warm barn, and internal combustion takes place - poof, spark, and your barn goes up in flames.

The rest of the hay story you will learn yourself through hard experience! Just use common sense and try to buy your hay in season (during the summer) because in winter it is liable to cost twice as much, and the harder the winter the higher the cost.

Good luck with the hay headache!

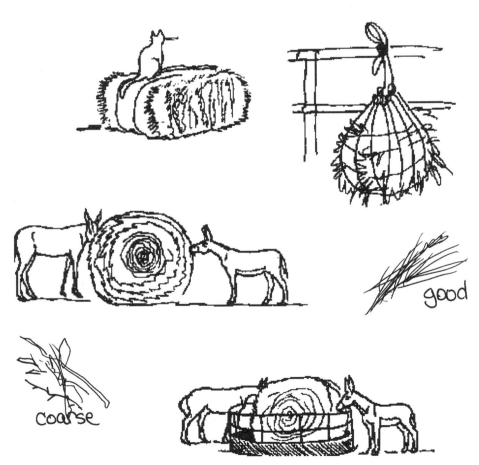

Square hay bale (with cat) tied in hay net, round bale on ground, round bale in feeder ring. All hay should be of good quality and not moldy or full of sticks.

Hot Rich, Fat and Foundered: From the BRAYER magazine:

(If you have fully read and understood the previous pages, most of this should now seem familiar! If not, read on - this is a good review!!!)

The ADMS Staff

There is that old myth that a donkey will never founder, that a mule won't overeat. Unfortunately, donkeys can and will will founder, and given free choice of a grain bin, the mule will treat itself to a buffet. There are plenty of fat donkeys that will testify to the fact that not all donkeys are skinny. In fact, a donkey can get fat rather quickly.

Although founder can stem from a number of situations, the problem with founder in donkeys most often stems from being fed too rich a diet. Donkeys do not need more than a 9 or 10% protein content **maximum**. Twelve percent is pushing it, fourteen percent is **too high**. Most donkeys can exist quite well given good graze in the summer and good quality hay in the winter. Youngstock, pregnant jennies, and show animals (animals that are expending some extra energy) might need a grain supplement but it should be of the lower protein type. Oats, and pelleted feeds with 10% protein or less should be fed once or twice a day, in small amounts. Even with the pelleted feeds, the donkey needs only about 1/4-1/2 of what a horse would need. The smaller donkeys need only a handful of grain if they need the supplement.

Corn is high in carbohydrates and thus is fattening. It is best only in limited amounts. It is sometimes labeled as a "heating" food - meaning the high carbohydrate level helps generate quick heat and energy - and used as a winter food. Only small amounts of corn should be part of the donkey diet.

Oats are high protein, but the fibrous covering around the oat head (the chaff) helps to keep from overfeeding. they are probably the safest grain-type feed you can give - the fiber will balance the content of the kernel.

If you decide to use a pelleted or sweet feed, be sure and check the formula and percentages in the contents. All feed bags should have the contents somewhere on it - if not printed on the bag, then on a label sewn into the seam. Some sweet feeds are not balanced diets, with the necessary vitamins and minerals. You might as well find a feed that has all the correct suppliments. If you do have a balanced feed, then *do not use additional vitamin and mineral (especially mineral) suppliments!*

If you are feeding good quality hay, there is no need to use hay/grain pellets. This is just a waste of your feed expenditure.

Alfalfa (also called Lucerne in some areas) is not recommended for donkeys and mules, or for horses that are lightly worked either. Alfalfa may be found as hay, in cubes, pellets, or in feed mixes. The protein content is VERY high. You might here the term Lush, or Rich used with this type of feed - and it's not what your longear needs. Good grass hay is much more preferable. You can tell good quality hay by the bright color and fresh smell, fine stems, little or no weeds and sticks mixed in. Don't feed last year's hay if at all possible, especially if the hay is no longer bright even in the center of the bale, and **never** if there is any sign of mold.

There are many different types of grass hay. Coastal, Bermuda, Timothy, mixed grass/clover, Prairie, the names and types will often vary with the region. Ask your supplier what types are common in your area, and ask a feed dealer or agricultural extension agent about the breakdown of the nutritional content of the different types of hay.

Be aware that Johnson grass hay is not usually fed to equines. It is better to reserve this type of hay for cattle. If the hay is not cut and cured at the right time, it can cause serious problems in horses. (The older the grass when cut, the higher the concentration of the toxins in the hay) Unless you are familiar with the time of cutting and baling for Johnson grass hay, it is best to avoid it. Luckily, if given any other choice, most donkeys will not eat Johnson grass hay.

Dog biscuits and dog food are for dogs - not for donkeys. Dog food and treats are high in protein, which donkeys do not need. Donkeys have been known to founder severely after eating just **one** bowl of dog food.

Chocolate chip cookies are fine as an occasional treat, and can come in handy when training or gentling animals, but better if you use the low-fat type!

Carrots, small slices of apple, even celery, lettuce, or bananas are the best treats you can give your donkeys. Just remember that treats mean reward, and in moderation. Ten pounds of carrots per animal per day is too much!!! The same goes for apples - too many apples (as in a tub full a day) can cause colic - have you ever drunk a lot of cider and gotten a tummy-ache? The same thing can happen to your donkey, mule or horse and a pile of apples!

Be careful if changing the diet of your animal. Fat animals should be brought down gently - cutting them off from feed and attempting to starve off some of the fat will not work, and could even result in a very dangerous medical condition (called Hyperlipemia or you may have seen it written Hyperlipidemia in some articles).

How do you tell if your donkey is in condition? Here are some basic charts to help you determine the overall fat content of your animal. Remember that the conformation of the animal will also play a role, so some of the items on a chart may differ if the animal is very narrow and shallow chested, as opposed to heavy-boned with a deep heart girth. These charts can also be used for mules and horses, although the particular shape of the donkey hip and neck structure are emphasized.

Figure 1 - the animal is emaciated - a walking skeleton. No donkey should ever have to suffer this condition. Very old animals who begin to look like this should be under constant vet supervision.

Figure 2 - The animal is thin and poor. This could be to a number of factors, ranging from old age, to neglect, to nursing a foal that is pulling the jennet down.

Figure 2A is of a horse or mule that is becoming poor. Note the "poverty line" on the hip. The donkey lacks the muscling curve over this region of the hip and will rarely show this line.

Figure 3A - this animal is in ideal flesh for its build. It is a lighter boned animal and the bones are well covered.

Figure 3B - is a well fleshed animal of heavier build.

Figure 4 is of a plump animal. The amount of feed should be cut down at once, to prevent any further weight gain. Some of this weight might be lost with proper feed and management.

Figure 5 - This animal is extremely fat. It has a "broken crest", hay belly, and "bubble butt". Unfortunately, most of it will never go away. The mane is tipped to the side on the fat neck roll, and will not stand upright again. This animal (if not already foundered) is in danger of serious health complications, including founder and hyperlypemia.

All of the above. This standard jennet is too fat, and has badly foundered. Her neck shows the "broken crest" of the obese donkey. Even if some of the weight were lost, the broken crest can never be made to stand upright again.

WHAT TO DO WHEN BRAYING IS A PROBLEM

From time to time we hear that one of our members has had to give up their donkey or mule because of braying and complaints. So many times this heartbreaking problem could have been avoided with a little care and knowledge.

Donkeys will bray if they are lonely, or have neighbors that are over the fence and within "long-distance" range. Another reason they will bray is if you do not make use of your newly aquired Feeding Knowledge and Feed At the Same Time Each Day. Never was there such a regular clock as a grumpy old jennet who is convinced she is starving to death if you are 5 minutes late with her daily feed!!!!

First of all, if you receive such a complaint it pays to examine the source. Often, such a gripe comes from one person or neighbor and may be an excuse for that person to work off an unrelated grudge or bad temper. Do not give in! This happened to us once and we fought it. In our case it meant going to court to prove that donkeys, burros and asses were not mentioned in the city ordinance, only mules, and we were allowed to keep our animals. Also check your city noise rules. Very often, they are only in force between certain hours, usually at night. If you can keep your animals quiet at that time you can fight off most attacks. CHECK YOUR RIGHTS - you have some in most cases.

The best thing to do of course, is to try to keep your animals quiet as best you can. Different animals vary so much in the amount of braying they consider necessary. Older ones seem to bray less. Any animal who lacks companionship or is hungry will bray all the time. Jacks are out of the question in this situation, they spend at least half their time in advertising by means of the bray. Older jennys or jennys kept with their own young ones, who are kept well fed (preferably three times a day with plenty of hay to keep them busy) and who have a shed for comfort and some room to roam, or a pair of geldings or a jenny and gelding or more are your best bet for noise control. Remember to feed their largest portion of hay late in the evening so their bellies will be full overnight, and the breakfast early enough so they don't start calling you before the neighbors get up.

Young animals shout for the fun of it, they are liable to bray for the sheer joy of living so be careful with them. Of course, you can, quite unconsciously train your animals to bray. If they call you to feed them or for your companionship DO NOT GO OUT AS SOON AS THEY BRAY! Very soon, they will find out that you come when they call, and like children they will call all the time in high hopes of your coming. Again, the closer to an exact schedule you can keep in feeding them, the happier you will keep both them and your neighbors. If you can work it to feed (at least twice a day) when your neighbors are out that will help. Also if you go out at imprecise intervals the donkeys will start braying when they think you just possibly might come out to feed, and will keep it up until you do so. So try to feed them at the same exact times every day, so they will not get into the habit of anticipating. I hate to say it, but when you go out to pet or play with them, do not take them treats if braying is a problem. They will bray loud and long whenever they see you. Give them their treats at feeding time instead.

If it is possible to startle them, (such as banging on their shed) when they start to bray every time), you may be able to break them this way also.

Finally, you should know of an alternative of **desperation** (and only in that situation!) There is an operation that a veterinarian can do to remove or alter the vocal cords to stop the animal from making braying sounds altogether. It is not cruel, but we have no idea of the expense. Thousands of donkeys and mules had the operation in WW II, to silence the pack trains and they came through quite well and happy, it has had a lot of use in that field. Also it is not an unusual operation performed on chronically barking dogs to save neighbor complaints. You can have your vet contact ADMS for information on this as a last resort when no other measures have worked.

DON'T LOSE YOUR PET THROUGH A GROUCHY NEIGHBOR - TALK IT OVER WITH HIM IN A FRIENDLY WAY - PROMISE TO COOPERATE IN ABATING THE NUISANCE AND THEN ... DO SOMETHING!

Remember to always be open and friendly with your neighbors and offer to do the right thing short of getting rid of your animals - this attitude will help both sides and may settle bad feelings before they ever happen!

GROOMING YOUR DONKEY

Your donkey will enjoy a good grooming whenever you can give them. He will enjoy it to the point of a droopy lip, lopped ears, and half-lidded eyes. He will even hold his tail off to one side so you can thoroughly groom his hip, then switch tail tilt for you to get the other. If you have more than one donkey, you may find they line up in a row to be brushed. One, two, three, four, five, wait a minute, I only have four! Yep, ol' Number One has rounded to the end of the line for another go-round. Your arm will fall off before they are satisfied.

And then, just to show you how appreciative they are of your hard grooming, they will go and find their sand patch and Roll and Roll and Roll - they will especially be glad to show you this after you have just given them a bath. Don't get mad, don't get even. You have just showed them how nice a grooming feels. They are just telling you that they also know how to groom themselves - see Mom, I can do it too....

You don't HAVE to groom every single day, but if you are keeping an animal in show shape, or training one, you will want to make brushing part of your daily work. Herd animals engage in mutual grooming as a social activity, and this is a good bonding experience with them. If the animal is clipped out short, you will need to check daily for rubs or scratches, or if it is heavy coated, for mats, burrs, sticks, or hidden injuries.

There are so many grooming brushes out there, how in the world will you figure out which ones you need? There are a few basics, all the others are really your own personal choice. (Just remember that no amount of work is going to keep all of the dust out of a donkey's coat - they will just add more, and some dust is thought to be beneficial to pastured animals.)

Rubber curry - this is a little round or oval brush, most have a hand strap, some have small knob. They come in a wide variety of colors and several sizes. Use the curry comb first, in broad, round sweeps to loosen hair. Knock it out occasionally to clear up the little round "mats" of hair it will form.

Body Brush - this is a stiffer brush, and can have a number of different bristle types (Nylon, natural, with brass bristles interspersed for thick-coated and thick-skinned animals). They are to remove the dirt from the coat and do the main work.

Dandy brush - with softer bristles, this sweeps the loosened hair out and gets to the finishing stages. If you have a thin-skinned animal, you may only be able to use a dandy brush and then a finishing cloth.

Finishing cloth or rub rag - gets the sweat, dirt etc off in the final stages, or can be used just to touch up small areas. (But most donkeys aside from show animals will never see a full-body, hard groom. Even lots of grooming will not gloss up a heavy winter coat like donkeys keep for much of the year - the hair is coarser than a horse's.)

If you plan to show, or need to spruce up a sale prospect, there is more information on grooming in the Showing Section of this book.

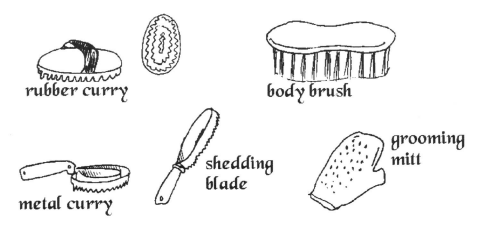

rubber curry

body brush

metal curry

shedding blade

grooming mitt

CLIPPING AND TRIMMING

Donkeys love their shaggy, wooly coats. They love them so much they are sometimes loathe to get rid of them. They will be hairy long past when all of the neighboring horses have shed off to slick, shiny summer coats. When they do shed, they are usually less glossy than a natural horse coat. Your good grooming can help. Then, as soon as the temperature drops only a few degrees, they start to wooly back up for the fall. They look as if they are getting ready to hibernate!

If you are going to show, or live in areas where it is just too hot to wait for the natural shed, you can clip your donkey out. You will want to have good equine shears - the people-kind of hair trimming clippers you can by at the local drugstore will die after trimming about 1/6th of your shaggy beast.

You will want to show the donkey the clippers, while turned off, and run them gently over the body. If he enjoys grooming, this will not bother him. It's the noise that will bother him. Some will get used to it quickly, others need a twitch. Make sure he is tied to a stout post!

There are patterns of trimming - body clip (the whole animal), head clip (used on Mammoths and Draft mules to show the face and throat line), Hunter, Trace, etc. The first time you clip you might have an experience friend help you. Otherwise you may have funny lines - clipper tracks - all over! If you are clipping for a show, practice in advance, or let a knowledgeable person help you. The neatness of your clip job will count in the ring!

Try to avoid clipping young foals unless absolutely necessary. The foal keeps his fluffy coat until the spring following his birth, it just gets thicker in the winter. If you must clip a baby, make sure his mom is tied right in front of him, and she can see the baby at all times. Breeders have taken little ones out of the stall to clip, and then put Mr. Slick in back with mom - who didn't recognize her non-wooly child! Chaos occurs... Even with the jennet watching, you may need to let her smell and touch him so she understands that the thinner, sleeker creature is still her little darling!

The Grooming Circle. *Bob* (of the slipper hooves), *Radar* (back) and *Senator* (front). Between these three, Colleen manages to groom six or seven rounds. Yes, she's surrounded by Asses!

DONKEY EARS

Most donkeys have fine, large upright ears, but occasionally you will find one who has lopped or damaged ears. Lopped ears may not be from damage, they can be caused by genetic factors (such as Poitou blood) or just very large, heavy ears; or from old age. Broken ears, where the tip flops over and is no longer upright, is usually caused by damage. Don't bend the tips of ears - the cartilage can become broken and will never stand again.

Eartips may also be damaged from frostbite. This is just cosmetic damage if just the tips are missing. If more than 1/3 of the ear is missing, you may need to provide extra ear protection for the animal in fly season. The ears are filled with hair that helps keep flies and insects out of the ear canal.

Ear mites can infect donkeys, and they can also have wax build up. A donkey that constantly shakes it's head in irritation may have ear mites or other ear problems. Have you vet check for mites, and follow any medical regimen to the letter to eliminate the problem. Take care in treatment not to fold the ear back to far.

NEVER grab a donkey by the ears as a method of restraint, or twist them as punishment. Very soon you would not only damage the ears, but you would have a donkey who is ear or head-shy and won't let you near it's head.

In some newborn foals, especially those of Mammoth stock, the ear cartilage may be weak and floppy at birth. This usually will settle itself without help by a week to ten days, but if it does not seem to get better after the first few days, contact your vet about taping the ears with paper towel rolls as support until the cartilage sets.

EAR TAGS ON DONKEYS

It should be noted here that the authors personally disapprove of the use of ear tags as ID on donkeys. Many breeders do it, we realize that, but just as many immediately remove these when a tagged donkey is purchased. The tags are too easily ripped out of the ear, permanently damaging the cartilage. If you have ever seen an old milk cow with shredded ears, you will see what can happen when youngsters chew on the tags and they have to keep being replaced. Freeze brands, microchips, or ankle bands are other (more supported) means of identification on your donkeys.

Fine, bright expression and large, upright ears are desired. compare this Mammoth foal with the ears of a Poitou - so large and heavy they are lopped almost horizontal! Lopped ears are not necessarily a fault, but are not attractive to most people either.

BLANKETING YOUR DONKEY

If you have a good, healthy young donkey, chances are 99% you will never need to blanket. Nature provides the correct thickness of coat for the season. If you blanket the animal at the first hint of cold weather, the coat will not come in as thick as it should and you will later HAVE to blanket. Only in extreme weather (such as an unexpected ice storm with cold, wet, icy wind) might you need to blanket, but if your animal is in good health and has adequate shelter, you probably won't.

If you have an older animal, you might go ahead and keep a properly fitting blanket on hand. If you are a breeder, it's a good idea to keep at least one foal blanket of the appropriate size (Mini, Standard, etc) on hand for those unexpected arrivals (early foals, rainstorm foals, mid-winter babies or heaven help you, twins).

To measure your donkey properly for a blanket you need a long string or a flexible cloth tape measure. Measure from the breastbone (chest) around the length of the donkey. Blankets usually come in 2" increment sizes, so if your donkey is 51" around, you would get a 52. Be sure and look at the way blankets are shaped as well. Some have distinct darts to help round the blanket over the rump, others have wrap-around chest pieces, still others have extra flaps at the withers or a wide belly band instead of straps. Buy the best blanket you can afford, but don't over-blanket. If you NEVER have 3 weeks of -0 temperatures, you will not need the heaviest, lined New Zealand rug made. However, if your winters are wet-cold, you will want a waterproof rug or a wool or chamois-lined one that will help consérve heat even when wet. Look through blanket catalogs, most of which tell you the weight and uses, before you invest.

Hint - for Mini breeders, you might look at the new dog blankets - many are scaled models of horse blankets (so your horse and hound will be rugged up in matching attire). There are also more manufacturers coming out with blankets for miniature horses and all the way up to 17+ hand hunters. The ADMS has a buyer's guide which can help narrow your search.

Too large   Good Fit   Too small

CARE OF THE FEET AND LEGS

The conformation is the key to the donkey's locomotion. The donkey like the horse is a working, active animal. Poor shape of limbs and feet causes deterioration of movement. The legs should be observed from a distance as well as closely, and still as well as in movement. A good judge does all this in the show ring, and you should too. The front legs carry from 60 to 65% of the weight. They are subjected to injuries from concussion and trauma more than the hind. In proper conformation the leg should be straight. A line dropped from the point of the shoulder should divide the leg equally. The toes should point straight forward and the feet should be as wide apart on the ground as the space between them at the chest. When seeing the front legs from the side, the shoulder should slope slightly and a line dropped from the point of the shoulder should equally divide (bisect) the leg to the fetlock joint, then carry to a point past the rear of the heel of the foot. The hoof walls should slope at the same angle as the pastern. These are a few common faults of donkeys:

Base Narrow: When the distance between the feet is less than the distance between the limbs at origin (chest or thighs).

Base Wide: Distance between the feet on the ground is greater than that at origin. This defect is seen in donkeys and is usually accompanied by toes pointing outward and in the case of the rear limbs the hocks pointing toward each other (cow hocked).

Toed In: (Pigeon toed) Where the toes instead of pointing out, point inward at each other. In your young donkey this can probably be corrected by proper trimming.

Splay Footed or Toed Out: This is usually inherited and is almost constantly seen to some degree in even the best donkeys. It is a defect because it is almost always due to crooked limbs. This can be helped or even corrected by trimming in youngstock. As a matter of fact, proper trimming can straighten the young limbs, while lack of trimming can cause the legs to grow crooked and set that way becoming permanent in later life.

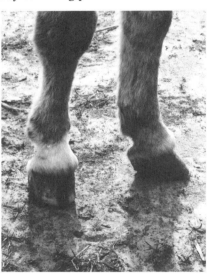

Even slightly from the side, these hooves point out from each other. The right forefoot is upright and the left is underslung, uneven growth from foundering.

A good view of forelegs. Rabbit has good straight legs, just slightly turned out the the hoofs. Note the more upright hoof shape as well, typical in donkeys.

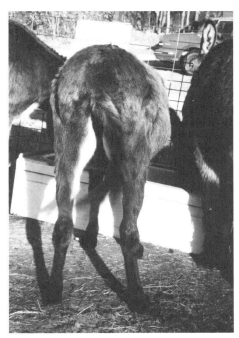

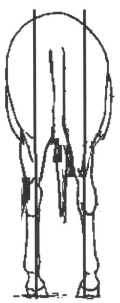

This donkey is standing spraddled in back. Have the animal move out and stop several times to see how the legs end up each time.

Dissecting this rear view shows the animal stands pigeon-toed and wide at the hocks.

The hind legs should be bisected in rear view (see diagram) but in side view a line dropped from the point of the hip should fall directly down the back of the rear cannon with the heel and hoof ahead of the line at the ground (see diagram). In the rear legs of

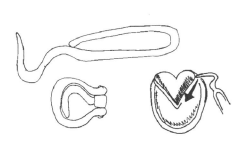

Pick in direction of heel to toe. This stone was wedged in the hoof, and if worked in hard, could have caused a bad stone bruise, lameness, and possible infection if the sole were to be injured. Always check hooves before you ride!

donkeys descended from generations of hard worked and underfed animals, you often see exaggerated instances of legs not only being base narrow, but deflected toward the front of the animal (sickle hocks), a deviation that enhances the ability to carry heavy weights, but slowly.

DAILY CARE - PICKING OUT THE HOOVES

You should own at least one hoof pick. Given that you can get strong, shaped plastic ones for about 50 cents - $1, you should have several. They have a habit of being anywhere other than where you last saw them. They can be hung on hooks by the stall door, in the tack room, in the grooming box. A flat-head screwdriver can suffice (for you guys that do the hooves) or they even make folding ones (where the curved head fits into the looped handle) that you can tie or clip onto your saddle for the trail. In a pinch, out in the furthest corner of the pasture, your car keys can suffice in some cases, but be VERY careful using makeshift picks. You can gouge too deep with the key, injuring the foot, or you can break the key!!! (Then you have to saddle up old Neddy and ride back to find the replacement pick-up truck key....) Never use a knife blade to pick out hooves, the danger of damaging the hoof (and your hand if he jerks his leg away) are far too great.

To pick the hoof, start with the near fore, closest to you after you have haltered your donkey. Some people are lucky enough to be able to do hoof work on their animals with no halter, but it's not a good idea, and you should always use a halter and rope on an animal in training. Tie the animal or have a helper hold them. Lift up the near foreleg, and hold it so the sole is pointing up (Hint, the leg bends at the knee like yours and the hoof will point to the back of the animal). Place the hoof pick at the side flare of the heel (there are two heel grooves) and slide the pick toward the rear (the front of the toe). Always clean hooves from back (the heel bulb) to front. The dip of the sole is deepest at the heel flare and it is easiest to get the pick in there. If you are lucky, the hoof will be clean and just need spot-cleaning. If there is dried mud, it often comes out in a big cake. Look at the quality of the sole and keep a nose open for unpleasant odor (not just regular manure smells). Don't dig into the hoof, one or two swipes will usually do it. Check for stones lodged between the heel and wall, or any discolored or tender area.

Move to the near hind, then proceed around to the off hind, and finally off fore. This is a good time to see if a trim is in order as well. You can pick hooves before or after your regular grooming session - after is nicer if your donkey leans a lot and is the type that gets REALLY dirty - you don't have the extra donkey dirt on your shirt or in your hair!

A well shaped hoof, cleaned.

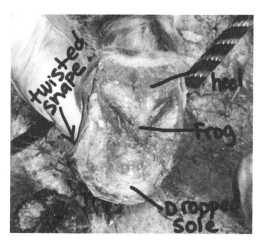

A foundered hoof. The walls have sagged on one side, bulged on the other. The sole has also dropped.

"In trimming a donkey's feet in my opinion you need a rasp, the same as for most equines. You never rasp the sole, which is far more concave that than in the horse, and very deep set. It appears to me from looking at the donkey's foot that the last quarter inch of the wall and the sole seem to be in contact with the ground. This is why there may be a different method for pushing the blood supply up for the donkey. Probably fairly similar but it looks to me, because the frog is not so well developed, that the donkey hits the ground more like a trotting horse. This sole and the wall, just the last part of the wall, is all having some effect on the physiology of the foot, and the whole thing would be an interesting study. Question: I read that donkeys have developed that concave foot because of the rough terrain: stones get into them and activate the frog. Answer: Yes. To substantiate that, last year I sent to look at some stock horses. Now a stock horse in hilly country is a very different conformed horse to oe on flat country and the good stock horse on hilly country has a foot fairly similar to a donkey's hoof. They are more "proppy" the pastern is a bit shorter, and this apparently makes them a little bit better for climbing hills. There, the type of horse demanded for rough country has a more upright pastern and a more concave sole. It must be for that reason, the gripping of the surface. A well developed frog could be a nuisance, making the animal slip and slide, so probably that is why it is recessed like the donkey. The donkey on flat country may have a problem but on hilly country it has the perfect hoof."

CARE OF THE FOOT AND LOWER LEG
by Lily Splane

Let me make it first understood that in caring for a donkey's foot the responsibility should take place at a very young age in order to assure a sound, mature donkey for future use. As a rule, not much can be done towards straightening a leg or pastern after the animal is two years old, and if such straightening is attempted it may permanently lame the animal. At this stage the bones have become fused and are not as elastic as they were in youth. All trimming of the foot should begin at weaning age or before, a week after birth for the first rasping is not too soon. When the foot is well balanced, stands flat and the legs are straight, they should be kept this way so that the leg bones will fuse to form a straight leg. When the leg is off angle in youth, the bones can be properly set so as to be more straight in maturity. Crooked legs in yearlings and two year olds can often be the results of being ridden too early which is not uncommon with an inexperienced handler. Or, crooked legs may result from off centred impact. An animal that is ridden too young is carrying weight over this physical capabilities and therefore his leg bones and ligaments (not to mention his back and spine) will be affected and even permanently damaged. A yearling's chest and shoulders are still narrow and to compensate for the lack of equilibrium in his stride, he will spread his legs to recover his balance. With repeated sessions the legs will soon fuse as a crooked angle because they have been forced to bow out in order to stand balanced.

The five main parts of a hoof are: 1. The **wall**, 2. The **sole**, 3. The **bulbs**, 4. The **frog**, 5. The **bars**. The frog and the bulb are considered to be sensitive tissues and their purpose is to absorb concussion or shock. The fetlock and tendons also absorb shock to some extent. The frog should be flexible and elastic as should the bulbs. The bars are not sensitive tissue, but act to regulate the expansion of the frog and absorb some shock. A hoof with the bars pared away is not a healthy one. The wall and sole act as absorbers of moisture to "feed" the hoof. Small tubes in the bottom surface of the wall and in the white line of the sole absorb water and moisture by capillary action. These small tubes may appear to the naked eye as tiny dots on the bottom of the hoof wall. These tubes are even more evident in a piece of freshly trimmed off horn from a donkey's hoof. As you can see, these tubes are the only method by which non-body moisture may enter the hoof.

The coronary band, commonly called the hairline is actually the casing for a small gland-like ring called the perioplic ring. This gland-like structure secretes a fluid known as periople oil which covers the outside of the wall with a tough, rubbery shield that keeps moisture in. It also prevents any other substances from penetrating the hoof wall. Instead of hoof oils the best way to treat dry hooves is to stand the animal in water for 10 minutes every day so that the hooves can absorb moisture naturally.

TRIMMING AND SHOEING

It is my belief that donkeys and mules should be left unshod whenever possible. This is because the wall is weakened by the nails and the foot cannot absorb moisture as well with a shoe on it. If you must have a donkey shod be sure that he is trimmed correctly first. He may have three sound feet and an abnormal one. If so, insist that the other three be trimmed first and the affected foot last so that it can be matched to the sound ones as well as possible. Keep an eye on the farrier's work. Human nature being what it is he may try to skip a difficult part to save time and because he thinks a donkey isn't an important animal like a horse is.

A good job of shoeing will have these eleven points well defined.

1. All feet the same size with front having rounder toes than hind.
2. All feet stand flat and in balance.
3. No flares at quarters.
4. Bars still intact, never pared away.
5. Axis of foot and pastern the same.
6. Nails well anchored and smoothly clinched.
7. Shoe fitted to foot, never foot fitted to shoe.
8. Heel of shoe extends slightly past heel of foot.
9. Shoe fits tight, no air space.
10. Sole and shoe concave.
11. No rasping above the nails.

No rasping of the foot on the outer wall should take place. It destroys the periople shield and weakens the hoof. If such a case is discovered apply a light coat of pure lanolin grease to the wall. Allow the dust and dirt to mix with the oil to form a crust on the hoof and repeat once daily for a week. By the end of the week the hoof oils should have taken over but if not continue the treatment. When a donkey's hoof chips, immediately rasp the edges smooth. For a crack, have an experienced person burn a half moon upside down just above the crack which prevents it from cracking any further. When the hoof grows out the horn with the crack may be slowly pared away.

Examining the hind hooves. there is a handler at the animal's head, while the second person lifts and picks and/or trims the hooves. You can tie the animal up if needed, but some animals do better if they do not feel confined while being trimmed. The donkey is leaning slightly on the woman, assuming the "jack stand" position!

CARING FOR YOUR DONKEY

Care in general is the same for all donkeys, whether Miniatures or Mammoth Jackstock. All need enough room to play, shelter from the weather, adequate feed, fresh water, preventative medical care (worming and vaccinations) and care of the feet. Care of ANY equine is very similar - just remember that all are individuals and need to be treated as such. You cannot assembly-line feed and treat all of your donkeys (or horses, or mules) the exact same feed and assume they will all grown and thrive the same way.

Many of you who may be reading this book have just purchased your first donkey, and that donkey is also your first equine. Don't panic, you can do well for your donkey and even get to the point where you, too, have contracted "Donkey Fever" (you can't own just one....). If you have had horses in your past, don't panic either - donkeys are not THAT different. You may have friends, vets, farriers, all do that strange jump and glance - ohmygosh, it's a donkey, it's a whole 'nuther critter, and claim to suddenly know nothing at all about general care for equines if it involves donkeys. It "just ain't so" folks. Donkeys are probably easier to care for in some cases than horses. They certainly love people and attention. They will be long-lived life-long pals. If you can care for your horse, you can care for your donkeys.

A lovely rose dun Miniature Donkey jennet, *Twilight*, resting after having won National Champion Weanling. Owned by Lynn Tackett.

CARE OF THE MINIATURE DONKEY from Arnold & Carolyn Sorenson

The Miniature donkey is a hardy animal and will get along well if it is not working hard on pasture grasses. They need a good supply of fresh water and need a freely available supply of iodized salt and mineral block. Good quality, clean hay should be provided in the winter time when pasture is not available. The donkeys can also be fed mixed grain horse feed, but this is only necessary for hard working animals, breeding animals, nursing jennets or growing colts. A Miniature donkey will do well on a minimal amount of 12% protein feed twice daily with hay or pasture freely available. A 70 lb. bale of hay (regular grass hay square bale) should last a Miniature donkey about a week.

The Miniature donkey is adaptable to any climate or altitude. They do need a 3 sided shelter facing south to protect them from the sun and cold in extreme weather conditions. Some donkeys do not like barns, and no matter how expensive and well laid out, they will prefer their shed or a clump of trees to the stall in most weather. The donkey can easily be kept in a small area. One acre is adequate for several of them although the pasture will soon be eaten up. The fence should be 3 feet high and of any style. (There is always controversy in the equine industry over the use of barbed wire, so you must make your own decisions on fencing materials) It is desirable to have a fence that will keep larger dogs and other wild animals out. This is necessary if you plan to breed the donkeys. The foal is very small when born and quite vulnerable to attacks from aggressive dogs, or coyotes. The donkey is also at home in pens of about 50 x 150 feet. It is desirable to lead or ride and exercise your donkey several times week when kept in a pen.

The Miniature donkey requires a minimum of grooming. They should be allowed to grow their shaggy coats, which should not be completely cleaned of dust during the winter as the dust trapped in the coat (from the donkey's favorite pastime of rolling in the sand) is an insulator to protect against the weather. If you plan to show your donkey during the spring and summer it may be necessary to body-clip him with horse clippers as he will shed his hair several months later than a horse would, in the spring. The hooves must be properly trimmed! They should be trimmed every 8 weeks when the donkey is on soft ground, and watched to make sure they do not crack or spilt from being too long. Long feet is a very common abuse of these animals and comes mostly through ignorance or laziness of the owner. Almost no medical care is required but the donkey should have the same immunizations that the horses in your area get. He should also be thoroughly wormed at least twice a year, spring and fall. One of the new paste wormers inserted into the mouth with a syringe works very well. Also horse wormers may be added to their feed, however some donkeys will discover this and not eat it.

MORE WORMING TIPS

We know of some places that have used the "loaded cookie" trick. Take the oreo-type creme filled cookies. Scrape the creme filling out, and put in paste wormer between the cookies. Feed cookies to critters. Drawbacks: you have to preset-the syringe to the weight marker, and will use a number of cookies for larger animals. Cookies are one of those no-no fattening treats for your donkey as well. Also, there is that very real possibility that you will get the munchies, and pick up the wrong cookie!!! Best to leave this as a last-resort effort for the animal you can't get to take wormer any other way!!!

Miniature donkeys, like larger animals, need the same basic care as a horse. Their tiny size and wonderful personalities make them instant hits wherever they go. This tiny baby jack is *TJC Riff Raff*, owned by Jean Chvapil.

HOUSING

Donkeys, whether one or one hundred must have shelter. Any person who buys a donkey, or other animal and turns it out in an open field with no shelter ought to be made to live out there with his animal. (Besides which, the law in most states says that animals must have adequate shelter, so don't buck the law.) Shelters can vary from simple to elaborate, but most donkey owners prefer simple, and so do many donkeys. The United States Department of Agriculture has many barn plans some of which are illustrated here. Your local county agricultural agent can help you obtain them or you can write to the USDA if you prefer. In parts of the country where the temperature does not drop below zero, and open shed, three sided with the opening to the South is usually all that is required. Many parts of the country are suitable to having a long loafing shed for the jennet herd, with a few stalls for foaling or ill animals, and a special stall and run for the jack.

If you have a pet, there are plans for one donkey size buildings, or you can build a simple one from sheet metal or plyboard and 2x4s. A very easy although somewhat temporary donkey home can be made by piling bales of straw (not hay or he will eat his house) bracing them with 2x4s and making the roof of sheet metal. This makes a very snug, well insulated home until a more permanent one can be made.

Housing breeding jacks is probably the biggest problem. They must have, in common with jennets and geldings, shelter from precipitation, cold winds and sun, as well as freedom to exercise, but must be kept restrained as well. A strong, safe fence of chain link, or safe horse fence around a grassy paddock with a stall or 3 sided shelter to go into would be ideal. The individual stall or building for a jack should have doors both on the outside and also shutting him off from his corral for restraint purposes. If a corral is impractical put up a long 150 or more foot - run for the jack. DO NOT FENCE A JACK IN WITH BARBED WIRE unless you want shredded jack. Make sure you use a safe type horse fence, many of which are on the market. NEVER, NEVER, NEVER keep a jack in a shut up, dark, box stall except for a very small amount of time -nothing causes a jack to become savage quicker. Also jacks kept close to other jacks must be in very strong enclosures.

One word of caution. Try not to put jacks in each other's stalls or runs. They are extremely territorial animals and may fall into a frothing rage and be quite dangerous if they see an "enemy" or "rival" jack in their own territory, or smell him on theirs. Try to keep your jacks in their own runs when possible. If they must be moved put them in places that don't smell like other jacks, especially ones they are used to. This warning applies most strongly to Mammoth donkeys but Standard and Miniature jacks are "men" too and they know it! So be careful!

Donkey pasture can be safely fenced with well stretched barb wire. However, if you are planning on seriously breeding donkeys it would be much safer to have pastures used by jennets and foals fenced with safe horse fencing which foals cannot get through, over or under or get their feet caught in - if a foal can damage himself in a fence or in an obstacle - he will! Keep your pastures and runs absolutely clean of dangerous obstacles, but there is no harm in tying a ball, motorcycle tire or some other safe plaything to a rope at head height for your confined jacks to fool with - just make sure it is safe - they like to throw things around with their teeth. A safe and harmless plaything may also be left loose in the run for the jack, but be sure he cannot injure himself in any way. (Try one of the big, colorful Horseballs made especially for this purpose.)

Feed hay in nets (racks are possibly better) hang them high enough so that even if the animal rears to its fullest height he cannot get his feet tangled in the net. The older rope nets are safer as they would break under pressure but the new nylon nets are traps and will not break if the animal gets tangled in them. If you feed in buckets be sure they are tied or clipped to the fence or stall and not loose.

Housing depends very much on your locality and individual circumstance, but it should be comfortable, convenient and safe no matter what type it is.

BUILDING CONSTRUCTION

Use only quality materials and good construction practices. The initial cost may be somewhat greater, but good quality will increase the life of the building, defer maintenance and replacement costs, and also contribute to such intangibles as personal satisfaction and pride of ownership.

The kind of building shell used will depend on:
- The building's function.
- The size of the structure.
- Local, state, and national codes. *Find out codes BEFORE you build!
- Personal preferences.
- Available funds.

Design and Construction of the structure and its foundations must be adequate to support the weight of the complete building, and the forces applied to it. The load that affect most buildings are:
- The weights of materials used in construction.
- Snow load on the roof.
- Wind loads on the roof and walls.
- Weights of materials stored in the building and supported by it.

Four-Stall Barn USDA 5994

Comfortable quarters for four horses are provided by this 20' x 60' barn. Four 12' x 12' box stalls, as well as a combination tack and feed room, open to an 8' covered way.

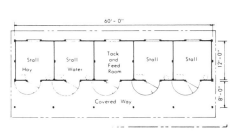

SNOW ZONE MAP

Snow loads and wind loads vary between states and are often different in various parts of the same state. While it is not practical to make buildings strong enough to resist tornadoes, they can be protected from severe damage from high winds by using preventative construction practices:
- Use foundations designed to resist overturning and lifting.
- Anchor the superstructure so it cannot be torn loose from the foundation.
- Make all joints between framing members strong enough to resist horizontal forces and uplift.
- Brace all walls to resist horizontal pressure and suction.
- If possible, locate buildings where they are protected from storms by hills or windbreaks.
- Use good materials and workmanship. Apply materials such as roofing in accordance with manufacturers' recommendations. Use mortar with not more 8 cu. ft. of sand per sack of cement. Use pressure-treated wood for poles set in the ground and for other wood in contact with the ground or foundations.

The foundation must be designed for the building it will support and the site it will occupy. It must resist the forces acting on it and the action of the soil below and around it:

- Building weight and roof snow load.
- Wind uplift and overturn forces.
- Soil load bearing value at the building site.
- Soil movement caused by changes in soil moisture content.
- Heaving during freezing and thawing of the soil.

CONSTRUCTION CONSIDERATIONS

Contractors should be knowledgeable about building material and their uses. Most builders like to erect good, attractive, buildings. But, the buyer must select the style, type, size, and quality of construction that fit his specific needs for the present and the foreseeable future.

Whether donkeys are owned for profit or pleasure, buildings and facilities should be in balance with the rest of the enterprise by contributing as much or more than can some other alternative. They can be out of balance because of:

- Under-improvement - performance and appearance could have been improved by investing additional effort and money.
- Over-improvement - needs could have been fulfilled with less investment, or
- Misplaced improvement - the buildings and facilities fail to perform as expected, regardless of quality of construction and appearance, because of under or over capacity, poor location, or because they do not fit the needs of the enterprise.

The most effective way to get a needed building is to select an engineered building plan with specifications that fit your situation, and obtain competitive bids from several reputable builders. Having a plan developed for you can be time consuming. Also, many builders and building manufacturers have their own standardized plans which they prefer to use, but which may not match your situation. Beware of plans that do not fit your need, and also of the builder who cannot supply a detailed plan of the proposed building. Most reputable custom builders prefer to bid on and work from an engineered plan and a good set of specifications.

CONSTRUCTION PLANS

The drawings in this book are more or less typical of the facilities associated with equine care and use. Except for a few equipment items, the illustrations should not be used as working drawings. They are intended to give information helpful in the preparation of working drawings. Working drawings should be prepared by a qualified agricultural engineer or architect to conform with local codes and regulations, and to adapt to local climatic and soil conditions.

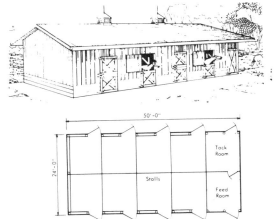

Eight-Stall Barn USDA 6010

Designed to give good protection in mild climates, this barn will house eight horses in 10' x 12' box stalls, placed back-to-back. Poles or posts are used as support members. The roof design provides for a 4' overhang on each side. The building can be enlarged in 10' increments.

YOUR TACK ROOM

You should have a section of your barn, shed or feed area designated as a tack room. If you ride and show, it can be as big as box stall, complete with wash racks and cross ties, or if you just ride occasionally or keep pets, it can be more like one wall of the feed room or closet-sized. Basically, it is somewhere to keep your halters, saddles, blankets and grooming supplies out of the wet and weather.

If you have the room to do up a full tack room, you can have as much fun furnishing it up as you did designing the barn. You can have custom grooming boxes or color-coordinated plastic Totes to keep your brushes and hoof pick portable. Want folding saddle racks on the wall, or shaped wooden ones painted to look like your favorite longear? Go for it!!!

If you are hanging up halters and bridles, a nail can suffice, but bridle brackets are better. These are shaped plastic, or the better ones are metal with a vinyl coating. They come in red, black or blue to compliment most color schemes. The are essential for bridles, to keep the leather shaped and from being stressed. If you just can't do bridle brackets, there is the old tuna-fish can trick.

Carefully wash out your flat tuna-fish cans, and take off the label. Decide where you are going to place the can (usually at shoulder height, if you are using several you would want to map out your hanging pattern). Using a large 16d (16 penny) nail, pierce the center of the can, and carefully nail it up, open side to the wall (closed end out). You can paint them, put labels on the end, or just use a marker on the can end to indicate who's halter it is. (This is for the friend, hubby or volunteer that is told to "go get a halter" and is faced with 12 various sizes of halters. They can see that the Red halter is Harry's, and the Purple one is Sally's without a panicked "WHICH ONE!!!" when you REALLY need the halter!!!)

Lead ropes should be neatly coiled and hung on pegs as well - this will save you a lot of time trying to untangle that heap left on the floor. Should you have nylon or cotton lead ropes? That is your choice. Cotton is thick, will wear out quicker, but is washable. Nylon ropes can be flat leads or round braided, and come in a huge variety of colors from purple to green to hot pink and every imaginable combination. Cotton ropes are usually 6, 8 or 10 feet long. Nylon leads come in 6, 8, 10, 20, and 30 feet (as lunge lines). It's up to you to decide, you may keep both. Just keep in mind though, if you are working with a flat nylon lead, and your donkey decided he's going to Timbuktu at a fast gallop, **let go** of the lead rope or he will take a good portion of your skin with him. Rope burns are possible from any lead, but nylon ones can be very bad. (And yes, you can still get deep rope burn through thin gloves!)

Other items you should keep in your tack room:

Stud Chain - this can be just the chain, or a lead rope with a chain end. If you keep a jack, this is something you should have on hand even if you feel you'll never use it. If you are training, you'll want one on hand anyway. If you never use it, great, and congratulations, but if you don't have it beforehand, you will certainly encounter a time when you desperately need it.

Crop or Bat - You never know when you'll need one. Not necessarily for riding, not for punishing the donkey - it is a training and riding aid (an extension of your hand or leg) but you can also fend off stray dogs in emergency situations!!!!

Boots and bandages (no, not your cowboy boots, although you might stand your mudders in the tack room: standing bandages, bell boots, shipping bandages, polo bandages. Poultice or inner tube boot (for soaking hooves or for protecting injured hooves). If you have small donkeys, you would be better off with the inner tube boot (an old bike inner tube and duct tape) than trying to find a small (and expensive) poultice boot - which are only made thus far for horse shaped feet.

Head bumper - if you trailer your animal a lot, and he/she is larger, you might want to get a head bumper. It is made of leather and felt, and is to keep them from whapping their head on the trailer if they are tall, or if they rear up. You might have to hunt to find one your donkey ears will fit through, or with smaller animals, you may decide not to use one. You will see lots of show Hunters that wear them, but many animals never do.

Emergency Kit - vetwrap, peroxide, Band-Aids (for you) cotton sheet (rolls of cotton). Duct tape (yup). Clean towels. Old T-shirt. Hankies(for wiping eyes). Old tube sox (for leg problems like cuts or flies) .

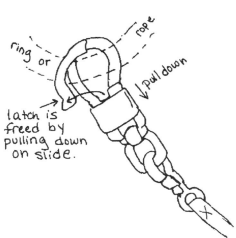

ring or

rope

pull down

latch is freed by pulling down on slide.

Panic snaps - If you have cross-ties, or ties on the rail or post where you usually work, you should have panic snaps on the ends. There are several types of snap ends on ropes. There are bull snaps, the big heavy kind you see on the white cotton leads. There are smaller smooth brass or nickel snaps, such as on show leads or lunge lines. Panic snaps are what you see on trailer ties. They are opened by a quick downward jerk, allowing you to free an animal that is, as they indicate - panicking or has fallen and in danger of injury or being hanged. You can snap a regular lead into the bottom ring on a panic snap if you are dealing with training situations. They are inexpensive, and may save you and yours from a dangerous situation.

Turnout halters - friend or foe?

Sooner or later, you will be faced with the situation where you must make a decision about leaving a halter on a donkey out to pasture. You've heard "NO, never do it"; You've heard "it's okay sometimes", and "Sure, why not?". There is good reasoning behind all of the answers

No, Never - Equines scratch with a hind hoof. The hoof gets caught between the face and halter. Animal panics, falls over, is injured or breaks a neck. Same situation if the halter becomes hung up on a fence post or branch. Nylon halters are designed not to break, and if they don't, the animal will be injured.

Okay sometimes - if the animal is turned out under supervision for exercise, such as in a round pen or paddock. Leather halters are supposed to be safer, as the leather will break easier than nylon. There are halters made of nylon that have a leather crown piece (behind the ears) so that portion would break. Then again, in personal experience, our nylon halters have broken, usually when the worst of the bunch rebels against being tied - he sets back and pulls - and the hardware - the buckles or leadline snaps - themselves have broken.

Sure - These people have been lucky and have never had an accident with a haltered animal. They have, however, probably lost 4-5 halters to Houdini animals who go out wearing that $30.00 headpiece and come happily hee-hawing home without it!!!

In a nutshell, only leave a halter on when it's necessary. If you have a problem-child who must wear a halter to be caught, don't rely on the halter, do more training. It's less expensive, less dangerous, and less frustrating in the long run!

Radar, a lovely Mammoth jennet turned out for show at the ADMS Nationals in Roseburg Oregon. Photo by Juanita Snyder

BREEDING BEAUTIFUL DONKEYS

CHAPTER FOUR

In the last twenty years, the breeding of high quality, good looking, pedigreed donkeys of all breeds and types has begun to become extremely popular as a hobby.

All people who engage in this pursuit have different reasons for doing so. However, most of them have three things in common. They all love the personalities of their donkeys, they are all captivated by the adorable foals, and they are not after big and easy money!

It is true that you are not likely to make much money breeding donkeys, but if you are sensible, prudent, careful and work hard you can make a profit. Three things contribute to this fact. Firstly, breeding stock of good quality is usually less expensive than comparable horse stock would be (especially in larger donkeys); secondly upkeep is so much less than with most other large animals; and thirdly, the market value of well bred, showable, registered donkeys has gone constantly upward in the past twenty years due to the formation of such clubs as the American Donkey and Mule Society, and the regional clubs and registries which work so hard to promote donkeys, and their offspring the mules.

The most profitable breed of asses in this country at this time is the Miniature Mediterranean Donkey. . These are used as pets, for driving and they breed very small miniature mules. This breed holds the top money record, with the averages for a small breeding animal being $2500-$4000. Following it is the Mammoth Jackstock. This very large ass breed is in great demand because of the popularity of mules for recreational uses. The average young jack for mule breeding purposes starts at $1,000. Standard donkeys come in various colors from slate (gray-dun) to black/brown to spotted and are the most useful breed being ridden, driven, packed and used in many other ways. They are less expensive than most, even very fine animals sometimes being available from people who do not know their true value.

Donkey breeding is a delightful hobby for those who are retired, or have small children, or even are working and busy most of the time. It can be absorbing without being nearly as time consuming or expensive as horse breeding. It does not take a great deal of land, fancy facilities, help and high overhead. It does take love, caring, attention and a sense of responsibility allied with a sense of wonder in nature, both for your animals as individuals and for the wonderful breed of asses as a whole, now and in the future.

Donkey breeders are lucky, happy people and we hope you can join them!

SELECTING BREEDING STOCK

The first thing to remember in selecting your breeding stock is that the jennets and the jack should be the same type of animal (both Minis or both Mammoths for example), and preferably of the same color or with the genes for the colors you wish to breed for. To breed animals of differing conformation and/or type together is a waste of time, because each foal will be different and many will be mismatched and ugly. Unless you are very experienced with upgrading stock and understand the workings of culling a herd, don't use poor quality animals. Also be sure that your jack is as near perfect as possible. He should make up in his strongest points of conformation what your jennets lack. If you simply must have a jack with some poor point in his conformation, pick each of your breeding jennets with that point in her favor in the hope that she will make up for his weakness. Buy the best overall stock you can afford. Three good animals are far better than twelve poor ones in a breeding herd.

Jacks should be picked not only for excellent conformation and outstanding color, but for breeding vigor, pedigree (if possible) and good health and physical soundness. If you do not know what to look for, you may pay the same for an inferior jack as you would an excellent one. Not all breeders geld extra jacks routinely. You should consider buying your first herd jack from a reputable breeder that practices the gelding of jack colts that do not meet their own standards. This will help you to match your standards against theirs. If not registered at time of purpose they should be inspected and registered immediately. It is a good idea to not only register with the American Donkey and Mule Society, but with any individual registry that takes care of these animals, such as the American Council of Spotted Asses, or the American Mammoth Jackstock Registry.

Be sure that jacks and jennets are free from inherited defects such as parrot mouth, are healthy and free from disease, and if possible, are proper breeding age. If you are a first-time breeder, you should start with one or two mature jennets and a jack, then add in younger jennets.

There is no harm in buying youngstock of course, and many advantages, but do not be tempted to breed your jennets before they are three years old, or you are simply cutting the ground out of your own herd in terms of the health and vigor of your jennets in the future and your foals in the first crop. A weanling pair (jack and jennet) have at least three years to go before you will see your first results in a breeding.

Remember that it costs as much to feed and maintain a good animal as a poor one, and good jennets carry their foals just as long as poor jennets. If you want the result to be worth the waiting then breed only to the best stock obtainable. The best possible way to build up your herd is to decide on your goals first, and then buy your stock. Most people aren't able to do this, but you should constantly work toward consistency in your herd, in size, conformation and color. If you want to breed two different types or sizes, then keep two different herds!

This may be a super breeding jack for miniatures, and you may be breeding for color or size, but....

(*Sunrise Mountain Augustus III*, 31" Miniature jack owned by Lil Longears Ranch, Lynne Tackett)

Photo by J Bar D.

...if he has his eye on this Mammoth jenny, you need to have a talk with the little man!!!

Ivy League Crimson, Mammoth jennet, owned by David & Kelly Ward, Enumclaw WA.

Photo by Creative Photo, Vicki Taylor

COLOR

Many people are interested in breeding donkeys of certain colors. Donkeys come in many color varieties although fewer than horses. No evidence has ever been found of a true golden palomino donkey, although they come in many shades of chestnut from "pink" to deep mahogany red. The Pink shade is the most likely candidate for the dilution equivalent of the palomino color in horses. Donkeys do have an overo-like spotting pattern, but no match to Appaloosa patterns. Many chestnut (sorrel) and gray (slate) ones have mixed color hairs which makes them sort of a red/gray roan. The Mammoth asses are often marked with dark reverse dapples which makes a very pretty effect.

Do not confuse true gray, which is born dark and turns lighter with age, with either roan, which is a mixture of white and dark hairs, or with "donkey gray" which if actually slate (silver-dun) or gray-dun. This is the color that the Spanish call grulla, and you will often hear called mouse color for some reason. Duns in horses can be told immediately by the distinct dorsal stripe running down the mane to the extremity of the tail where the long hair starts. Most donkeys have visible crosses and stripes regardless of color (slate, brown, smoky black, sorrel, pink, etc) and the slate color may actually be a "self" color, with dun modifiers as well.

Breeding donkeys by color is interesting and it is very important to call the colors what they actually are because they breed quite differently genetically. Some donkey colors are a confusing visual mix (such as brown/slate) and in breeding, they produce both of these colors! An overview of coat color genetics is included in this chapter to help you with this problem. The prettiest herd is the herd where all members are consistent for type, size, conformation and color. A herd of all spotted, all black or all chestnut donkeys is more impressive than a herd of mixed colors to many observers.

(More about color can be found at the end of this chapter and in the appendix.)

A beautiful dark brown Spotted Ass jennet and her one month old jack foal (Large Standards). Photo from Conter's Spotted Ass Ranch, Billings, MT.

ESTABLISHING GOALS

To begin breeding donkeys with the intent of establishing a well bred herd, whose offspring are in market demand, the breeder must sit down and plan and decide on the goals he will be working toward.

Here are some samples of the type of goals breeders of donkeys might choose.

1. Elegant, light limbed, straight legged, high actioned harness animals.
2. Heavy boned, large, strong pack animals.
3. Very tiny miniature donkeys.
4. Medium sized, moderately boned, well conformed show donkeys for general use.
5. Fancy spotted animals for show and parades etc.
6. Great size, black color, or sorrel color, heavy boned mammoths for draft mule breeding.
7. Medium size, heavy bone but refined mammoth stock for saddle mule breeding.
8. A herd of all white or all dark brown or all sorrel donkeys.
9. A herd or animals that all are the image of a particular animal you admire.
10. Etc. Etc. Etc

You cannot have a good herd of any type of stock unless you know the end goal you are working for. And remember, just because an animal fits the superficial description of your herd does not mean you should acquire it if it has poor conformation. One foal out of an elderly but superb jennet is better than five out of a scrub!

BUYING BREEDING ANIMALS

If you are buying breeding stock there are some specific problems you need to watch for. Examine the jaws and teeth of the animal. If there is more than a 1/4 inch over- or under-bite do not buy the animal for breeding purposes. This is an inherited fault and these animals may not be registered. In addition, you should really have a vet examine the jack or jennet to make sure they have no reproductive tract infections. Such infections prevent good breeding performance and not only may make the animal worthless, but may spread to the whole herd causing untold damage and high veterinary bills. If you are buying a breeding jack or any type and are paying a good price for him, ask that not only a vet examine him for breeding soundness but a sperm count be taken to be checked as well. Remember, a jack that has been used on mares for mule breeding may refuse jennets and vice versa, so make sure he will breed the way you want him to.

If you buy a bred jennet and it matters to you that she really is bred - make sure you have a guarantee of some sort (part of your money back if she isn't or something) or have her examined by a vet. Some of them look completely pregnant and ready to foal when they are barren, even experienced breeders are often fooled. A vet can do a pregnancy check in a few minutes and settle the problem. Of course your best bet if you want prime breeding stock is to buy registered stock from a reputable breeder. A jenny should have a foal at her side, should just have weaned one or should be pregnant, and if you are lucky you will be able to see her last foal - or the last foal or foals of the jack you are interested in. Your other best bet is to buy young, well bred animals that have never been bred. The normal young donkey should be a perfectly good breeder with maturity and proper health care.

Make sure the mature animal fits the height specifications for the type you wish (under 36" for a mature mini or over 54/56" for a mature Mammoth), then go for conformation, temperament, and then color. Color is an added bonus, that, if you understand color breeding, can be added in later.

BUILDING THE BREEDING HERD

What do you want from your donkeys? Sometimes this is a fairly simple question -more donkeys! However, a truly excellent breeding program begins with a WELL THOUGHT OUT, AND PRECISE DEFINITION OF THE BREEDER'S GOALS.

What you want from your donkeys is only the first goal. After that is settled, and you have chosen your breed or variety, you have to become thoroughly knowledgeable about the variations within the breed. You need to know what is allowable and what is not, both on general principles and by your own judgment. Most of this comes from experience, some can be gained immediately by checking out the requirements of the individual breed registry for your animals and with the American Donkey and Mule Society.

Whatever the goals, the same rules pertain to success. These rules are important whether you are just starting out or re-evaluating for improvement. To be worthy breeding stock, animals must have desirable physical and mental characteristics and if at all possible good pedigrees.

Pedigrees are a new, and sometimes worrisome complication to old line donkey breeders at times, but to anyone starting to build a herd, they are a necessity and a responsibility. We should define a "good" pedigree. A good pedigree has two main elements. First, the outstanding individuals which are shown in the ancestry of the animal should be "close up", that is in the first three generations, preferably parents or grandparents. Second, all the good animals in the pedigree should blend, or "nick" well with all the others. For an example, a champion miniature jack, bred to a champion mammoth jennet, might well show champions on each side of the pedigree sheet, but certainly does not fill the "nicking" requirement!!! (Don't laugh too hard. It's been tried…not necessarily deliberately by the breeder either!!!)

No matter how good the individuals, if the pedigree is a hodgepodge, especially if it has some good individuals that share the same faults and weaknesses, then it is not a good pedigree. Keep this in mind when breeding and establishing your own pedigrees. When buying pedigreed animals try to see as many of the closely related animals as possible, ie. sire, dam, brothers, sisters etc. When filling out a pedigree sheet make it as complete as possible. Be sure you put the height at the withers and the color of each animal listed. On the back you might want to list any outstanding show wins or siring an animal in the pedigree has done. This is excellent, almost a necessity for your own easy reference and a useful thing to the person who buys the animal. A pedigree sheet is only as good as the detail about the animals listed on it. Names and registration numbers are NOT ENOUGH. Be sure all of your breeding animals are inspected and registered as soon as possible. One thing a registry does is keep track of your string of animals for you, that is one of its benefits, but of course it cannot take the place of careful and detailed records of your own.

Many good breeding programs have been founded on a single pair or trio of outstanding animals because the breeder could not afford, or find more. Also, whether the program is new or old, it must be clearly understood that it cannot succeed without rigorous and constant objective **culling**. If all youngstock looks beautiful to you and you cannot trust yourself, get someone who is really knowledgeable to come and help you, and don't let sentiment mess you up. On the other hand never sell all of your top animals just because somebody wants them, or even needs them badly, or is willing to pay an extravagant price. You will never build a good herd for yourself if you make a practice of doing this. Offer to sell them breeding stock from the same bloodline that might suit them as well and keep the one that fits your own particular requirements perfectly - otherwise you will never build up and keep up an increasingly good herd.

Culling, if you have the determination, is pretty simple. What is hard, is selection! If you have a real breeding operation and it is a commercial venture, you really have to sell good animals to stay in business. There in a fine line between offering top animals to buyers and impoverishing your own herd. When selling pet donkeys, some of this difficulty can be overcome by selling jack colts as geldings and selling only geldings as pets, reserving jennets for breeders and your own herd where possible.

However, do not fail to cull!!! Within every herd there are degrees of good, bad and otherwise. Some of your animals will be Grade A, some Grade B, some Grade C -

by whatever set of standards you use. It can be subtracting faults on a scale of 1-100. Not all of your animals are going to score 90+ - and if they do, then you are donig EVERYTHING right and can afford to sell your colts for the best prices. Just remember that eventually, if you keep everything, and use only your own established stock to breed back too, sooner or later you are going to run out of genetic diversity. Everyone on the place will be related, and where do you go from there? You either have to sell both sons AND daughters and keep breeding to the same herdsire, or you retire dear old dad and bring in a younger, unrelated male to keep up further generations.

GENETICS

In all of this you must enlist the aid of genetics. This is a tool only recently appreciated in the equine world. Meat animal breeders have always followed a policy of breeding like to like, so why can't we take the long view and build up a herd of asses to a standard goal through several generations, just the first Mammoth Jackstock breeders were so successful in doing? To put genetics to work for you, you don't need to take a college course, but for openers learn the meaning of these words.

Chromosomes: Are the "rods" upon which the "genes" are placed. These carry the genetic or hereditary composition.

Genes: There are two of these for every characteristic (such as coat color, size, conformation of each part etc.) except for sex. When a mating is made, the chromosomes from the female eggs split in half - also those from the male sperm split in half. Half from one and half from the other make up the new pair in the resulting offspring. In other words each foal gets half its characteristic genes from each parent.

Homozygous: It means *the same*. If there is a variation in characteristics (such as the color of sire and dam being different for instance) there are a couple of things we need to know. First, the genes coming from the jennet and jack may be the same in any particular case. An example is both parents giving the offspring a gene for red color. This is called "being homozygous" for that particular gene and that particular characteristic. The foal will be chestnut (sorrel) . The equine color chestnut (sorrel) means the animal is always homozygous for the chestnut gene since the gene is "recessive" or hidden, and to show up there must be two of them in the animal's hereditary make up.

Heterozygous: (hetero means different) The genes given from each parent may be different. Such as one for non-gray and one for gray. In this case the offspring is "heterozygous" or mixed for this characteristic.

Dominant: If the offspring is heterozygous for a particular characteristic, the gene which is "Dominant" or more powerful, will determine the characteristic. In the above instance the animal will be gray, the gene G (for gray) is dominant over the gene g (for non-gray) and a Gg animal will show gray. Capitol letters are always used to indicate dominant genes and small case letters for recessive ones.

Recessive: The gene which is masked or overshadowed by a dominant gene (in this case c for chestnut) is called a "recessive" gene.

Complete: - works with homozygous, having two doses. There are Complete Dominants, where both copies of a gene will effect the outcome (such as the roan gene in horses - the genes would be RR - a complete dominant. Only one dose is needed for roan, Rr, and in this case two doses of roan (RR) is a lethal.)

Incomplete - heterozygous, used to indicate that only one copy of a gene is needed to produce the desired effect. In donkeys the Spotted Ass coloration is produced by an incomplete dominant - meaning only one parent must be spotted to get spotted foals. The same is true of the roan in horses - only one parent needs to be roan to get roan foals (Rr). For more on genetic projections, see the appendix.

With an understanding of these simple terms you can learn much. Study the chapter on color genetics with you new knowledge and start your genetics education.

If you wish to learn more, libraries have agricultural sections and also can borrow books through interlibrary loans for you. There are several books on horse and equine genetics including one large one called GENETICS OF HORSES, which your library may be able to borrow for you.

If you are going to inbreed, there is a formula for inbreeding coefficients which you can get from books on livestock breeding. Even without this formula you should know certain facts such as the closest mating being full sister and brother, the next closest parent to offspring. Most important of course is **to understand to purpose of inbreeding, its power and its dangers.** Inbreeding should be only done with careful study, never by accident. In a nutshell, inbreeding is going to INTENSIFY the characteristics of the offspring. Of course exactly the same intensification of good and bad points can occur, so you must use the best possible genetic material to start with.

What you are doing with inbreeding is making your animal's genetic structure more homozygous. If you learn which genes you are concerned with are dominant, and which are recessive you can inbreed good animals to try to get the good genes homozygous. One from each parent contributed to the offspring. If we breed good sires and dams, and cull poor offspring we are making them more and more homozygous for their good characteristics and eliminating more and more of the bad ones. Every animal however is going to have something "bad" about him and it may be that with a great deal of inbreeding these faults will become intolerable.

You should also know about **Hybrid Vigor.** It is one factor that makes mules so hardy. Basically, hybrid vigor is where the offspring is hardier than either of the parents, and usually has some of the best characteristics of each parent. Generations of inbreeding are going to have the effect of causing a loss of this vigor in your stock. Foals may be born dead or weak, breeding efficiency may go down etc. When we introduce into our *inbred* herd a complete *outcross* it is likely that we will experience this hybrid vigor. One program which is good for people who have room and which has been followed successfully by breeders of miniature donkeys, is to keep two or more inbred lines with their own characteristics. They would need to be lines that cross well and "nick" together. Each should be strong where the other is weak so that when they are finally crossed with each other, there is a better chance of getting what is wanted than by just mating two animals chosen because their outward but not genetic characteristics are complimentary.

Miniature Donkey jennets *Quarter Moon Rosie* and daughter *Sophie*. Owned by Pete and Carolyn Christian, Quarter Moon Ranch, Franklin TX.

To keep your breeding program progressing, you should constantly re-evaluate it. Is the goal still valid, and if so are you moving toward it? If you can say that these two things are true then you are a true stockman or stockwoman and a true donkey fancier, and you are contributing in your own way to the gene pool of the ass breeds of the world

A TYPICAL EQUINE PEDIGREE OF THE TYPE ALL DONKEY BREEDERS SHOULD USE ON ALL STOCK:

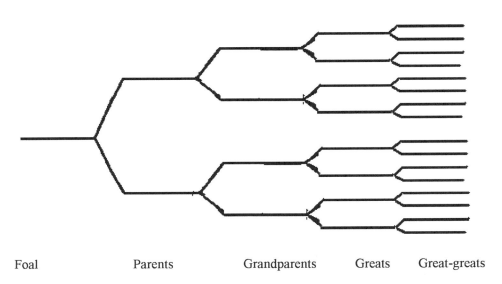

| Foal | Parents | Grandparents | Greats | Great-greats |

5 Generation pedigree

Choose your jack carefully by evaluating type, conformation, size, temperament, pedigree. Color is important, but only after other factors have been weighed.

Mammoth Jack owned by Bess Jackstock, Dexter MO.

SYSTEMS OF BREEDING

Editor's Note: Everyone should read these condensations from Dr. M. E. Ensminger's book [HORSES AND HORSEMANSHIP -3rd Edition, by Dr. M. E. Ensminger, Ph.D., published by the Institute Printers and Publishers, Inc., Danville, Illinois]. Many breeders already know the definitions, advantages and disadvantages of the various systems of breeding. Those is that category can refresh their knowledge in the following review. Others may read this for complete enlightenment. By thoroughly understanding this material we will be more informed breeders.

"THE CHOICE OF THE SYSTEM OF BREEDING SHOULD BE DETERMINED PRIMARILY BY THE SIZE AND QUALITY OF THE HERD, BY THE FINANCES AND SKILL OF THE OPERATOR AND BY THE ULTIMATE GOAL AHEAD."

PUREBREEDING

A purebred animal may be defined as a member of a breed, the animals of which possess a common ancestry and distinctive characteristics; and he is either registered or eligible for registry in that breed. Breeding purebreds may offer unlimited opportunities for it is a highly specialized type of production. Generally speaking, only the experienced breeder should undertake the production of purebreds with the intention of furnishing foundation or replacement stock to other purebred breeders. However, this need not discourage the small operator - the owner of one mare, or of a few mares - from mating to a good purebred stallion of the same breed. in order to produce some good horses.

INBREEDING

Inbreeding is the mating of animals more closely related than the average of the population from which they came and includes closebreeding and linebreeding.

Closebreeding is the mating of closely related animals; such as sire to daughter, son to dam, and brother to sister. It might appear that closebreeding is predominantly harmful in its effect - often leading to the production of defective animals lacking in the vitality necessary for successful and profitable production. But this is by no means the whole story. Although closebreeding often leads to the production of animals of low value, the resulting superior animals can confidently be expected to be homozygous for a greater than average number of good genes and thus more valuable for breeding purposes. Perhaps closebreeding had best be confined to use by the skilled master breeder who is in a sufficiently sound financial position to endure rigid, intelligent culling and delayed returns and whose herd is both large and above average in quality.

LINEBREEDING

Linebreeding is that system of breeding in which the degree of relationship is less intense than in closebreeding, and in which the matings are usually directed toward keeping the offspring related to some highly admired ancestor. The degree of relationship is not closer than half-brother and half-sister or matings more distantly related; cousin matings, grandparent to grand offspring, etc. Linebreeding may be practiced in order to conserve and perpetuate the good traits of a certain outstanding stallion or mare. Because such descendants are of similar lineage, they have the same general type germ plasm and therefore exhibit a high degree of uniformity in type and performance. It is a more conservative and safer type of program, offering probability to either hit the jackpot or sink the ship. Small breeders can safely follow this program to their advantage. Usually a linebreeding program is best accomplished through breeding to an outstanding sire rather than to an outstanding dam because of the greater numbr of offspring of the former. The success of linebreeding is dependent upon having desirable genes with which to start, and an intelligent intensification of these good genes.

Herds of only average quality should almost never be closebred or linebred. Here more rapid progress can usually be made by introducing superior outcross sires.

OUTCROSSING

Outcrossing is the mating of animals that are members of the same breed but which show no relationship close up in the pedigree (for at least the first four or six generations). This is a relatively safe system of breeding, for it is unlikely that two such unrelated animals will carry the same undesirable genes and pass them on to their offspring. Defects in inbred animals may best be remedied by introducing an outcross through an animal or animals known to be especially strong in the character or characters needing strengthening. In general, continued outcrossing offers neither the hope for improvement nor the hazard of retrogression of linebreeding or inbreeding programs.

GRADING UP

Grading up is that system of breeding in which a purebred sire of a given breed is mated to a native or grade female. Its purpose it to impart quality and to increase performance in the offspring. The greatest single step toward improved quality and performance occurs in the first cross.

CROSSBREEDING

Crossbreeding is the mating of two animals, both of which are purebreds but members of different breeds. Any merits that crossbreeding may possess are and will continue to be based on improved "seed stock". From a genetic standpoint, it should be noted that crossbred animals generally possess greater heterozygosity than outcross animals - with the added virtue of hybrid vigor. As in outcrossing, the recessive and undesirable genes remain hidden in the crossbred animal.

IN SUMMARY IT CAN BE SAID THAT **CROSSBREEDING** HAS A PLACE, PARTICULARLY FROM THE STANDPOINT OF INCREASED VIGOR, GROWTH RATE, AND EFFICIENCY OF PRODUCTION; BUT **PUREBREEDING** WILL CONTINUE TO CONTROL THE DESTINY OF FURTHER IMPROVEMENT IN ANY CLASS OF LIVESTOCK AND FURNISH THE DESIRED HOMOZYGOSITY AND UNIFORMITY WHICH MANY STOCKMAN INSIST IS A PART OF THE ART OF BREEDING BETTER LIVESTOCK."

HOW CAN WE CROSSBREED DONKEYS!!!

A lot of people always ask, what is the difference between a donkey and a mule. Tell them donkeys produce more donkeys, and donkeys to horse gives a mule, that's all they want to know. They tend to lump donkeys together as a single classification. Donkeys. Not Mammoth, Miniature, Catalonian, like they do Thoroughbred, Arabian, Clydesdale. The truth is, since very few established BLOODLINES to give BREEDS of donkeys remain, donkeys really are lumped together. The closest we can come to crossbreeding is using different size types together. There is Standard blood in the minis, and in Mammoths as well. Some people laugh when they point out that those very shaggy minis look like tiny Poitous, hey, wonder if it's possible....Our answer is yes, *anything* is possible. Pedigrees on donkeys are still not as well kept as they should be. If every Donkey had a pedigree the way an Arabian does, you could look back 10 or 12 or 20 generations and see a name you know for a fact was a Poitou, or a Mammoth, or an Egyptian White Saddle Ass. Then we would know for sure.

In recent times there have been known crossbreedings of standard to Miniature - that's fine, as it adds that much more to the genetic diversity of the "Breed"/type. If you crossed only Mini to Mini, given the small gene pool they started with, it would not take long for every Mini to be related. You breed related animals, you are line breeding, and then inbreeding, and all the faults start showing up. The quality of your herd takes two drastic directions - the best and the worst. It's happened already in the Poitou - in order for there to be any viable population, the Poitou has had to be outcrossed with "common donkeys". The partbred daughters are put back into the re-breeding effort, and over generations, you get something that approaches 100% in purity. THAT is why crossbreeding works, and why it is sometimes essential.

SYSTEMS OF BREEDING
from the BRAYER Magazine
by Leah Patton

The goal of any breeding facility should be to produce animals of quality and, in the long run, improve the breed as a whole to the point that all of the animals are of high quality. In order to reach the goal, there are several methods of breeding that can help the breed flourish. Line breeding and inbreeding both can be beneficial if the right foundation is used. On the other hand, you have heard about "too much of a good thing". Overuse of linebreeding can lead to inbreeding. This, if not carefully supervised, can turn on you and produce all of the wrong traits.

Linebreeding is inevitable in some breeds (such as the miniature donkey) where a small gene pool of foundation stock is involved. Be it 6 animals or 100, those foundation animals must be bred to one another, and their offspring crossed back again, over a period of time until the population grows in size. Look at a miniature donkey with a 5 or 6-generation pedigree and you are very likely to see *Luigi* 95 in the pedigree. He was one of the original imports, and the source of the sorrel color in miniatures today. You might even see his name on the sheet more than once. If you see his name three or four times in the whole pedigree, that can be considered linebreeding.

So where does linebreeding end and inbreeding begin? It all has to do with the concentration of the bloodlines you are using. By tradition, breeders have considered distantly related crosses to be Linebred, while close-up crosses were Inbred.

Inbreeding is a technique where animals that are closely related are bred back to each other. These include father-daughter pairs, mother-son, or brother-sister. Inbreeding in the strictest scientific definition also means all crosses that are duplicated on both sides of a pedigree (sire and dam). Therefore if *Luigi* was the grandsire top and bottom, this is inbreeding, no matter how distant the duplication is on paper.

The good side of line and inbreeding is that you can try to select the best traits. Good head, good hip, cross back to a closely related animal (also good head and hip and of course, similar pedigree) and have a great foal with the best of both worlds. Your super-jack can now be outcrossed to unrelated jennets and pass on his genes to future generations.

The bad side is that all the little faults, the recessive genes, have suddenly been crossed back in. Remember from previous pages our discussion that it takes two doses of a recessive? Homozygous is two doses of an identical gene (BB) and heterozygous is one dose each of different but paired genes (Bb) All animals have some kind of recessive genes. If your A jack has a recessive for an underbite, and his full sister B jenny also has the recessive (and these can be hidden for many generations) you have suddenly increased the chances not only for future foals to carry the bad gene, but for them to get the underbite themselves as well. You have increased the chances of Homozygous pairing in the genes.

Although at times the goal is to produce animals with homozygous genes, some homozygotes should be avoided. Double doses of the sorrel gene are the only way to get sorrel, and a homozygous spotted jack would guarantee all his foals would be spotted, but would you really want to assure that every foal from your jennet would have weak loins and an overbite?

The dangers of inbreeding and the "bad" recessives could mean that a foal is born with all kinds of faults, from being just plain ugly to real deformities. If a breeder is going to practice inbreeding, they should be aware of the consequences. Are you willing to put down a newborn or very young foal because it has legs so deformed it cannot stand, or a cleft palate (a hole in the roof of the mouth). Yes, expensive horses have had corrective surgery for this kind of thing, but are you willing to go to the time and expense to have this done? **Surgery might correct the problem physically, but genetically, where it counts, the fault is still there.** It's not that donkeys are inferior to horses and don't deserve to have the best of care, but can we afford to continue breeding animals with severe faults? This is why culling (removing) poor stock from herds, and making sure that pet-quality animals are pets only and not bred is important.

If you decide that your stock is of good enough quality to use in line-breeding or inbreeding (by a physical examination of conformation and temperament), then study the pedigree closely. If you know you already have a large amount of concentration on one side, but the other is "Untraced", you might think again before breeding this animal back to their mother, father, son, or daughter. You might get "*the Great*". But you should be aware that you are also gambling with the unknown on that untraced side. Again, here is another reason to make sure that you register your animals, and keep track of bloodlines.

Arabian Horse breeders use linebreeding with success, but Arabians also have strict pedigree rules. Theirs is a closed book, meaning only purebred foals from registered, purebred parents may be called Arabians. We don't want to close the books on donkeys. You can't confuse a donkey with any other breed, the way you might confuse some Arabs with certain types of Morgans, or some lines of Quarter horses with Thoroughbreds. A donkey is a donkey, no matter the size or color. But we would like in the long run for all donkeys to be able to show that they have traceable pedigrees. The pedigreed donkey is invaluable to research, whether it be for dwarfism traits, sorrel color, or height. Having records that go back 5 and 6 generations, where you can look and see that this 33" tall jennet had ancestors who were all under 34" tall can make a great difference to the breeders of the future.

How can you look at your pedigree and tell how much concentration of a particular animal is too much?

If you break pedigrees up by generation, and assign a percentage to each generation, you can see how much of each animal "concentrates" in your pedigree.

The sire is 50% of the contribution. The Dam is also 50%. Therefore each grandparent is 25%. In the next section, the great-grandparents are 12.5% each (12.5 x 8=100). The great-greats are 6.25% each and so on.

Below are pedigrees based on real animal's breeding to show examples of animals with no linebreeding, linebreeding, and inbreeding.

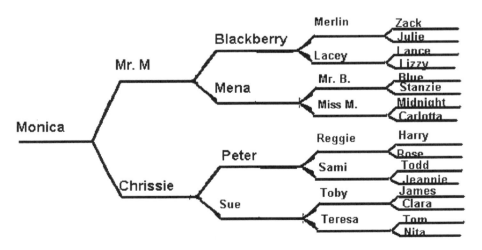

"*Monica*" shows no evidence of inbreeding or line breeding. There is no duplication of names showing in her 5-generation pedigree. If you wished to cross her with an animal that also had "*Lance*" as a Great-great grandparent, it would be far enough removed that it would not even be considered linebreeding.

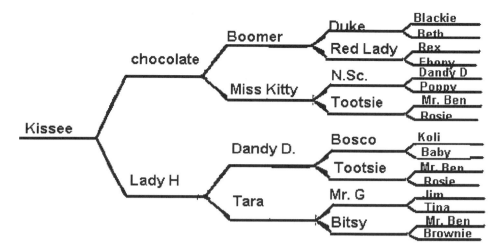

"*Kissee*" shows line breeding. The concentration of "*Tootsie*" is 12.5 % (in the Great-grandparent field) and *Mr. Ben* is concentrated to 18.75 percent in the Great-Great Grandparent line. The normal percentage should be 6.25% for each great-great grandparent.

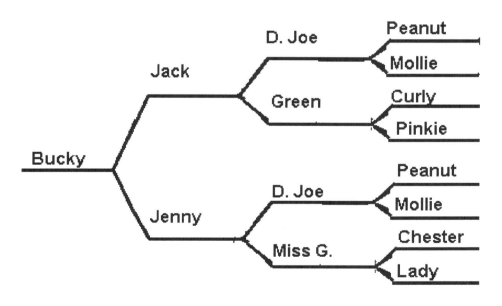

Bucky" shows where the line starts to get fuzzy between linebreeding and inbreeding. If there were 6 generations, and "*Peanut*" kept showing up throughout, then you could say he was linebred for "*Peanut*. In reality, both "*Jack*" and "*Jenny*" have the same sire, "*D. Joe*". This makes the concentration of "*D. Joe*" blood 50%. If you look at the concentration of "*Peanut*" is it 25% - half the total blood line contributed by the 4 great-grandsire slots.

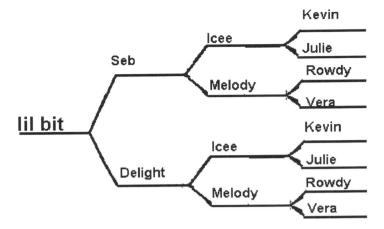

"*Lil Bit*" is inbred. Her parents are full brother and sister. If you break it down, "*Lil Bit*" really has 50% "*Icee*" and 50% "*Melody*" blood. This is where all those dangerous recessives can start to crop up. It would not be a good idea to breed "*Lil Bit*" to any animal with "*Icee*" or "*Melody*" up close in the pedigree, and even the great-grandparent blood should be avoided since there is such a high concentration already. An untraced animal should probably also be avoided, since you would have no way of knowing if any of these animals would be in that background.

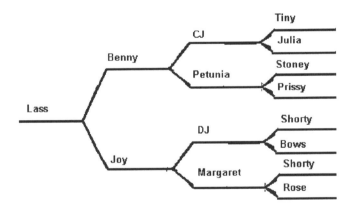

"*Lass*" has a degree of inbreeding, but it is far enough removed in her pedigree it ought to be okay to cross her back to an animal with "*Shorty*" back in the breeding. Breeding to an animal with "*Shorty*" up closer - like the grandsire - would be linebreeding, but hedges on in-breeding. This is when careful visual examination of the animals involved (especially the parents) and any other offspring they have produced is necessary. If there are faults starting to crop up, then it is essential to go to outside, unrelated bloodlines.

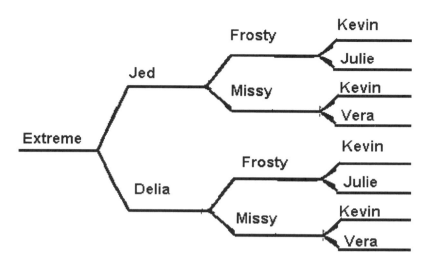

This is either a "Worst case" or "Absolute best" case of inbreeding. With a limited gene pool, this type of breeding might be necessary, but it is more likely to produce serious faults. The resulting animal should absolutely NOT be bred to an animal with any duplicate bloodlines. If you break this down, "*Extreme*" is not really 50% "*Jed*" and 50% "*Delia*", it is really 50% "*Frosty*" and 50% "*Missy*. To make matters worse, the full percentage of male input, top and bottom, is "*Kevin*". This animal has no genetic diversity in the male portion of the pedigree.

By making sure your animals are registered, you can keep the breed records more complete. Having "Untraced" in the middle of a pedigree might mean you are unknowingly duplicating bloodlines. Should color be a consideration in linebreeding? Linebreeding, perhaps, but inbreeding for color might be sacrificing conformation. Breed the best, geld the rest, and good luck with your donkeys!!! 🐎

DANGERS IN OVERSELECTION

It is true that inbreeding can occasionally cause mutations. The Przewalksi horse, the last known "true wild horse" is down to such a tiny gene pool that inbreeding is necessary simply to maintain the breed. In recent generations, white markings never before associated with that breed have begun to crop up. Forehead stars, facial white, socks, white belly splashes - all the apparent manifestation of a "Crop-out" white gene. Somewhere along the way, the genes for color had a mutation, and changes began. Scientists in Russia breeding for fox pelts tried an experient to breed tamer foxes that would be easier to handle in raising for pelts. The animals who exhibited the best tame personalities were crossed back again and again. In a very few generations, they not only had tame foxes that wagged their tails like dogs, they had white Border Collie-like marking, blue eyes, and curved tails. In breeding for one trait, they had strengthened the recessives for others (the markings and the personality) and lost the original goal - good fox pelts for the fur trade. There are other animal species in serious danger of losing their genetic diversity - the remaining Cheetah population is this world is all apparently interrelated - they are all line bred and every single living animal today shares at least one or more common ancestors with the rest of the global population.

In a species where there is no other similar type or species to outcross, the loss of genetic diverisity could eventually mean the loss of the breed. With donkeys we probably have a large enough overall population that such inbreeding can generally be avoided. Learn to spot names in pedigrees that might overlap with those in other animals in your herd. 🐎

CAUSES OF INFERTILITY IN MARES, JENNETS AND JACKS
by Paul E. Hoffman, DVM.

Infertility: A failure or inability to conceive or produce offspring.

Conception Rate: Average conception rate in equines is usually lower than in other domestic animals. National average between 70-75%.

INFERTILITY IN THE MARE OR JENNET
Three major problem areas:
1. Failure to come into heat
2. Failure to conceive
3. Failure to carry pregnancy to term

REASONS FOR A MARE OR JENNET FAILING TO COME INTO HEAT:
PREGNANCY
    A. Rectal exam will detect
    B. Hormones detrimental
SEASONAL INFLUENCE
    A. Mares are seasonally polyestrus (come into several heats through the season)
    B. Southern breeding season March to October, however Estrus cycle more regular and conception highest from April to June
    C. Anestrus mare with no pathology

Heat may be induced by:
1. Exposure to artificial light (simulates increased length of day)
2. Improved nutrition including green vegetation
3. Warm intrauterine saline douche
4. Follicle stimulating hormone
5. Scientific neglect
PYOMETRA
    A. Infection produces pus which distends the uterus
    B. Vaginal discharge may not be present
    C. Shows no receptivity to stallion or jack
    D. Enlarged pus filled uterus easily misdiagnosed as a pregnancy by rectal palpation
SILENT HEAT
    A. Phlegmatic and never show external signs of estrum
    B. Show no receptivity toward male
    C. Can be detected only by typical changes in vagina, uterus, and ovaries which requires repeated rectal and vaginal exams by a vet.

MARES AND JENNETS THAT DO NOT CONCEIVE :
LONG PERIODS OF ESTRUM (HEAT)
    A. Most common early in breeding season (Feb. to April)
    B. In heat for 10 to 20 to 30 days
    C. Not a true nymphomaniac
    D. Repeated covering useless
    E. Continued teasing only seems to prolong estrus
    F. Stop teasing and turn her out
    G. Hormones usually of no value except to further complicate the problem
    H. Most will develop regular cycles and conceive later
LONG PERIODS OF DIESTRUM (NONHEAT)
    A. Show heat but go long periods before showing again
    B. Regular teasing necessary
    C. Generally poor breeders
IRREGULAR PERIODS OF ESTRUM
    A. "In" greater number of days than "out"
    B. Often become regular later in season
    C. Require follicle palpation to determine if and when to cover
    D. Most will eventually settle

ANESTRUM IN MARE SUCKLING FOAL
    A. Probably experienced a foal heat but was not covered
    B. May go one to two months without showing heat
    C. Usually seen in mares or jennets in poor condition or with phlegmatic temperament
    D. Correct any nutritional problem
    E. Tease mare with foal at her head. May 'lie' to you because of protective instinct, watch her closely around other mares
    F. Some mares are routinely anestrus while suckling a foal, become "every other year" mares

ANOVULATION OR DELAYED OVULATION
    A. Cycle normal, teases in, gets good cover but does not conceive
    B. Reason: No egg released from the ovary (anovulation) follicle regresses

DELAYED OVULATION
    A. The heat period is prolonged 2 to 5 days
    B. The egg is not release until very late, maybe even after the mare has gone out of standing heat
    C. Diagnosed only by repeated rectal exam of the ovary
    D. Most will eventually conceive
    E. Treatment - gonadtropic hormone
    F. Cover or inseminate mare on last day of heat

GENI'I'AL INFECTION
    A. Cycle may be normal but due to inflammation and infection in the mare's reproductive tract either the egg and sperm do not join or the egg does not become implanted or if it does is later rejected.

BASIC CONDITIONS CAUSING GENITAL INFECTION
PNEUMOVAGINA "WINDSUCKING"
    A. Vulva tilted forward under anus
    B. Aspirates air and filth into vagina when she runs or turns sharply, worse when in heat
    C. Seen more commonly in old and thin mares
    D. Most common cause of infection
    E. Treatment: Caslick's Operation - Freshen edges and suture vulva lips together

PATHOLOGICAL FOALING
    A. Foal has to be taken, dead foal, retained placenta, severe trauma to birth passage
    B. Infection picked up from ground, instruments, hands
    C. Mares reproductive tract slow to shrink to normal sine often fills with air and fluid

INFECTION PRODUCED BY COPULATION
    A. Good breeding hygiene very important
    B. Excessive frequency of covering increases likelihood of infection

INFECTION PRODUCED BY MAN
    A. "Opening the mare", before service by human hand a "no-no"!
    B. Improperly sterilized instruments such as speculums, douching equipment etc.
    C. Poor artificial insemination techniques

MARES & JENNETS THAT DO NOT CARRY PREGNANCY TO TERM
The incidence of equine abortion is higher than that experienced in cattle, maybe as high as 5 to 15 percent. The highest percentage of abortion occur during the first four months of gestation and are apparently not associated with infectious agents.

MILD BACTERIAL INFECTIONS
    A. May conceive but return to heat after 40 to 45 days
    B. May have late abortion (2 to 6 months), diseased foal, retained placenta
    C. Aborted foal shows autolytic changes

VIRAL ABORTION
    A. Respiratory virus capable of causing abortion 3 to 4 months after a very mild "cold" which often goes unnoticed

B. Abortions occur from 8 to 11 months gestation

C. Infected foals often born alive but die within a few minutes or hours

D. Aborted fetus "fresh"

E. Prevention, vaccinate with rhinomune
   1st injection 2nd month of pregnancy
   2nd injection 4 to 8 weeks later up to 7th month of pregnancy

TWINNING

A. Approximately 10 % of equine abortions caused by twinning

B. Abortion often occurs before 4 months but goes unnoticed

C. "Seen" abortions occur during 5th to 7th month

FESCUE GRASS ABORTION

A. Grass does not cause it but it may be caused by a mold that grows on tall grass

B. Most are probably Rhinopneumonitis

INFERTILITY IN JACKS

THERE IS USUALLY LITTLE TREATMENT OR THERAPY CAN DO TO SIGNIFICANTLY IMPROVE THE LEVEL OF FERTILITY IN A CONGENITALLY INFERTILE MALE.

LACK OF SEXUAL DESIRE AND/OR ABILITY TO COPULATE:
NUTRITION

A. Low plane influences adversely; high seldom influences directly

B. Protein content little or no effect

C. Vitamins seldom if ever a factor

AGE

A. Very young or very old

MANAGEMENT - PHYSIC FACTORS

A. Jack raised with jennet may not want to breed mares due to unacusstomed smell of different species

B. If he associates sex with pain or punishment he may give up

C. Rough, noisy or abusive hand breeding practices

D. Injury by mare

E. Lack of competitive stimulation

F. Excessive A.I. collections with too few natural covers

G. Improper A.I. collection technique or A.I. Vagina too hotH

F. Unacceptable scent on mare or jennet, such as medicinal

I. Excessive use by natural or A.I. services or masturbation

ORGANIC DISEASE OR INJURY

A. Hormonal deficiency - rare

B. Joint, muscle, nerve, bone and tendon injuries

C. Disease of penis or injury to penis, or presence of stallion ring

INABILITY OR REDUCED ABILITY TO FERTILIZE :
SEMEN OF NORMAL QUALITY BUT INFERTILE

A. Inherit enzymatic disturbance causing early death of sperm in female

B. Defects in genes and chromosomes

ABNORMAL SEMEN PRODUCTION - CONGENITAL

A. Testicular pathology

B. Congenital or hereditary hypoplasia

C. Treatment unsuccessful and ill-advised

D. Sperm cell defects such as abnormal heads, middle piece or tails

TESTICULAR DEGENERATION

A. Thermal influences, cryptorchidism, high or prolonged fever

B. Vascular defects, trauma excessive exercise such as racing

C. Shipping under adverse conditions, usually temporary sterility only

NUTRITIONAL FACTORS

A. Underfeeding

B. Diets sufficient for growth and maintenance are adequate for fertility

C. Nutritional "aphrodisiacs" no use at all

A NEW LOOK AT PASTURE BREEDING
by Charles A. Hutton, Extension Animal Scientist, University of Georgia

Pasture breeding is a real option to be considered by the serious mule or donkey breeder who wishes to improve breeding efficiency while reducing cost. This system of breeding seems too often to be dismissed today as "too dangerous" or simply "too old fashioned". Pasture breeding does have its disadvantages, but it also has its place. Let's consider the advantages and disadvantages of pasture breeding and then discuss the management necessary to make this system work. First we should distinguish between managed pasture breeding and random mating in a pasture. The latter situation is too common already and doesn't need to be promoted!

The primary advantages of managed pasture breeding include:
1. High efficiency of foal production
2. Lower labor requirement
3. Lower facility and building cost
4. Reduced veterinary expenses
5. Eliminates certain breeding problems

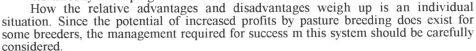

The main disadvantages of the mating system include:
1. Fewer mares can be booked, sometimes no outside ones
2. Increased risk of injury to jack
3. Possibility of disease transmission
4. Difficulty in keeping accurate records

How the relative advantages and disadvantages weigh up is an individual situation. Since the potential of increased profits by pasture breeding does exist for some breeders, the management required for success m this system should be carefully considered.

One real principle of agriculture is to work with nature, never against it. Since pasture breeding is a natural situation for the equine species, it follows that the environment should be in harmony with the natural state for a band. In particular themanager of pasture breeding operations needs to take into account the social structures and behavior of mares and donkeys. Horses tend to develop a strong herding instinct with a set social order or dominance hierarchy as do jennets. This development takes time and requires that the band of mares or jennets be assembled well in advance of the foaling and breeding season. Introducing new mares or jennets during the breeding season will upset the entire band, increasing the chances of injury to all. Also the entire band or part of it may reject the newcomer. This situation makes breeding outside mares or jennets in a pasture breeding situation next to impossible. Two options are available however that will allow limited public service.

While the pasture band should be wintered together, the jack can be stabled and hand bred early in the season. Also some jacks can be brought in from the pasture for occasional hand breeding and then returned to the herd. Others may refuse to serve an outside mare in these circumstances.

Another problem in pasture breeding involves mixing maiden and barren mares with nursing and foaling mares, and foals. Mixing mares upsets the herd and often leads to injuries.

Also, it is desirable to feed and handle mares with foals separately. A "split pasture" breeding demonstration was conducted at the Extension Horse Center in Athens during the 1977 breeding season. The objectives of the trail was as follows.
1. To determine if a modified pasture breeding system could be adopted to outside mares.
2. To determine if one stallion would serve two groups of mares.
3. To evaluate the management of foaling and non-foaling mares in separate groups. The procedure was as follows:
1. Divide foaling and non-foaling mares into two pasture groups.
2. Remove stallion from pasture each morning. Feed and rest in barn during day.
3. Release stallion into pasture in late evening alternating pastures daily.

The stallion accepted all mares without incident and displayed typical behavior patterns of a pasture breeding stallion while with each group of mares. Although the two pastures were separated only by a farm road the stallion did

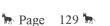

not seem distracted by the other group of mares. The foaling mare group was kept relatively stable through the breeding season but mares were added and removed from the non-foaling group frequently. The overall system was easy to manage and substantial savings in labor and veterinary assistance were realized. Although the conception rate and cost reduction realized are most encouraging, more work is needed before this 'split pasture' system can be fully recommended except on an experimental basis.

The danger of injury to the jack in the pasture depends largely on past conditioning and on having the mares or jennets of the proper size so that the jack can manage them physically. It is fascinating to watch an experienced pasture stallion or jack at work. He checks each mare frequently but quickly and efficiently. He is both cautious and commanding in his manner, giving himself room to operate and disciplining mares or jennets that become too aggressive during teasing. Contrary to popular opinion the male is not likely to "wear himself out" by frequent services if several mares are in heat at once. He will usually select the mare that is in the most intense heat and concentrate on her until she ovulates. Such an experienced breeder is probably no more likely to be injured in the pasture than he would be in the breeding shed.

The real danger of injury is to the inexperienced stallion or jack. The best hope would be to select a few quieter mares to begin with, including one gentle mare in full standing heat. Hopefully the inexperienced animal will adjust with no more serious losses than a little hair and hide and a lot of pride. A better system of conditioning a prospective jack is to begin at an early age. By wintering the yearling jack with a few pregnant mares he will learn a healthy respect for the mare that isn't "in the mood". Since the yearling is naturally submissive he will be unlikely to be hurt unless he is cornered. Until the jack becomes thoroughly experienced it is best to limit his band to fifteen or less. Thirty mares is about maximum for any stallion and should be less for most jacks.

Good fences are a necessity for pasture breeding. They should not only be safe and secure, but also designed to eliminate narrow lanes and corners where horses or jennets can congregate. A woven wire fence with a top board is a practical one for many conditions.

For disease prevention and control it is best to use a closed herd situation insofar as possible. Barren mares being added to the herd should be given a complete examination, including a close screening for genital infections. Mares with a tendency toward windsucking (pneumovaginitis) should be avoided in the pasture breeding situation.

It is critical to maintain the health and condition of the jack at a high level of fitness. He should be prepared prior to the breeding season with emphasis on exercise and adjusting to weather exposure. Naturally he as well as the mares or jennets must be fed a balance diet and kept free of internal parasites. Foot care before and during breeding season is crucial to good performance.

JACKS CAUSING ABORTIONS

You may hear tell that letting a jack re-breed a pregnant jennet will cause her to abort. As yet, there has been no verified scientific proof. However, there are some instances where these acts may be related. A newly introduced jennet, already in foal, is going to have to adapt to her new herd. If she is in those crucial 36-40th days, the fetus is "Settling" at that point, and things are already touchy. Stress itself could cause her to slip the foal. There may also have been problems with the fetus, and it would be spontaneously aborted anyway. It is estimated that only about 40% of all conceptions result in viable births anyway. Those other 60%, while natural, may be seen to have been caused by some other factor, and aggressive breeding by the jack would be one.

TEASING

With donkeys a teaser is often a young colt, which is walked through the field under firm control, and allowed to mount the jennets to see if they are in season. Or a jack may be brought to the fence and he and the jennets are allowed to sniff each other. Jennets will show they are in heat by making a funny 'mouthing' gesture which is unmistakable and unique to donkeys. It is the same gesture sometimes shown to an adult by a foal which is indicating submission. Of course the jennet may or may not raise her tail, urinate and obviously show heat. Some jennets do not come into season at all unless they are actually mounted by the jack. If you have one of this kind, keep careful records on her and "try" her at the times she should show heat until she comes in. When she does, breed her every day during the heat cycle - being sure to keep very careful records of it.

IN HAND BREEDING

This is the way most serious breeders do most donkey mating. It is simple, the jacks are not overworked or out of condition through chasing and being kicked. Records, which are so important are much easier to keep, and proper cleaning of the reproductive organs of jacks and jennets may be carried out easily after each service.

The jennet must be restrained in some way. Some people use a breeding chute which is quite nice. One or two people may hold her, or she may be cross tied with QUICK RELEASE (panic) snaps and strong rope. It is very important to make sure she can take a step or two forward while being served. It is not really safe to tie her to a fence or gate. A non-slip surface is very important. If a certain spot of grass or earth is used, make sure it does not become slippery or muddy.

Breeding should always be carried out in the same place when possible. This way the jack knows he is here on business and will be less likely to try to breed every jennet he sees in other places. If he never breeds anywhere else he will stick to business better also. I have seen this backfire however, when an expensive Mammoth jack was shipped cross country - and then refused to breed a mare until he was taken to his regular place again - a thousand miles away! However, this is standard practice and the safest and most efficient way.

Wash the genital area of the jennet without killing her smell with strong disinfectants; very mild soap and water is best. Place her in position for breeding. Lead the jack quietly up to her and make sure she knows he is there and that they both have time to get ready. The jack should be allowed to sniff her and trial mount a time or two if that is what he wants. The jennet will probably kick or hump up her rump as if she would lash out. An older jack can usually manage this, but with an inexperienced one try to stand him where he will not get hurt. If the jennet is a bad kicker, restrain her with the breeding hobbles.

Sometimes, especially early in the year when it is cold, the jack will not be able to cover the jennet. If you bring the animals indoors, whether for warmth or protection, make sure the roof is high enough so that the jack will not bump his head. When the jack is ready to cover the jennet, move her tail to one side, with donkeys, tail wrapping is not necessary as it is with horses. She will move her tail herself usually but you need to keep the tassel of hair out of the way. If the jennet is too tall for convenience the jack may need to be guided. Three strong pulses may be seen as the semen is ejected. Let the jack remain mounted for as long as he wants and be sure he gets down quietly. Lead him and the jennet away in different directions, remembering to turn her head toward the jack so nobody gets kicked. If you can do it now, a bucket of warm water and diluted disinfectant (not one with a very strong smell) may be thrown over the jack's penis. If you can't you will have to douche (externally wash) him in a few minutes. Most people walk the jennet around for about 10 minutes to prevent her from urinating or straining at this time.

If you do not have breeding hobbles you may be able to keep a jennet from kicking by twitching her. Twitches can be made in many different ways, and if you do not own one, you can make one from heavy cord and a short broom handle.

You may douche the jack with an enema syringe using a mild solution of disinfectant. Just spray it over his penis. Repeat two or three times if necessary and use warm water. He should have his chest and belly wiped down with a cloth dipped in the same solution. After he is cleaned in this way he will not smell too strongly of jennet and you may take him near other jacks with less trouble. If you have a jack you have raised, part of his training should have been to have his "parts" handled so he will allow you to clean him with no protest.

To train a young jack for service, bring him to a very quiet jennet who is strongly in heat and does not kick. Have him wear a halter with a stud chain run under the chin and a strong lead. Let him mount her two or three times and sniff her and then make him stand quietly beside you until he is ready. Keep him disciplined at all times, but be as gentle as possible with it. Always carry a stick or stout whip. You may never need it and should not use it under normal circumstances, but when it is needed, it is needed very badly, so keep it there.

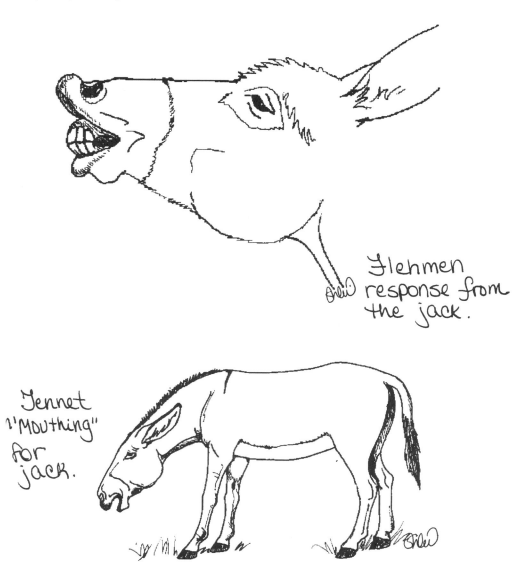

Flehmen response from the jack.

Jennet "Mouthing" for jack.

BROOD JENNETS

The most aggravating thing about maiden (never been bred) equine ladies is a habit they seem to have of coming into irregular heat in their first breeding season, either they don't come in at all or they come in and stay that way for a month at a time! Wait until later in the spring before breeding these, and be persistent with them. Usually a maiden is accepted as "clean", that is sound for breeding, but a vet might look for one or two things. The first, which is rare is an infantile genital tract. It can affect the uterus, vagina or any of the reproductive organs. They may have failed to develop to maturity. If this is true, sell the jennet for a pet, unless the vet says she is developing. If so, check her a year later, while perhaps using her for work or show meanwhile. The other condition is imperforate hymen. The hymen is a thin membrane that closes the vagina of a maiden jennet. It ordinarily has one or two small openings and is very thin and easily ruptured. Even though mechanical means aren't used to rupture the hymen before breeding it can be done at breeding time with very little damage, although in some instances there is a very tough, thick membrane that absolutely will not give. If a jennet with this condition is bred she will get very badly torn and is likely to hurt herself and some of her handlers in the process. When such a hymen is suspected have your vet open it surgically. It is always best if the hymen is broken down two or three weeks before breeding time and allowed to heal. If you find the jennet has a problem, do not attempt to solve this yourself, or let the jack keep trying. Call the vet and mark the jennet down for a later foal!

Teasing is quite a problem early in the season, but it is a matter of persistence. The large percentage of jennets fall into a regular pattern and probably the maiden is the second easiest to get in foal. The barren is probably first, and then jennets with foals at side.

Proud Jack. Photo by L.G. Smith, Benton City WA.

TRAINING JACKS TO HANDLE

The belief among some people that a jack is a vicious animal is not based upon actual facts but probably upon a remembrance of some individual that had been spoiled as a result of poor management. After being properly trained a jack is one of the easiest of workstock to handle. The earlier the training begins the less difficult the undertaking. The colts produced in this study were halter-broken and trained to lead during the suckling period. They have been handled almost daily since with the exception of the periods when they were on permanent pasture.

After a colt is about 18 months old he begins to become unruly when handled with a halter. It is necessary therefore to start "bitting" him or training him to be handled with a bridle. The important point in this connection is to provide a bridle that is easily put on and taken off. Most jacks are touchy about the ears and any jack can be completely spoiled by careless management. The ears should never be touched except when they are to be trimmed or the mane roached. (ed. note: further investigation has been found to show that the best way of making jacks and mules gentle around the ears is to handle them gently and caressingly from early foalhood on. Most love to be rubbed on the inside of the ears with a finger - once they know you are not going to hurt them. The ears should NEVER be used for disciplinary purposes, under any circumstances.)

Jacks are usually handled with an ordinary snaffle bit and a bridle made from 1 ½" strap of leather bradded to the bit on one side and to a snap on the other side. No brow band or throatlatch is needed. A strap of leather 1" wide and 8' long with a chain chin piece makes a satisfactory lead. The chain run through one ring of the bit under the chin and snapped to the ring on the opposite side is sufficient.

Jacks should be trained to be approached in the stall from the left side. The snap end of the bridle is first thrown across the neck from the opposite side with the handler standing on the left, the bit placed in the mouth and snapped to the bridle. The bridle on top of the neck can now be gently moved to just back of the ears and the jack is ready.

TRAINING JACKS TO SERVE MARES

The "Breaking-in" period represents one of the most critical periods in the life of a jack. The natural inclination of most jacks is to serve jennets rather than mares and for this reason every precaution should be taken after jacks are weaned, to handle them in such a way that they will not become "jennet-spoiled". In this study, a horse filly about the same age as the jacks was allowed to remain with the colts during the first winter and the following grazing season. As has been mentioned, an effort was made not to allow the jacks to see jennets or mules at all. At about 20 to 24 months of age, the colts were bred to a mare. The mare used was gentle, and fully in heat each time the jacks were tried. Hobbles were placed on the hind legs of the mare to prevent any danger from kicking. No trouble was experienced in getting all of the jacks as two year olds to breed a mare. They were allowed to serve five or six times at weekly intervals.

The plan at the beginning was to breed each jack to a definite number of mares for experimental purposes. Two of them served the alloted number of mares readily, but one refused. He was worked with, two or three times weekly for about two months without any results. On August 1 this jack was tried on a jennet fully in heat and served her in about 10 minutes time. The following day he was tried on the same mare that he had served as a two year old but again he refused to serve. The training was continued and no trouble was experienced on the following day in getting the jack to serve a mare after a jennet had been placed near him.

This jack is a typical "jennet-spoiled" individual. He was developed under the same environmental conditions as the other two that served mares normally. These details are mentioned in order to point out the fact that each individual is different from all others, and must be handled as such.

HANDLING UNCASTRATED JACKS

Although many people are against castration of male donkeys for many reasons, a pet male donkey not intended for breeding purposes is best gelded. Handling an entire jack is sometimes tricky. Some people have found that their jacks are so quiet, kind and gentle that there is supposedly no need to go to the trouble and expense of castrating them. Others feel that the sale value of a castrated male is too low.

Before we discuss the safety aspects I would like to state, that every person that is sincerely interested in the ass breed should realize that ALL males of such conformation as to render them poor specimens of the breed should be castrated. This way they make loveable, valuable pets, but do not pass their conformation faults on to their offspring. In all probability, 90% of male donkeys produced should be gelded and not used for breeding. However, you will find that sadly, the figures are much lower than this, almost to the point of being inverted!

There are two elemental, simple facts that must be learned by people that deal with donkeys.

1. ALL MALE EQUINES CAN BE DANGEROUS AT TIMES.
2. Jacks, unlike stallions are not particularly nervous animals. This makes the handling of a jack a matter for some thought.

Some people will tell you that a jack is a "tricky" animal. Except for the occasional individual spoiled animal this is not so. His donkey nature sometimes betrays him. Donkeys are not nervous and uptight all the time. They are basically affectionate, trusting and gentle. So, when his "baser instincts" take him over and the jack does something to injure or frighten his handler he is accused of being sneaky. Actually it is a matter of his better qualities being overcome by impulses he cannot control and may not expect. Any entire (uncastrated) jack can do something dangerous in the heat of the moment! Nature just forces him to it sometimes.

Never give a child or an inexperienced person a jack to handle habitually. Let me give two examples. A Mammoth jack of kind disposition and beautifully trained, a show ring winner, badly savaged his owners hand. (It could have been her neck if she had been standing differently.) This happened because he was put in another jack's stall and could see his rival in his own territory. He simply went mad. When he calmed down he seemed to be terribly distressed and crouched in the corner shivering even though he was not punished. His handler knew enough about animals to realize what had happened, and after she got back from the hospital the situation was remedied and the jack was not punished. But what if this animal had belonged to an inexperienced person - severe injury and even death could have resulted from a savaging by this large jack in his insane mood - and a less understanding owner might have beaten him or even had him killed.

The other example was a horseman who had learned to look for a certain kind of behavior in Stallions! He was lulled into carelessness by the gentle and truly loving nature of his Standard jack. When the man walked into the jack's stall smelling of mares the jack attacked him on an instant's notice and savaged his arm very badly. (Jacks catch hold with their teeth and hang on and shake what they have - large ones will get a person or another jack down, kneel on the victim and proceed to tear him apart if they can). Immediately after the attack the jack in questions was gentle and loving again. The same instinctive reaction that makes a jack bite and kick a jennet or mare will cause him to do the same to a human that smells like a female. Smell is much more of a trigger to most animals than sight or sound and it can have this effect.

ALWAYS BE ALERT AND AWARE OF THE NATURAL REACTIONS WHEN HANDLING AN ENTIRE JACK. NEVER LET YEARS OF KINDNESS AND GENTLENESS BLIND YOU TO THE FACT THAT HE IS A MALE EQUINE WITH INSTINCTIVE REACTIONS THAT MIGHT BE DANGEROUS TO A HUMAN OR ANOTHER EQUINE, ESPECIALLY ANOTHER JACK OR A GELDING.

HANDLING JACKS

Anyone who owns a jack should give him plenty of normal good care, love and affection. If it is possible to let him run with other animals, geldings or a gentle mare or jennet it is best for him. Do be careful, especially if he lives alone and not with other animals, not to come to him smelling of mare or jennets. If he lives with a little herd be careful when you approach him that his herding instinct does not cause him to defend his herd against you as if you were another jack or a stallion. If he can see or hear females when you are handling him be careful with him. "Vicks" rub comes in very handy in some cases. A very small dab in each nostril kills the smells and makes most jacks behave much better at shows and other places where they are not supposed to breed. However it will completely kill the breeding instinct in some so do not use any time that breeding is contemplated.

If you lead or work with a jack, make sure he is properly haltered and tied short if you are grooming or working around him. If you are leading, have the chain under his jaw, or in some cases through the mouth or over the nose. Do not make it painful, but a sharp jerk of the chain will often bring him to his senses. Many people show jacks with a bit in the mouth for control, this works well also. Your jack may be gentle enough at home to work with no halter or a halter only with no stud chain, but you should own a stud chain, keep it handy, and know who to fasten it properly. It may never be needed (and you will be very lucky). But if you need it, you will need it right that minute, and that instance is no time to stop and figure out HOW to use one. A stud chain used properly will be a helpful tool.

If you buy a young jack, train him right away to behave perfectly when confronted by members of the opposite sex. Most people do this with stallions because without it, they could not be handled at all. Because the average jack is kind tempered, or small (Miniatures can bite too you know), they may neglect this training with a jack. At all times remember that he has both feet and teeth and may use them under stress.

Do not use harsh punishments on jacks - the old time mammoth breeders will tell you that nothing makes a jack as dangerous as a lion as quickly as either shutting him up in a dark stall or whipping or beating or hurting him. This treatment will turn a good natured jack into a monster, in a very short time. Unlike horses, donkeys are not so inclined to be afraid of people - when a bad jack attacks he is not doing it in a panic -but with malice - forethought - and he will not be easily frightened off. (Remember that old saying that a mule will never forget the person who abuses him, but will wait until the right moment for revenge? It's not quite all true, but the mule does get part of that "remembering" from the jack.)

Do not allow any children or inexperienced people around a jack without supervision. It is much the best if you are holding his lead with the chain on. Especially do not let them around if they have been around other horses or donkeys first. You may trust your jack to the Nth degree. You know he would never harm anyone. But you can't control the actions of the other person, and as we all know, it's that one time we don't do every single thing right that it all falls apart. You wouldn't want that one time to be at the expense of a friend or your animal.

I would like to stress the following point as much as possible. A jack is an animal that if properly reared and handled will not want to hurt its handler. The smaller Standards and Miniatures are especially friendly. They will try never to hurt you. But please - allow the jack his dignity as an entire male, and respect him for his instincts. Do not punish cruelly his occasional lapses - but handle him sensibly. Treat your jack with respect and he will do the same for you.

IF YOU ONLY WANT A PET, GELD YOUR JACK!

MANAGEMENT OF THE JACK
from The Brayer

Don't wait until just before breeding season to get that stud jack into condition. Prime condition means good health from top to toe, to perform well, he must feel well. Condition the jack the year round, don't cram condition him in late winter for the spring season.

The following steps can be taken to keep your jack doing well.

1. Inoculate with yearly booster shots for equine influenza, tetanus, distemper and sleeping sickness. Shots should be completed 6 weeks before breeding starts.
2. Feed a complete ration with all necessary vitamins and minerals and a good grade of hay free choice. Also salt and all the clean fresh water he wants.
3. Allow him the freedom of a large pen or pasture for proper exercise.
4. Control parasites with a regular program.
5. Do not allow mares or jennets to kick the jack.
6. If you must tease, don't use your most valuable jack.
7. Try to watch his semen count.
8. Sore mouthed animals don't breed well, have the vet check his teeth.
9. Keep his feet (hooves) in the best possible condition.

10. Provide food increases gradually, do not boost feed intake immediately when breeding season starts.
11. Any lameness should be seen immediately by a vet.
12. Washing the jack's genitalia as well as the mare's or jenny's before and after breeding can help the conception rate and lower chances of disease transmission.
13. Provide shade in hot weather, shelter in cold.

CONSERVING THE JACK

A vigorous two year old jack may breed 8 to 12 mares at the rate of one to two a week. A three year old may breed 25 to 40, a four year old 50 to 60, and a mature jack in a four month's season, 70 to 100. The number of jennets will probably depend on the experience of the jack. The mature jack limited to two mares daily on weekdays with none Sundays, remains virile and lasts longer than one allowed to breed a greater number. Overworking jacks is often responsible for a low ratio of foals to total mares bred. Jacks in heavy service require ample feed and hay of good quality. He should be fed at least twice daily, the stall should be kept clean, airy and dry and should be sprayed regularly with the proper dilution of disinfectant. Much jack trouble can be avoided by keeping feet trimmed, and by regular exercise. Try to arrange to keep the jack in a good two acre grass paddock adjacent to his stall.

RISK FACTORS IN BREEDING

Aside for the risk of infection from the jennet or mare, and the possiblity of reduced fertility from overuse, there is one other factor in breeding that should be mentioned. It is more likely to occur in larger jacks who are breeding mares, but it could theoretically happen to any breeding male. Some jennets and mares may be overly aggressive, and kick the jack when he attempts to mount. Restraining the jennet in a breeding chute or control hand-breeding can reduce this risk. However, there have been several recorded incidents where a mare has kicked the jack and scored right on the scrotum - rupturing one or both testicles. In this case, castration is usually the only alternative in order to save the jack's life. You have then lost your breeding jack and have a perfectly wonderful gelding, but as a breeder this was not your goal. If you have a situation where the jack has been injured in a breeding situation, let your vet check him immediately to prevent the situation from going from bad to worse.

photo by Leah Patton. ADMS Nationals 1998

BREEDING THE JENNET & MANAGEMENT OF THE PREGNANT JENNET

Most jennets show that they are in foal by ceasing their heat periods. However, an occasional one will fool the breeder and come in heat when she is already pregnant, or get a year's bed and board with nothing to show at the end of it but a fat tummy from all the good grain she got. So, if you are in the donkey breeding business you should work out some type of pregnancy testing program with your vet.

Taking the first day of the jennet's season as day 1, the 36th to 40th days are rather ticklish. She should not be upset or disturbed during this critical period as she may reabsorb or abort her foal. Don't show her, worm her, trim her feet or disturb her in any way during this period. Just continue her normal routine.

For several months you will not notice any change in the jennet's tummy size. She may get either more quiet and staid or more irritable, or perhaps somehow different from her usual temperament, but she should not get any rounder unless you are overfeeding her. The pregnant jennet does not require any extra care other than her normal (not more) good nutrition, good grass where possible and ample opportunity to exercise. She should not be overfed as obesity may make it difficult for her to give birth. The feed given should be a balanced ration with all the necessary vitamins and minerals. She should have plenty of salt and fresh clean water also. At about 5 months or so you will notice her becoming progressively rounder. Jennets that have had foals before show this more than first timers usually, as their muscles have been stretched before. At foaling time, a small jennet usually looks alarmingly like she swallowed a barrel, but all will be well shortly, and much of that is fluid.

While a jennet is in foal she should have her feet trimmed properly, as the extra weight can cause pain and deformity of the legs if the feet are not kept level. Try not to trim her feet in the last month or so however. She may be irritable from the advanced stages of pregnancy, and shifting all that weight to three feet (especially if she has had hoof problems before) may not be her idea of fun.

If the jennet is used to being ridden or working regularly she can keep it up until she looks large and it becomes obvious that carrying a rider and her foal is rather much of a strain. However do not put her into heavy work at any time while she is in foal. It is not the best idea to show her while she is in foal either. She won't look all that good in the ring, and the stress and disease possibilities of showing could be dangerous for her or the foal. Likewise, if she has just foaled, or is suckling, she may not be able to keep enough flesh in the right places to be in show shape.

In summary, adequate space for exercise, congenial companions, light work, proper nutrition without getting fat, and careful watching by the master will be just what the pregnant jennet needs. Of course have the vet prescribe her worming program while she is pregnant, as some medicines are dangerous and having worms is very bad for the foal. Be sure she has the proper immunizations for your area.

BREEDING THE JENNET

Some people prefer to run the jack out with the jennets and let nature take its course. It is however, much safer to breed by hand and let them run with the jack only after they are safely in foal, or not at all. If the jennets are out with the jack, two may come into heat at the same time, and the jack may completely ignore one while courting the other. Jennets may fight, and kick the jack and may injure him. Some jacks are very rough with their jennets. They usually bite when mounting to give themselves leverage and to hold the jennet still, but may catch an ear and greatly damage it as well as causing intense pain. Also he may bite her and cause injuries in other places. Most jacks, especially inexperienced ones that are turned out with jennets or mares will be scratched, bruised and scraped with kick and bite marks on them before the breeding season is well started. Older jacks may escape much of this, but may be equally rough on the females to keep them under control. In a young jack, he may become a reluctant breeder.

Usually the jennets have to be chased around until they are so tired they are forced to stand for breeding, which is hard on both animals and may cause injury, loss of condition and fatigue. If there is barbed wire fencing the dangers are both obvious and frightening. The same holds for dangerous obstructions or objects in the pasture. Do not put strange jennets in with as established herd which is set up with the jack for breeding. The other animals can practically torture her to death because she is a stranger, and to have that happen while the jack is frantically chasing her to try to breed her is cruel and inhumane. If you must put a new jennet in the breeding herd, do it outside of the breeding season, or have the jack hand breed her and put her in after she is safely in foal. One method of easing the transition is to put her in a roomy enclosure with the "top" jennet or one of the jennets at the top of the pecking order in the herd. Let them come to an understanding, or better yet, let them be pals an then put the two of them back. If you can't do that you can put the jennet in and keep close and careful watch for about eight days, taking her out at night if the other jennets are being especially violent to her.

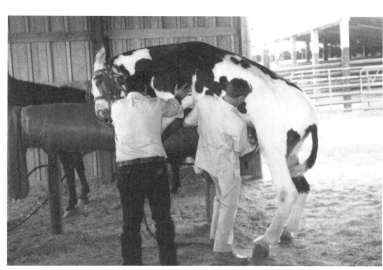

photo courtesy of American Jack Sires, Dr. Marco Oviedo, NM.

Whether you are using artificial insemination and collecting the jack, hand-breeding or pasture breeding, you should take precautions for the jack's safety. this jack is being collected, and mounts a phantom or "dummy" mare. A real mare is in the background to provide a visual (and odor) stimulus. The jack also wears a muzzle. Some jacks take hold with their teeth and can injure the jennet or mare. If your jack runs in pasture you should not muzzle him.

INJURY AND SPREAD OF DISEASE
Hopefully in selecting your breeding animal, you made sure they were free of any disease, and this includes warts. Warts are caused by a virus, and can be spread among your herd, as well as to humans. Check the muzzle of all animals to make sure they do not have warts. Treat them before release into a breeding herd, or the entire herd may possibly have to be treated.

Donkeys and mules are more prone to Sarcoid tumors (which in themselves are not cancerous but can lead to cancerous changes). The sarcoids look like small, hairless lumps at first, but can become as large as grapefruits. They are also apparently caused by a virus, but are not known to be contagious. They are, however, susceptible to further injury. Scratching, rubbing, or biting can cause them to bleed. If your jack or jennet has a sarcoid tumor, have it surgically removed. Some donkeys will chew on them, causing further damage. Unexplained small bloody patches on broodstock should always be carefully examined, and any injury to the breeding jack should be attended at once.

EXAMINING FOR BREEDING SOUNDNESS

The greatest cause of failure in breeding is insufficient exposure. Start at the beginning of the breeding season and keep breeding your jennets that didn't settle as long as you can taking into account the weather at the time of foaling in your area. Most will go out of season by October, but you can usually keep trying the stubborn ones through September. Most people feel that a foal born in September, although needing extra care because of winter weather, is better than a barren jennet eating her head off for a year before trying again. Although you may start breeding early, most will not take until the spring grass has had time to take a "tonic" effect on their systems and the daylight lengthens.

When you ask your vet to examine your herd for breeding soundness he will first make a complete examination of each genital tract. A rectal examination of the uterus and ovaries (in larger jennets) and an examination with the speculum of the vagina and cervix for old tears and adhesions may disclose enlarged or malfunctioning ovaries. The speculum examination shows if there is redness or discharge. If there is a bacterial infection, culture should be made. This enables the vet to treat it most effectively.

Early cycles can be quite confusing. A jennet may appear to be coming in one day and perhaps "show" for six to eight days before she is actually ready to breed. The result is that there is a tendency to breed a barren jennet too early in the cycle in those early days. In the early period you don't breed a jennet until five or six or seven days after she first shows in heat. Later on she may come in heat one day, will be bred on the third day and be out on the fifth day.

There are no real rules for teasing or breeding a jennet. We have only rules of thumb, or guides. There is no doubt at all that the more personal attention each individual animal receives, the better results will come from breeding.

The physical condition should be thrifty without being fat. Extremely fat jennets or those who are poor are not in correct breeding condition, as pregnancy could cause a great strain on her. Her hooves must be sound, an old chronically foundered jennet is going to have a lot of added weight, strain, and possible pain on those damaged hooves.

Likewise, the jennet you just bought that is 16 years old and never reportedly had a foal is not a good candidate as a brood jennet. If the jennet has had several foals, rather regularly spaced (but not overbred with a foal every 13 months) you have a better chance of getting an older jennet in foal. If you know for sure it has been more than 3 or 4 years since the jenny last had a foal, let your vet know and have him/her do a complete examination. This type of jenny is usually very hard to get in foal and to carry to term. She may also be out-of shape as well, which just compounds matters.

AFTER SHE IS BRED

The first thing to worry about after you determine by vet inspection that the jennet **is** in foal is abortion. We will consider first physiological abortion, of which there are two or three forms. The first is due to a glandular upset. We know little or nothing about most of those and fail to explain what is meant when we say there has been a hormone or glandular upset resulting in the death of the embryo and abortion. Other abortions can be due to a weak sperm or ovum. One type occurs between the 40th and 60th day. Shortly after 40 days of pregnancy there is a shift in the production of the hormones from the ovary to the placenta. What happens is that during this shift there may be a little slip up in Nature's technique that will allow an abortion to occur at that time. The fetus is not big enough to attract attention, and if the jennet is at pasture it will probably pass unnoticed. If a jennet is prone to this we can supplement the proper hormone from the time she is found in foal at 40 days and keep her supplied until foaling.

When twins are conceived they are not considered normal and often abort. Infectious types of abortion are due to various bacterial diseases including streptococcic infections, B Coli infections etc. and are purely mechanical. That is, the infection occurs either in the uterus at the time of breeding or is introduced at that time and develops. Whenever you have an abortion and can find the fetus it is well worth whatever it costs to have a laboratory make a thorough examination and find out the reason if possible. To control infectious abortions there are vaccines, such as a contagious abortion vaccine which is made from Salmonella Equi. While it is agreed by experts that Virus Abortion Vaccine is not a specific vaccine, it is used because it is all there is available at the moment.

GESTATION

Everyone seems to have his own number of days that he calculates foaling dates on. In the mare it is approximately 340-345 days (eleven months) but jennets take approximately 365 or twelve months. According to her own personal calendar, some may carry as short as ten and a half months, others may carry thirteen. One breeder was certain of the date the jack was removed, and the jennet was still carrying at fourteen-plus months. If a jennet delivers a big, healthy foal she's had a normal gestation period regardless of how long it took. However, no matter how far into the pregnancy, if she begins to look ill or begins to drop flesh rapidly, have your vet make sure she still has a live foal. Late-term foal deaths can cause all kinds of infection in the jennet, and you could possibly lose her as well.

JEALOUSY AMONG JENNETS

Although as we have seen, jacks may do harm to other jacks or occasionally to humans through jealousy of other males, this reaction is much less common among females. You may see this in jennets you thought were pregnant but turn out to be barren. You should watch jennets who don't seem to be advancing normally in pregnancy, especially if you felt she was due and all the others jennets have foaled, but not her. It is less common early in the pregnancy, more common after other foals start to arrive.

In a herd of breeding jennets one will sometimes try to take a foal away from another, and sometimes will succeed. Obviously this couldn't be worse for the foal since the new "foster mother" has no milk.

However, even more serious is when a jennet does harm to a foal or to a human because of jealousy. The causes usually have to be extreme however. The following is a case which came to our attention and will illustrate the type of situation to be on guard Two jennets ages approximately 7 and 8 were constant companions for over a year. Suddenly, two new young donkeys were introduced, and almost at the same day the Standard jennet had an unexpected foal.

The Miniature jennet was immediately driven away by her former companion and not allowed to approach the Standard jennet or her foal for two weeks. At the same time the two animals that had been introduced rejected her because they were "pals". At this time the Miniature and the mother came into heat. The young jack that had been introduced to the herd proceeded to serve the Standard jennet with the foal, ignoring the Miniature.

One day the Miniature jennet was observed making aggressive gestures toward the foal of the standard jennet who, however, would not let her get close enough to harm the foal. These aggressive gestures did not look serious, so a young boy, who was very familiar with all these very gentle donkeys, went out to pet the Miniature jennet. This jennet suddenly turned on the boy (apparently because he was approximately the same size as the foal), knocked him down and bit him several times. Only one bite was severe but there were quite a few grazes. Upon the intervention of an adult she sprang off the boy and retreated to a corner. She showed "guilt" (or whatever passes for knowledge of wrongdoing in the donkey world) for a day or so afterward.

Luckily the owner, instead of condemning all donkeys and this one in particular as vicious, was an experienced animal lover, and was able to examine in detail the physical and psychological reactions that caused this problem. Various combinations of veterinary treatment, breeding, separation etc. will see that the incident does not reoccur.

This jennet was brought to a peak of hormonal and psychological excitement at a bad time, and not meaning to cause harm to her human master, simply turned on an object approximately the size of the foal and took out her frustration on it. It could just as well have been a dog or the foal itself.

This is an EXTREMELY RARE incident for a jennet, but it is best for the owner of pet donkeys to keep in mind the intense attraction they develop for each other, and take steps in advance to provide comfort for the jennet that may be left out or rejected in this manner.

THAT LONG AWAITED FOAL

You have waited the required 12 months. You have dilegently recorded the breeding dates of your jennet. Now you just have to wait for the foal to arrive. Or, in the opposite case, you have purchased a jennet, and she seems to being her best every day to get so wide as to not make it through the barn door. She's in foal and you have no idea when Baby will arrive!!! How can you tell??? What can you do???

The signs of impending birth will vary with every single birth. Don't have your hopes up about catching her in the act - it's unlikely. Then of course, as soon as you read this, you will be like the people who called the ADMS office in uncontrollable excitement - not only was their jennet foaling in the daylight, but she came up onto their wide porch - in the midst of a garage sale, and laid down in public view for the birth!

There are some signs you can look for. The first is slack muscles over the croup. If the jennet is very fat or very poor, this will be harder to tell. The vulva will also seem larger or slack.

BAGGING UP AND WAXING

"Oh, she'll bag up two weeks (or two days, or two hours) before she foals. Already you can read this sentence again and see that the "Bagging" rule doesn't hold. Maiden jennets might bag only hours before the colt is born. Old pros might look like a nanny goat for weeks. Even is she never appears to bag up, unless the newborn appears to be getting weak and you never see any milk on the teats or whiskers after it has nursed should you worry. Some jennets are just smaller-bagged than others!

Everyone will tell you the nipples will wax just before she foals. Face it, some jennets wax weeks beforehand and lose the wax droplets, some will wax 24 hours beforehand, some will never wax where you can see it. If you do see tiny yellow beads on the ends of the teats, this is wax. Don't knock them off, and under NO circumstances should you milk the jennet.

POINTY BELLY

The most reliable indication we have found for foaling is the "pointy belly". Within 48 hours of foaling, the foal will move into the birth canal, preferably forefeet and nose first. He is mostly leg at birth, and has been pretty much curled up inside Mom. As he gets in position, the legs are stretched out in front of him, and he is quite literally "sitting" in the womb. His little butt will be the lowest part, and it makes a distinct point on the jennet's belly. If you see this angular look, she is almost ready!!! Check to see if her muscles are slack on the tailhead. she may be irritable, so don't upset her. Don't attempt to examine her internally either!!!

MOOD AND MANNERS

Studies show that the fetus actually starts the birth process in motion by releasing hormones, although there is also some evidence that the jennet or mare can have some control, such as holding off when the weather is bad (or making sure you are gone on vacation, or until you have left the barn to go to the bathroom or get a cup of coffee...). When this happens, all the other factors begin to shift into place. Her tummy is big and droops past her knees. Her back may hurt. Her bag (udder) may be hot and tight as it fills. She is certainly not in the mood to have last year's youngster or the jack enticing her to play!!! She might take it out on the nearest creature - if she seems irritable, leave her alone, but stay near her where she can hear or see you. You don't want to push it on being there for imprinting, but you don't want to miss it either. Above all, if she starts acting funny, try and bring her up to the barn (or pen her away from the other donkeys), and don't get yourself hurt.

DAY OR NIGHT?

Being prey animals, most equines foal in the wee hours of the morning. Nocturnal predators are usually on the way home, and those that hunt in the day probably aren't awake yet. Since the newborn foal is up and moving within an hour or so of birth, foaling at 5 am in the morning gives a fairly safe margin. The jennet can rest and recover from the birth, and baby can find his legs.

In the wild, a Mustang mare will often have an "aunt" attend the birth with her. The aunt watches for predators while mom and baby rest and get aquainted. If your jennet seems to have a pal attached to her at the shoulder, don't attempt to separate them. Just bring mom and auntie both up into the pen, or place them in stalls next to each other. Mom may need her pal for comfort.

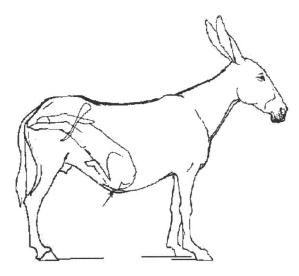

Proper postition of the foal immediately before delivery. Note that the lowest portion of the foal, the haunches, forms a "point" on the jennet's belly.

Various abnormal presentations - one leg back, sboth legs back (nose only) , breech (butt first)., head back (legs only, no nose presented).

If any of these presentations occur - CALL THE VET IMMEDIATELY!!! DO NOT PUSH OR PULL on the foal's legs unless instructed by the vet!

Our sincerest thanks to the owners of jennets who made it possible to share this special sequence with our readers.

Close to foaling, the tailhead is slack and other muscles are relaxing.

Rear view - a distinct pear shape. The bag and teats are filled.

Closeup, the vulva is enlarged, the bag bulges out between the hind legs. The jennet is also holding her tail out and away from her rump.

Perhaps not the best spot to foal near droppings, but once the jennet lays down, do not attempt to move her. She may get up and down on her own a few times. In this photo, the amnion (sac) is begining to emerge.

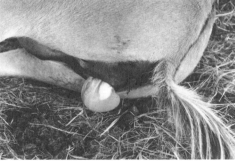

A hoof is visible in the bubble of the fluid-filled sack. Both hooves are actually right alongside each other, although only one can be seen clearly. If only one presents, be ready to call the vet!

This jennet has decided to stand up in the early stage of labor. Both hooves are visible.

The jennet has laid back done, and both forelegs are emerging.

The foal's head and shoulders emerge, still partially enclosed in the sac.

This foal is born except for the hind legs. The sac is clear of the nostril, but if it were over the face, you woud want to pull it gently away. Approach the jennet quietly, but speak to her so she will not be startled. You do not want her to rise at this moment.

The foal is completely delivered. The membranes are not around the face, and the umbilical cord can be seen still attaching the foal and jennet. Let them both lie quietly as long as they like.

The jennet has curled back around to sniff the new arrival. This is vital bonding time, especially for maiden jennets. Let the pair be alone, you can move in and imprint in a few minutes. You can rub the foal with a towel, and begin to handle it, but always monitor the jenny's reactions. If she starts getting upset, leave and let her calm back down.

Those first attempts to stand - the jennet is on her feet but has not yet expelled the afterbirth. Within a few minutes she will deliver the placenta. If possible, remove it from the birth area, and spread it out to make sure it is intact. If you vet is coming, he/she will want to see it, so put it in a big garbage bag. If it appears to be breaking up or is only partial, call the vet and let them know. Retained placentas can cause serious infection.

All wobbles, and they will fall down, at least the first couple of times. The foal should attempt to stand within the first 30 minutes or so, some sooner. If it makes no attempts at all to stand, call the vet! It should be alert with it's head raised. If it just lies and shivers, or cannot raise it's head, call the vet immediately!

On our feet and drying into fluffy curls. The foal may make several attempts to find the udder - even on the wrong end. If the jennet will allow, you can gently direct, but let the foal explore and learn.

EMBRYO TRANSFER And ARTIFICIAL INSEMINATION

II. Embryo transfer foals from registered parents will be registered in the usual manner providing the following rules are complied with;
1. Any jennet may be used for embryo transfer regardless of age or past reproductive performance.
2. There will be no limit to the number of foals registered in any given year.
3. The ADMS shall be advised in writing of the intent to embryo transfer a jennet prior to the date of transfer. This notification shall include the sire or sires to be used.
4. The ADMS shall be advised in writing of all successful transfers during a calendar year no later than March 1, of the following year. The sire, dam, transfer date, and description of the host jennet or mare shall be given.
5. An association representative or association approved veterinarian must be present during the collection and transfer procedure.
6. In the event of questionable parentage, the ADMS has the right to require blood tests to verify the pedigree. If the question cannot be resolved the foal will be registered by inspection only. All expenses incurred in this testing will be paid by the owner.
7. The ADMS may inspect the premises and practices of any party using or intending to use embryo transfer procedures to produce registerable asses.
8. Written verification of the transfer shall also be made by the attending association representative or veterinarian.

Embryo transfer is a recent advance in breeding management of considerable significance in donkeys, with especial reference to the breeder of mammoth jackstock. Since mammoth jennets are rare and excellent ones are even more rare, embryo transfer permits a breeder to obtain many offspring from the best jennets, using smaller donkeys as substitute mothers. The technique itself is relatively simple. The donor jennet is bred according to conventional practices and recovery of the embryo is usually attempted on day 8 or 9 after ovulation. After washing of the external genitalia and wrapping of the tail, a Foley catheter with a 5O cc inflatable cuff is inserted through the cervix into the uterus. The purpose of the cuff is to secure the catheter and prevent flushing medium from leaking past the cervix. The flushing medium is then introduced into the uterus either by gravity flow or by injection with a large volume syringe. The fluid is then allowed to flow back through the catheter carrying the embryo with it. The fluid containing the embryo is collected and examined under a microscope. Assuming that a healthy embryo is obtained it is then placed into the uterus of a recipient jennet which is at the same stage of her estrous cycle as the donor. The acual transfer can be done either surgically through an incision in the body cavity, or non-surgically by going through the donor's cervix. Obviously because of both convenience and expense the latter approach is preferred but success rates are much higher with the surgical procedure. At present the chances of success with surgical transfer are nearly twice as high (35%) as with the non-surgical technique (20%).

In addition to the expense of the surgery, the maintenance of large numbers of recipient jennets to insure synchrony between donor and recipient also adds to the costs of embryo transfer. Although equine embryo transfer is now commercially available, research is needed to further evaluate transfer media, method of transfer, sites of transfer and the degree of synchrony necessary between donor and recipient which will insure maximum success. The expense of maintaining large numbers of animals could be eliminated by the development of technology for freeze storage of embryos. This has been accomplished in laboratory animals.

No facilities are known currently to have quantities of frozen embryos of donkeys.

The current known usage of embryo transfer in donkeys has been as host mothers for some endangered species, and experimentation on inter-species transfer. Mare mules have successfully carried horse and donkey foals, donkey jennets have carried horse and mule foals, and horse mares have carried zebra foals. However, the cost involved is highly prohibitive for this practice to become commonplace for breeders.

ARTIFICIAL INSEMINATION (A.I.)

Although this technique is becoming common in horses, it is more unusual in donkeys. There are Mammoth and Large Standard breeders who use it, especially on jacks that breed mares. Since some jacks tend to show a preference for breeding either mares or jennets, if a breeder wants donkey foals from a mule jack (a jack used only to breed mules), he uses A.I. on select jennets. Many vets are now equipped to perform A.I. Fresh or fresh-chilled semen is the norm. It is still under debate whether or nor frozen semen has a decent viablility. The known trials thus far have not produced very favorable results.

A.I. is less common in the smaller donkeys. Although it is just a matter of technique, there are enough Miniature jacks that live cover is the most common form of breeding.

A.I. breedings take more time and planning than live cover. You must consult with your vet if you plan on using A.I. It may require cycling your jennet so that when the semen arrives, the A.I. can be done immediately. A close sense of timing and a good working relationship with your vet (or one that does A.I., not all do) is essential.

What all the fuss is about - a nice jennet and a healthy baby! *Ruby* and her foal *Charlotte*, Large Standards, owned by Ann Wagonseller, Southlake TX.

ORPHAN FOALS

There are dozens of ways to raise newborn or older orphan foals. Some people would not use anything but goats milk, others realize that the most sensible way is to foster the orphan on a milking jennet. But goat's milk and milking jennets that will accept two foals are not always available. The first thing you should do is consult your veterinarian and work out a program with his help.

The following is taken from the booklet THE BORDEN GUIDE TO THE CARE AND FEEDING OF ORPHAN AND EARLY WEANED FOALS, and will give you some idea of at least one way to raise such a baby.

Foals can be orphaned at any age and the feeding of the foal will depend on the age, condition and eating habits when orphaned.

If the jennet dies and the foal has not yet stood and suckled, you should try to milk the jennet immediately and get some colostrum into the foal. Keep in touch with your vet and let him/her direct the procedure, but if it possible to get the jennet's own colostrum into the foal, that is best. Otherwise, let your vet know immediately so they can help you locate a source of frozen colostrum.

The charts and discussions following are to be considered as GENERAL GUIDELINES and the owner must evaluate the animal's condition and eating habits to know whether these directions should be modified. Any foal which has been nursing or even a foal taken at birth should be started on Foal-Lac carefully and slowly so the digestive system can adjust to the new milk.

FOALS ORPHANED DURING THE FIRST WEEK OF LIFE

For this age foal the feeding schedule should be followed as though the foal were just born. Feed 4 times per day (every 6 hours if possible) for the first week. If the foal adapts well to the feeding schedule and handles the increases without difficulty, it may be changed to three times per day (every 8 hours if possible) during the second week. If the foal does not readily consume the increases in feeding, it should be continued on 4 feedings per day. Three feedings per day should be sufficient for the third week, and this can be reduced to 2 feedings per day during the fourth week. Finally the feedings should be reduced to 1 per day a couple of days prior to discontinuing liquid feeding.

You will note two different feeding schedules. One of these should be used with a ration formulated for young foals containing a minimum of 16% protein, supplemented with vitamins and minerals. The second should be used with a simple grain mixture or low protein horse feed. These feeding schedules including the introduction of Foal-Lac pellets and the grain ration should be self explanatory.

You will probably be most successful feeding liquid Foal-Lac in an open bucket. To start the foal, rub a little on its mouth and place its nose in the milk. It sometimes helps to hold the bucket for the foal until it starts to drink. Then lead it to the permanent feeding area with the bucket. The bucket should be placed about the height of the foal's shoulders and tipped slightly toward the foal so that all the milk can be readily consumed. The foal may require 1 or 2 hours to drink the milk during the first couple of days. Wash the bucket with hot, soapy water after each feeding. Rinse thoroughly and invert the bucket to dry. Consult your veterinarian if there are any signs of disease, fever, parasites, etc. A worming program should be established, even for a young foal, to keep it free from parasites. Foals less than one week old should be out of the weather, especially at night. A heat lamp in the stall is desirable if the foal is orphaned during the first 3 days of life, and especially if foaling occurs n cold weather. Place the lamp in such a position that the foal can get away if it becomes uncomfortable. If it is doing well, the lamp can be removed after the first week.

At the start of the second week some grain, or a special complete foal ration should be offered. You may find it desirable to place a couple of handfuls of good quality heavy rolled oats in the feeding box along with the grain. Foals generally like rolled oats and the oats will encourage them to start eating the grain ration. If the grain is not consumed in 2 days, remove it and offer fresh feed. The foals can be allowed to eat all the grain ration they want providing there are no stool consistency problems. They may be eating 1 to 2 pounds per day by the time they are 1 month old (horse foals remember). During the third week Foal-Lac pellets should be introduced and mixed with the grain ration. Just add a small handful at first until the foals eat the pellets readily. As the Foal-Lac powder is decreased on the 30 day liquid schedule, Foal-Lac pellets should be increased so that by the time liquid feeding is discontinued, or shortly thereafter, the foal is receiving 2 pounds of Foal-Lac pellets per day. If the 8 week liquid feeding schedule is followed, Foal-Lac pellets should be fed at the rate of 1 pound per day until the 50th day. Then increase Foal-Lac pellets to replace the powder as it is reduced so that the foal receives 2 pounds of pellets per day by the 60th day. (Ed. Note. for donkey foals unless Mammoth, we would believe that 1 ½ pounds is plenty)

Good quality dust free alfalfa hay should be made available at about 3 weeks of age. This is particularly important if pasture is not available or if alfalfa is not included in the grain ration. If the foal consumes too much hay or seems to get diarrhea from the hay, grass hay should be substituted. (Ed. note - probably a good recommendation for donkeys anyway.) Provide fresh water. A salt block may be used. A complete foal feed will probably provide adequate salt. Foals should be exercised daily. After they are 1 to 2 weeks old, depending on the condition and the weather they can have free access to pasture as long as there is a protected feeding area and a place they can go for shelter from wind and rain. (Remember this is for horses, you may need to drop some of the amounts for donkey foals, especially if they are Miniatures. They really don't get much out of the grain and hay until they are several months old, but a foal would naturally begin to sample the feed beside it's dam at only a few days old.)

FOALS ORPHANED DURING THE SECOND OR THIRD WEEK OF LIFE

In general these foals will be from 20 to 25 lbs. heavier than the foals orphaned during the first week unless they have not been receiving sufficient or healthy milk from the dam. If the foal is in a weakened condition, follow instructions for foals orphaned during the first week.

Foals orphaned during the second or third week should be started on a 1 pound level of Foal-Lac powder for 1 or 2 days. If the foal readily consumes this and shows no digestive disturbances due to diet change from its dams milk, it can be brought up to 1.5 pounds and then 2 pounds of Foal-Lac powder over a period of a couple of days. The schedule can then be picked up for a 8 week old foal as shown in the feeding schedule. These foals can start right off at a 3 times per day feeding frequency.

Foals that have been on the dam as long as 2 weeks are often more difficult to get on Foal-Lac. Do not be disturbed if they do not readily consume all the Foal-Lac liquid. Introduce them as soon as possible to grain and Foal-Lac pellets and encourage them to drink as much Foal-Lac liquid as they will consume up to 2 pounds of powder per day.

GENERAL FEEDING AND MANAGEMENT CONSIDERATIONS

Foals that are weaned at 4 weeks or older and occasionally foals orphaned after they are 2 or 3 weeks old will become nervous and may not eat well because they miss the company of other equines. To overcome this problem you may place another gentle farm animal - a kind dog or a "motherly" gelding or barren jennet with the foal. As the Foal-Lac is increased there may be a temporary stool looseness. If this gets very watery and persists for 24 hours the Foal-Lac should be reduced to the original level for two days and then increased perhaps more slowly than indicated in the feeding directions. If the condition does not correct itself the veterinarian should be consulted. They may recommend the use of a human product such as Pepto Bismal © but ASK FIRST!

The hair around a foal's muzzle may by lost after a couple of weeks, due to contact with the liquid. This should not cause concern and the hair returns normally when the foal is off liquid feed.

FOAL-LAC DIRECTIONS

The following schedule for mixing and feeding can be followed for light horses (900-1200 pounds mature weight). Ponies and donkeys will require about one-half these quantities.

Note that there are two sets of directions. The quantities of Foal-Lac pellets recommended depend on the quality of grain ration. figures in parenthesis are suggestions for use with a simple unfortified grain ration. The other figures are for use with a ration formulation for foals containing a minimum of 16% protein and fortified with vitamins and minerals.

Age of Foal	#/Feeding per day/Liquid Foal-Lac	Warm Water Pints	Total Daily Foal-Lac powder, Lbs*	Total Daily Foal-Lac Pellets, Lbs
0-3 days	4 (4)	4 (4)	1 (1)	0
4 days	4 (4)	6 (6)	1.5 (1.5)	0
5 days	4 (4)	6 (6)	1.5 (1.5)	0
6 days	4 (4)	8 (8)	2.0 (2.0)	0
7 days	4 (4)	8 (8)	2.0 (2.0)	0
2nd week ***	3 (3)	8 (8)	2.0 (2.0)	0
3rd week	3 (3)	8 (8)	2.0 (2.0)	1/4 (1/4)
4th week	2 (3)	6 (10)	1.5 (2.5)	1/2 (1/2)
29 days	1 (2)	4 (10)	1.0 (2.5)	1 (1)
30 days	0 (2)	0 (12)	0 (3.0)	1 (1)
31-35 days	0 (2)	0 (12)	0 (3.0)	1 1/2 (1)
6th week	0 (1)	0 (12)	0 (32.0)	2 (1)
7th week	0 (1)	0 (8)	0 (2.0)	2 (1)
8th week	0 (1)	0 (4)	0 (1.0)	2 (2)
9-12th week	0 (0)	0 (0)	0 (0)	2 (2 1/2)
13-16th week	0 (0)	0 (0)	0 (0)	1 (2 1/2)
17th-20th week	0 (0)	0 (0)	0 (0)	1/2 (1)
21st-24th week	0 (0)	0 (0)	0 (0)	1/2 (1)
Total Foal-Lac consumed in 6 months			**50 (113)**	**169 (240)**

* Three level cupfuls equal one pound.
**Divide the total daily water and Foal-Lac powder allowance equally into the number of feedings indicated.
*** Start offering grain ration in small amounts. Fresh water should be made available at this time. Provide a small quantity of alfalfa hay unless the roughage is provided in the mixed grain ration or the foals are allowed access to pasture. A salt block should be provided with a home-mixed grain or low-protein horse feed program.

After 6 months of age the protein content of the grain ration might be reduced to 14 % protein.

The continued use of Foal-Lac after 6 months will help provide extra condition and bone development. Some research has shown continued growth stimulation from this low level Foal-Lac feeding after 6 months, but some research has shown no increase when a 20 % protein ration was continued after 6 months.

(Remember these protein values are based on horse foals)

Age of foal	Amount of warm water (pints)	Amounts of Foal-Lac Powder/day (pounds)	Amount of Foal-Lac Pellet/day (pounds)	Amount of Grain Ration/ Day (pounds)
5th week	4	1	1	1
6th week	0	0	1 1/2	1 1/2
7th week	0	0	2	2
8th week	0	0	2 1/2 (3)	2 1/2
9th week	0	0	2 1/2 (3)	2 1/2 (3)
10th week	0	0	2 (3)	3 1/2 (3 1/2)
11th week	0	0	1 1/2 (2 1/2)	5 (5)
12th week	0	0	1 (2)	7(7)
5th & 6th month			0-1/2 (1/2-1)	Full Feed
after 6 mo			0 -1/2 (0-1/2)	Full Feed
Total Foal-lac Pellets			**100-150 (150-200)**	

EMERGENCY SUBSTITUTE FOR FOAL-LAC

If you temporarily run out of Foal-Lac powder for liquid feeding, the 2% fat cow's milk can be used as a temporary formula. This should be supplemented with a teaspoonful of white corn syrup per pint of 25 milk to increase the carbohydrate portion of this emergency diet.

It should be emphasized that this is an emergency formula.

Other foal feed substitutes:

One of our long-time breeders has used this formula quite successfully in raising orphans - the last she raised was a horse colt that recently topped out over 16.3 hands....

3 pints low fat (2%) cows milk
1 pint water
1 tablespoon plain yogurt
¼ package Sur-Gel (or 20cc 50% Dextrose)

Always mix each feeding fresh, and discard any unused portion of mixed liquid.

FOALING AND CARE OF THE NEWBORN

Ronald Marten, DVM., Associate Professor Department of Large Animal Medicine & Surgery Texas A&M University, College Station, TX 77843

Parturition, or in this case, **foaling,** is the terminal phase of one of the most complex phenomenon known. Although we are often dismayed by the frequency of abnormal births, whether it be due to poor presentation or a malformed foal, we should in fact stand in awe at the regularity with which perfection dominates.

Realizing that nature has devised an almost infallible system, I would like to emphasize the normal perinatal period, or that period immediately surrounding birth. I shall also discuss some of the abnormalities encountered, relaying what I feel a layman should or should not attempt to do, and present some guidelines to follow in knowing when a veterinarian should be consulted.

FOALING

The precise stimuli which initiate the birth process are so complex that they have eluded investigators for centuries. The cervix, which is the portal of exit from the uterus to the vagina, relaxes under the influence of hormones. The uterine muscles begin to contract, forcing the fluid filled chorioallantoic sac or placenta into and through the open cervix. This stretches the cervix even further and is accompanied by the crampy or colicky signs with mild sweating, which we observe. As the pressure increases on this sac, it bursts, expelling its contents to the outside. This is commonly called "breaking of the water bag". At the same time the muzzle and front feet normally come through the cervix. Once a portion of the foal enters the bony pelvic canal, the abdominal muscles are stimulated to contract. These contractions progressively in-crease in intensity and, compared to most other species, are extremely forceful. The mare will usually experience several such contractions and then rest for a few minutes rpeating the process for a period of from 5-45 minutes.

Our first impulse is oftentimes to get the foal out as rapidly as possible. This may result in irreparable damage to the mare and foal if the birth canal is not sufficiently relaxed and the cervix dilated. The best advice is to be patient but know what signs might indicate a pending problem. Although nature periodically makes mistakes, they are insigninicant when compared to those created by humans who attempt to "help" without adequate knowledge. By the time the mare strains lightly several times, both front feet and possibly the muzzle will be observed protruding.

SIGNS OF PENDING PROBLEMS

If nothing is visible, only one leg up, the knee or hock, or a head and no legs, or the soles of the hooves are uppermost, the jennet should be examined. Strict cleanliness must be observed. The mare's genital region as well as the operator's hand and arms should be washed with a mild soap and disinfectant. An obstetrical sleeve should be used and the hand well lubricated with a water soluble lubricant. Reach in only as far as in necessary to determine whether the head and both front legs are in the canal. If so, sit back and wait; if not, call the veterinarian. It is much better to call unnecessarily than to wait too long and perhaps lose the mare and foal. If trouble is apparent, walk the mare until the veterinarian arrives. If a mare or jennet is kept walking she does not have the tendency to exert the forceful abdominal contractions which oftentimes compound a relatively simple problem.

CHANGES OCCURRING AT BIRTH

The time during which the foal passes through the birth canal and immediately thereafter is probably the most difficult and stressful period it will ever encounter. It must adapt to an entirely new environment, coming from a warm fluid bath in which many of its functions such as respiration and nutrition are performed by its dam, via the placenta, into one in which it must essentially live on its own. Normally, nature provides the necessary preparations so that the newborn can survive. The digestive tract, kidneys, heart, etc., have been functioning for a number of months so that their adaptation is somewhat of a graduation rather than an entirely new beginning. The respiratory system is somewhat of an exception to this rule. Although the fetus may make respiratory movements characterized by gasps while in the uterus, the lungs are filled with fluid and no gaseous exchange can take place. In normal respiration or breathing, air, which contains oxygen passes from the lungs into the bloodstream and carbon dioxde leaves the blood, entering the lungs to be exhaled. In the fetus or unborn foal, this exchange of oxygen and carbon dioxide occurs across the placenta or membranes. It gets its oxygen from the mother's blood and transfers its carbon dioxide to the mother, which she exhales. Therefore, as soon as the umbilical cord breaks, is sufficiently compressed, or the fetal membranes begin to separate from the uterus, the foal must start breathing on its own. The initial expansion of the lungs requires about ten times as much force as that needed for subsequent expansion. Consequently, if the foal is weak or depressed, it may not have enough energy to take this all important first breath. Whereas, the blood in the fetus was directed away from the lungs and to the placenta, gross cardiovascular changes must occur concurrently with the initiation of respiration to redirect the blood to the lungs for gas exchange.

DEPRESSED FOALS

Now that we have a better understanding of the urgency of this conversion, we can relate back to some of the factors which may result in depressed in stillborn foals.

1. Anything which causes compression of the umbilical cord will decrease the amount of oxygen which the foal receives and result in depression.
   a. The foal's umbilical cord is normally twisted in a spiral fashion, and although extreme twisting could result in occlusion of the cord, it rarely, if ever, occurs. However, it is commonly incriunated.
   b. In a normal delivery, the umbilical cord is long enough to allow complete delivery of the foal. At least the head is presented so that if compression of the cord does occur, spontaneous respiration can be initiated.

   In a posterior presentation, if delivery does not ensue without delay, the cord may become compressed and the foal cannot breathe because its head is still contained within the uterus. Therefore, if the foal is presented posteriorly with both legs present and is not progressing with each contraction, traction should carefully be applied in a downward direction toward the mare's hocks, concurrently with her abdominal contractions.
2. Each time the mare has a hard labor contraction, the blood flow to the uterus decreases momentarily which may reduce the amount of oxygen available to the foal. There is also some indication that these periods of decreased blood flow may initiate the separation of the fetal membranes and thereby reduce the surface area across which gas exchange can take place. Therefore, any cause of dystocia or a prolonged delivery may result in hypoxia or insufficient oxygen for the foal. The result may be a depressed or dead foal.

RESUSCITATION OF THE DEPRESSED FOAL

When a foal is born it should start breathing within seconds after the hips are delivered. If respiration is not initiated or if the foal is only gasping:

1. Rub it briskly with towels, burlap sacks, etc., to stimulate it.
2. Wipe the mucous out of its mouth and nostrils with a gauze sponge or clean rag.
3. Position it with its head lower than the rest of the body to facilitate the drainage of fluid from its upper respiratory tract.
4. Attempt to stimulate a cough reflex by inserting a piece of straw or similar foreign material into the nostril
5. If these procedures fall to initiate breathing, artificial resuscitation must be administered. This is best accomplished with a "non-rebreathing" resuscitation bag, after the mucous and amniotic fluid have been cleaned from the upper respiratory tract and with the head and neck extended. When compressed the resuscitation bag forces air into the lungs and when released allows exhaled gases to escape through a one-way valve. Non-rebreathing implies that the exhaled gases will not get back into the system to be rebreathed. The resuscitation bag is attached to a large canine face mask or padded plastic bottle which is held firmly over the foal's muzzle. The bag is intermittently compressed and

released at two second intervals until the foal begins to breath on its own.

a. If that apparatus is not available, extend the foal's head and neck to assure an open airway, close its mouth and cover one nostril with you hand. Place your mouth firmly over the other nostril and blow, thereby giving mouth to nose resuscitation. One must blow hard enough to expand the foal's chest and the procedure should be repeated every two seconds until the foal responds and begins to breath on its own. Oftentimes only a few breaths are necessary to initiate spontaneous respiration; however, this depends upon the degree of depression. The heart rate or beats per minute, determined by placing the hand over the left side of the chest, just behind the elbow, is the best indication of recovery. A favorable response is signaled by an increased rate and as long as there is a heart beat present there is hope for survival.

There are other resuscitation techniques such as correction of the profound acidosis and the administration of oxygen which your veterinarian can institute, if he is available at the time of delivery.

TEMPERATURE REGULATION

In a weak or depressed foal, temperature regulation is extremely important. The newborn foal has a normal temperature range of 99-101 degrees F. If its temperature drops below this range, it shivers in an attempt to maintain a normal temperature. thereby expending more energy which may result in further deterioration. When a weak foal is wet and lying in a drafty stall, it loses a great deal of body heat. Supplemental heat should be provided with heating blankets, lamps, etc., and the foal must be protected from drafts.

NORMAL BEHAVIOR OF THE NEWBORN FOAL

1. Before the body of the foal enters the bony birth canal a withdrawal response can be elicited by pinching the forelimbs. However, once its body enters the canal, the foal is usually unresponsive until its hips are delivered. During this period of unresponsiveness. the foal may appear to be depressed or dead.
2. Within second of delivery, a respiratory rhythm is established and the foal is able to turn up on its sternum or chest.
3. A foal will usually stand, unassisted, within 1 ½ - 2 hours and nurse within three hours.
a. Following the initial nursing, they will generally repeat the act with increased vigor every 30 to 60 minutes.

ROUTINE CARE OF THE NEWBORN

MEMBRANES

As stated previously. the chorioallantoic sac or water bag breaks early in parturition. The foal, however, is still encased in another bag called the amnion or amniotic sac. This membrane normally covers the foal throughout delivery and may prevent breathing if it does not rupture when the foal struggles. A weak or depressed foal may not have enough energy to initiate this rupture and consequently will suffocate. Therefore, if the membrane is intact when the head protrudes from the vagina, it may be ruptured manually and pulled back over the head.

UMBILICAL CORD

The umbilical cord contains two veins which carry the oxygen enriched blood to the fetus and two arteries which carry the used or relatively depleted blood away from the fetus and back to the placenta. The urachus, which is a tube coming from the bladder and emptying into the chorioallantoic sac, is also contained in this structure. The umbilical cord should be allowed to rupture on its own and this usually occurs within 15 minutes, when the mare and/or the foal struggles to stand. It has been estimated that from 1-3 pints of blood may be transferred from the placenta to the foal following birth and one can readily feel the pulsations of blood flowing in the cord prior to its rupture. If the cord is ruptured or clamped prematurely the foal will be deprived of this blood. Occasionally, the umbilical vessels will hemorrhage excessively as evidenced by this active spurting of blood. This can usually be controlled by compressing the cord for several minutes with your fingers, however, it may be necessary to ligate or tie off the umbilical stump. If this is necessary, a non-absorbable suture material may be used and it should be removed in three to four hours.

UMBILICAL DISINFECTION
Strong tincture of iodine used to be frequently applied to the umbilicus shortly after birth. Recent evidence has indicated that this solution may on occasion be too irritating and thereby cause the umbilical cord to swell closed prematurely. The umbilicus is in a position which promotes ventral drainage and if we artificially close it with strong disinfectants or by tying it off, bacteria may be trapped in and cannot drain out. Therefore, this procedure in itself may add to the incidence of umbilical and urachal abscesses. Your vet will probably recommend the daily application of a mild disinfectant such as **2% tincture of iodine**, iodine and glycerin or Betadine solution, for three to five days or until the umbilical stump becomes dry and hard. Application of the disinfectant is most effectively attained by immersing the umbilical stump in a shot glass or similar container which is held up against the abdomen.

ENEMAS
Although enemas are not necessary in all newborn foals, their routine use seems to decrease the incidence of meconium impaction. While in the uterus, the foal is constantly swallowing amniotic fluid. The fluid portion is absorbed from the intestines, but the particulate matter remains in the large intestine until after birth and is called meconium. It frequently forms into small hard balls, resulting in constipation. Various solutions may be administered; however, extreme caution must be employed and only a soft flexible tube should be inserted into the rectum.
1. Fleet enema (Eaton Laboratory). Four ounce human adult or veterinary preparation.
2. 1-2 pints of a warm mild soap solution (i.e., Ivory Soap).
3. Two ounces glycerine.
Be gentle and do not apply excessive pressure. Repeated attempts or carelessness in the administration of enemas may result in a ruptured rectum and death.

TETANUS PROPHYLAXIS
Tetanus antitoxin is oftentimes administered immediately after birth. Longer lasting and perhaps higher levels of protection can be obtained by vaccinating the mare yearly with tetanus toxoid. The annual booster should be administered at least one month prior to foaling. The antibodies, which protect the foal against tetanus, are then passed to the foal via the colostrum of first milk. Find out from your vet if you should give a combination injection such as a "3-way" (usually Eastern/Western/Tet).

ANTIBIOTICS
Antibiotics are often given prophylactically to the normal foal on the first day. It is felt that the indiscriminate use of antibiotics may result in the formation of resistant bacteria. The bacteria learn to live in the presence of this particular antibiotic, and it may be of no value it the foal contracts an infection at a later date. It is also possible for the foal to become sensitized to this particular antibiotic and therefore more prone to an allergic reaction if it receives the same drug at a later date. If the foal resides in an enzootic disease area, one in which there is a higher than normal incidence of disease, such as a breeding farm, prophylactic antibiotics are indicated but should be administered in therapeutic doses over a three day period.

(In other words, don't just give antibiotics unless it is absolutely necessary. Too many recent studies are showing that bacteria are quickly becoming resistant due to the procedures we use daily, such as antibacterial handcreams and soaps, and over-use do antibiotics. The foal gets immunity from the colostrum - let it work first, then only if needed, have your vet give antibiotics.)

IMMUNITY
Once the foal has normalized following its perilous journey, the next most important consideration is to assure the acquisition of sufficient antibodies which

provide protection against many infectious agents. The immune system of the term fetus is competent or able to produce antibodies against various infectious agents, however, it is rarely exposed to them since the mare generally inactivates them before they reach the privileged uterine vault. In the human, immunoglobulins or antibodies are acquired by the fetus, across the placenta, from its mothers blood. The foal does not receive antibodies across the placenta, therefore, it lacks this important disease fighting mechanism at birth. As we stated earlier, the foal is capable of producing antibodies, however, it takes 2-3 weeks following exposure to an infectious organism for it to establish adequate protection. Obviously, the foal could get sick and die before it could ever fight off the organism so it needs immediate protection to carry it through the 3 week transition phase. This protection is obtained from the colostrum or "first milk" which it ingests. The jennet's immunoglobulins which have been stored in the mammary gland are absorbed from the foals' small intestine and enter its blood stream. The failure to absorb adequate immunoglobulins is termed "failure of passive transfer" (FPT) and is probably the single most important predisposing factor in the acquisition of infection. It is estimated that between 10-20% of all foals have some degree of FPT.

The foal can only absorb these immunoglobulins for about 24 hrs. after birth. The ability to absorb them is greatest at the time of birth and diminishes over the ensuing 24 hours. Consequently, the earlier he receives colostrum the better protection he will have.

Several factors are known to result in failure of passive transfer:
1. The foal not nursing early enough or adequately
2. The mare not producing adequate colostrum with sufficient immunoglobulins
3. The mare running milk prior to foaling and losing the colostrum
4. The foal ingesting colostrum but not absorbing it adequately, primarily due to a stress reaction
If the history or tests of the immunoglobulin levels indicate inadequacy, supplementation with stored colostrum from another mare or a plasma transfusion should be considered.

INFECTIOUS DISEASES
The progression of signs and symptoms of disease differ from patient to patient; the course may be fulminating, leading to death in several hours or more protracted. The earliest clinical signs are non-specific and include lethargy or dullness, irritability, poor nursing or the observation that the foal is not doing as well as previously. Additional alterations may reflect primary or secondary involvement of any organ system.

The most common manifestation of infection in the foal is pneumonia, whether it be the primary site or secondarily involved. It may be acquired: (1) across the placenta, (2) by aspiration of infected materials during or after delivery, (3) by inhalation of aerosols containing infectious organisms or, (4) via the blood.

CAUSES OF INFECTION
A significant proportion of neonatal infections are opportunistic in that the foal is infected by organisms which can readily be cultured from the reproductive tract, skin or gastrointestinal tract of normal pregnant mares or from the immediate surroundings. Infection can thus originate in the uterus, at the time of delivery, from the environment or from other horses. Therefore many organisms which cause no apparent problems in a normal foal can invade one which is more susceptible due to stress etc. and cause disease.

Bacterial pneumonias are the most common and may be primary or secondary to previous lung damage caused by viruses or parasites. Streptococci (Strep.) are the bacteria most commonly involved in pneumonia. It is estimated that they may account for 75 % of the cases in foals. Fortunately these are also the cases which are the most responsive to therapy.

Corynebacterium equi on the other hand produces the most devastating type of pneumonia. It usually appears in 1-3 month old foals and by the time the foal looks or acts sick, a large portion of its lungs may already be involved with multiple abscesses.

Effective therapy is often impossible because the drugs will no adequately penetrate these abscesses. Early diagnosis of the infection is essential to successful therapy, however, there is not much known about the specific host organism interactions and early diagnostic tests are not currently available. Although not as many foals are affected by C. equi, the mortality rate is much higher and the economic losses, due to prolonged expensive therapy and many failures, are staggering.

A myriad of other organisms can also cause pneumonia and often several of them combine to form a mixed infection. This usually presents an even greater diagnostic and therapeutic challenge.

DIAGNOSIS

The vast majority of the organisms which cause foal diseases do not produce specific clinical signs which would enable the veterinarian to pinpoint the causative agent and institute specific therapy. Therefore, an organized and intelligent diagnostic approach must be utilized.

The following are some of the diagnostic aids which may be useful:

1. History
   a. The age of the patient, season of the year, nutritional, immunization and parasite control programs
   b. The post-natal progression of the foal
   c. Previous therapy and the outcome of previous cases on the farm

2. Physical Exam
   a. Temperature, pulse and respiration
   b. General attitude and presence of a nasal discharge and/or cough
   c. Auscultation with a stethoscope
   d. Distinguish between an upper respiratory infection and pneumonia - every young child with a cough and nasal discharge is not placed on massive doses of antibiotics

3. Hermatology or Blood Work
   a. Complete Blood Count (CBC) - may give an indication of the cause of the infection and how the animals body is responding to it.
   b. Immunoglobulin levels - may indicate whether the foal has sufficient antibodies to effectively fight off an infection.

4. Transtracheal Aspiration
   a. A catheter is passed into the lungs through a small incision over the trachea. Saline is flushed into the trachea and some of the secretions from the lungs are drawn out for culturing so the specific bacteria can be identified and the Appropriate antibiotic therapy instituted

5. Radiographs (X-rays)
   a. These can be very helpful in determining the type and extent of lung involvement
   b. Currently the equipment necessary for this procedure is only available in the larger institutions

6. Necropsy (Post-Mortem Exam)
   a. Every foal which dies should be examined in an effort to determine the specific organism involved especially in cases where the cause of death might be termed to be genetic or inherited.
   b. This may prove very helpful if other cases should develop on the farm.

THERAPY

In discussing a therapeutic approach, we must take into consideration the many changes which are occuring in the diseased foal. Clinically, we often consider destruction of the causative agent as the endpoint and final goal of our treatment regimine. Unfortunately there are many alterations occuring that will not be reversed merely be "sterilizing" the foal.

The use of appropriate antibiotics for sufficient lengths of time is vitally important, however, an integrated approach to the treatment of disease is imperative for optimal results. A complete approach also consists of supporting the homeostatic or life supporting mechanisms with nutritional support. fluids, electrolytes, etc., so that the foal and/or the antibiotics can overcome the causative agent and the resuitanL damages. As stated earlier, stress must be minimal and the foal kept as comfortable as possible.

In many cases we lose the battle long before the therapeutic agents have chance to be effective.

PREVENTION OF DISEASE

1. OVERCROWDING

In their natural state, donkeys live in small, widely dispersed herds, with minimal psychological stress and maximal disease dilution. In the unnatural domestic state, donkeys are kept in large numbers and in relatively small areas. These factors produce maximal psychological stress and disease concentration, with constant contamination of pastures, feed, water, bedding etc. Grass pastures are reduced to sand and dust, and rotation of pastures is impossible.

2. Housing
   a. Poor ventilation is a major factor. Keeping the barns closed and providing supplemental heat during inclement weather is the wrong thing to do. The barns should remain open and/or an adequate ventilation system installed. For detailed recommendations, contact state extension agricultural engineers.
   b. Bedding provides a suitable "culture medium" for several pneumonia causing organisms. Sawdust, shavings and moldy dusty straw are prime offenders.
   c. Foaling quarters should be thoroughly cleaned and disinfected between uses.
   d. Mares and foals, if healthy, should be moved to pasture 3-5 days after foaling, even in freezing weather. Run out sheds are advisable in extreme weather.
   e. Foals should be kept away from transient horses; i.e., segregate resident foaling mares from the show string and "outside" mares by double fencing with at least a 30 foot gap between the fences.
   f. Avoid buildings that stay damp, such as concrete block structures.
   g. Whenever conditions permit, jennets should be allowed to foal outside.

Ideally, foaling jennets and foals should be maintained in areas completely isolated from other donkeys, horses or mules until the foals are 3-4 months old. This is not usually possible, but the closer it can be approximated, the lower the risk of disease.

3. Nutrition
   a. Subclinical malnutrition, produced by poor-quality feed and/or improperly balanced rations, may serve as a contributing factor in disease processes.
   b. "Push" rations constitute a stress.

4. Handling Procedures
   a. Almost all handling procedures are stressful to foals physically and/or psychologically. Stress induces include:
      1. Transporation for breeding or shows.
      2. Separation from mother for breeding or other purposes.
      3. Training and weaning.
      4. Treatment procedures.
      5. Any stressful condition for the mare which reduces her milk production level.
   b. Handling Recommendations
      1. All handling procedures involving young foals should be kept to a minimum and accomplished in a quiet and gentle fashion.
      2. Young foals in a diseased state should not be subjected to weaning and/or training procedures. Total rest is one of the most important factors in the treatment of sick foals.
         3. As early as is managerially possible. a foal should gradually (five minute dally periods) be conditioned to walk quietly at halter and to submit to gentle handling in the presence of its mother.

5. Dust
   Many important pneumonia-producing organisms are dust-borne. Therefore, all possible measure should be taken to reduce the exposure to this irritant.

6. Weather

   a. Heat and humidity aggravate existing problems and predispose a foal when other stresses are present.

   b. Foals should not be overprotected from cold by putting them into poorly ventilated facilities.

   c. Severe temperature fluctuations - either hot days and cold nights or moving foals in and out of doors are detrimental.

7. Parasites

   a. Lung migration of certain parasite larve such as ascarids or round worms may produce the initial damage necessary to allow certain bacteria to invade the lung tissue and result in disease.

   b. Parasite incidence is directly related to overcrowding and poor sanitation.

   c. A good parasite control program is imperative in the prevention of disease and must include all donkeys on the farm.

8.   Immunization

   a. The foals immune system is generally capable of producing antibodies at or shortly after birth. However. the immunoglobulins derived from the dam via the colostrum interfere with the efficiency of vaccines in the foal until it is about 3 months old. At that time the foal is usually vaccinated against tetanus, influenza, rhinopneumonitis and occasionally strangles.

   b. Autogenous vaccines which are made from a specific organism isolated from a problem herd are helpful in some situations.

   c. Sufficient booster vaccinations are necessary to assure adequate protection.

9. Hereditary Predisposition

   It has been observed that some mares consistently produce foals that are particularly receptive to disease processes. It has also been observed that some mares consistently produce foals that are particularly resistant to disease processes. This observation may relate to immune transfer of antibodies to the foal. or it may be a partial or complete immunodeficiency on the part of the foal.

   It has been well documented in other species that disease resistance and/or susceptibility can be genetically selected. This would also include inherited genetic factors related to color, or dwarfism, etc.

NON-INFECTIOUS CONDITIONS

PATENT OR PREVIOUS URACHUS

   The urachus is the fetal portal of exit for urine into the chorioallantoic sac or water bag. Normally, this structure closes prior to birth, but. occasionally, and more frequently in the horse than other domestic species, it remains open and is characterized by continual drainage of urine from the umbilical stump. This structure should not be tied off since it may be the foal's only outlet for urine, and again, it will prevent natural drainage. If the condition persists for longer than two days, a veterinarian should be consulted.

RUPTURED BLADDER

   This condition appears most commonly in colts and is thought to be caused by extreme pressure on a bladder which is full of urine. The pressure is created by the mare's strong abdominal contractions during labor. The affected foal appears normal at birth and the symptoms of progressive weakness and abdominal weakness and abdominal distention or swelling develop over the first two to three days. Even though the bladder is ruptured some urine may be observed passing via the normal channels, when the foal strains. The diagnosis must be confirmed by a veterinarian and is accomplished by the removal and analysis of some of the abdominal fluid. The defect or tear in the bladder can be repaired surgically and the prognosis or expected outcome is quite favorable if it is corrected early.

HIGH MECONIUM IMPACTION

   Occasionally, meconium becomes impacted or stuck in the large intestines and is not eliminated following the routine enema. This usually occurs within the first two days and is manifested as severe colic. Appropriate analgesics or pain killers and antispasmodics may be necessary to control the pain. Cathartics, such as mineral oil and/or fecal softeners, administered via a stomach tube will oftentimes result in passage of the meconium and an uneventful recovery. If these measures are unsuccessful, surgical intervention may be necessary.

FOAL HEAT SCOURS
As the name implies, this condition usually occurs at about 7-9 days of age and coincides with the mare's or jennet's first heat period after foaling. There are several theories regarding the cause of this condition. It may be due to excessive milk production by the mare, intestinal parasites, increased fiber in the diet or a change in the normal bacterial inhabitants of the intestine. It has not been correlated with any compositional alterations in the mare's milk or contamination of the udder by yaginal secrections. Therapy is generally not indicated unless the condition becomes severe, persists longer than a few days, or the foal stops nursing, in which case a veterinarian should be consulted. The management of diarrhea in the foal should always include daily washing of the buttocks with a mild soapy solution. Application of vaseline to prevent scalding of the skin by the feces is recommended by some vets, banned by others. Ask your vet if preparations such as a human Diaper Rash creme or vaseline should be used.

HERNIA
Hernias are a defect in the body wall which permit some of the abdominal viscera or guts to protrude. They usually occur at the navel and are presented as a skin covered lump of varying size or through the inguinal ring, whereby the intestines may be contained within the scrotum. The inguinal ring is the normal portal of exit for the testes as they descend from the abdomen into the scrotum. Umbilical hernias, in which the abdominal opening is less than two fingers in diameter, will usually close spontaneously in several weeks, depending upon their severity.

The greatest danger associated with hernias is the possibility of a portion of the protruding intestine becoming trapped outside of the abdomen and its blood supply being occluded or shut off. This results in decay of the tissue and, of course, can be fatal. There are various means by which hernias can be repaired, however, I feel that surgical correction is the method of choice.

HEMOLYTIC DISEASE (Neonatal Isoerythrolysis) (NI)
This is a condition in foals which is similar in many respects to Rh incompatability in humans. If the mare's blood is exposed to the red blood cells (rhc's) of the fetus and they are of a different type than hers, she becomes sensitized to that type and produces antibodies against it. These antibodies are capable of destructing the foal's red blood cells, if they come into contact with them at a later date. In the human, these antibodies can cross the placenta so that the fetus' red blood cells are destroyed, rendering it anemic. However, the horse's placenta is too thick to permit ths transfer and the foal can only receive these, as well as beneficial antibodies via the colostrum. Since the foal must ingest colostrum to receive the antibodies, it is completely normal at birth. It becomes progressively weaker, due to its anemia, as it absorbs these antibodies through its intestines and they enter the bloodstream. Although the foal may show signs of icterus or jaundice, as indicated by yellow mucous membranes of the eyes, mouth, etc., this is not a steadfast symptom and may not occur for several days. Therefore, the absence of jaundice does not eliminate the condition. In fact, many foals, particularly in the early stages of the disease, may only present a weakened condition and pale mucous membranes. Conversely, the presence of jaundice does not confirm the diagnosis since there are many other conditions which produce this same sign. This is most common in mule foals.

There have been some reports of NI-like symptoms in donkey foals. If the foal becomes depressed and weak in the first few days, NI could be possible. In these cases the foal should be muzzled to prevent nursing, and the vet contacted immediately in order to take blood tests. Death is possible especially as the foal will be weakened and secondary infections could set in.

WEANING THE FOAL

You look out across your pasture, and suddenly realize that your foal is almost as tall as his mamma. Should you wean him? Doesn't his mamma do that? And at what age??? There are no hard-and-fast rules for weaning, but there are some good guidelines.

AGE

Foals will suckle off their dam for many months. If you have a sweet old jennet, she may let him nurse for a year or longer. This is not necessary, the foals really can be weaned at about 6 months, and certainly it's not necessary after 8 or 9 months. Four to six months is the average weaning time. Foals under the age of 4 months should not be weaned unless absolutely necessary. The guidelines for "necessary" should be based on the health of both animals. After 6 months of age, the nutritional content of the milk drops off, and the foal should be eating grain and hay anyway. In many cases the jennet is already pregnant again, and the strain of nursing a big foal at side may start pulling the jennet down.

HEALTH

If the foal is big and healthy, starting to eat grain and hay well, and the jennet is already in foal again, you may decide at 4-5 months to go ahead and wean the colt. However, if it seems to really need to nurse, needs extra suppliments, you may want to leave it on the dam until it is 6 months old. The only time you would want to pull a foal off before 4 months of age is medical reasons, or if the foal is growing so rapidly it is taking too much out of the jennet. Consult with your vet about nutritional needs for both animals. Under no circumstances barring life-threatening illness of one or the other animals do we recommend weaning foals before age 3 months. Routinely weaning foals at 2 months of age is not sound husbandry. The foal is not capable of independent intake at that age, without CLOSELY monitored feeding. See the tables in this chapter about Foal-Lac Milk Replacer for orphan foals. If you wean at 2 months, you should be prepared to follow a schedule like this on your foals.

CASTRATING

Should you take the opportunity when your colt is castrated to go ahead and wean him too? This depends on too many factors. If you **know** the colt is going to be a gelding when he is young, you should go ahead and castrate him as soon as possible, usually in the fall. If he was an early colt, you will probably want him weaned before the fall gets here. If he was born late, then he may not quite be old enough to wean. In most cases, you would not want the double stress of weaning and gelding both. Do one, then the other. Look over all the factors, find out when your vet feels is the best gelding time, and decide from there.

SELL AND WEAN?

You may already have a buyer set for your foal. You have a contract saying you will deliver the colt after it is weaned. Do you pull the baby off mom and send it off to the new owner? Or should you wean it, give it a week or two to calm back down, and then ship it off? You are dealing with a double-stress situation any way you look at it. First and foremost, you need to make sure the new owner is willing to cope with a foal just off his/her momma. If this is their first foal, it's usually not a good idea to have the owner and foal both go through this process. If they are experienced with equine babies, and understand the process, then work it out with them.

In some cases, it is best to go ahead and take the foal off the mom, and straight to his new home. He can make new friends and be weaned at the same time. In other cases, this just might backfire - he wasn't ready in his own mind to be weaned, and in getting acquainted with his new family, he either takes it out on them, or finds a substitute mamma willing to offer him a nurse whenever he feels like it.

CONFINEMENT

When you get ready to remove the foal, if you have several colts near weaning age, you should try and doing them all at once if they are ready. This way you have a pasture full of long-eared peers who are all going through the same thing and can cry together and make new friends. Some mammas will cry too, but if she is an experienced brood jennet, she will quickly recover. One thing you must do is make sure the place you pen the colts in is completely safe. Youngsters who are determined to get back to mamma can perform extraordinary feats. They can jump tall fences in a single bound, they can crawl under or through wire, they can nurse through panels.

Breeders used to put the foal in one stall, and the mare or jennet in another stall way at the end of the barn - they could hear each other, not see each other, and foals often literally climbed the walls. Mangers, buckets, hayracks would all have to be removed. If there are bars between stalls, they must be such that the hooves cannot be caught between the bars.

MOVING THEM AWAY

If you can get them far enough away from each other, this is sometimes best. If you have alternate pasture, you can put the jennets in one and colts in the other. Or perhaps a neighboring breeder will work out a temporary deal with you. Just be sure if this is the case you have a written agreement regarding liability if one of the foals becomes injured, etc.

HOW LONG DOES IT TAKE?

The jennet must have some time where the colt is not actually suckling daily for the milk production to stop. Put them back together too soon, and she may actually begin producing milk again. This has also been known to happen after several months of separation, so there is no set rule. Hopefully your jennet is not too lenient and will discourage the foal from nursing again if you put them back together again later. In short, three days is usually not long enough, 3-4 weeks is better.

NO PALS, NO PEN

If you are a one-donkey owner who suddenly becomes a two-donkey owner when your jennet surprises you with a foal, you may not have the resources to separate the pair at weaning time. Cross your fingers and hope the jennet will start the process herself - ears laid back when the youngster nurses, little side-wise kicks at him/her, a nip on the bottom, moving off before the foal has nursed for more than a minute or two. She's impatient, and thinks baby has had enough. This kind of behavior will usually result in a weaned colt fairly quickly. If both are healthy, the jennet is not bred back or losing weight, don't worry if the foal is over 6-8 months old. She will wean when she is ready.

Otherwise, if she is too sweet to wean the little guzzler, you can try special weaning halters that have spikes to poke her in the belly if baby nurses (from experience - this rarely works) or you can put something on the udder to make it disagreeable in flavor to the baby. Just check with your vet before applying anything to the bag - you would not want something that would be poisonous to the foal, or that would cause discomfort to the jennet.

WHEN TO GIVE UP

Don't get too worried if the older foal is still suckling when both animals are in good condition. It's usually just a "comfort" thing. The nutritional content of the milk has gone down, and it means your jennet and probably the foal too have sweet personalities. However, if you have a jack colt, you don't want him in with mom after he is 6-9 months old without being gelded. Take the advantage of this time to wean. Take him to the vet and perhaps make arrangements to board him for a while.

On the other hand, the big colt that nurses until he is three is just too much. Separation didn't work (he jumped the fence), putting him at a neighbors didn't work (he just started again when he came back) even having him away at 5-day shows... so you either live with it or sell him. In worst-case scenarios, all you can do is talk with other breeders and your vet and try different methods!

COLOR GENETICS OF DONKEYS

Colors and color genetics in the donkey have not been researched or studied anywhere near the extent that horse colors have over many, many years. Terms were established for Mammoth Jackstock, but other donkey colors have either been vaguely described, or horse terms have tried to be adapted.

Plain and simple, donkeys are not horses, and the terms must differ. However, research into this field of color genetics is in it's infancy, and much more is waiting to be learned. The research is by no means complete, but enough generalizations are understood to offer some help in determining coat colors and their workings.

Colors of the donkey:

Slate (Gray-dun) (lt -silver, med, dark - charcoal)
Brown (Lt, med, dark)
Brown/Slate (Brown/Gray-dun)
Smoky Black
Black/Brown
Jet Black
Sorrel (Chestnut)
Russet
Bay/Brown
Rose Dun/ "Pink"
Lt Sorrel/ "Pink"
Ivory

Modifiers:

Frosty Roan
Frosted Roan
Dappled Roan
Spotted (pinto)
Ivory

The ADMS has researched and come up with the following explanations and terms of usage for donkey colors. Following is information about the known genetics and their workings.

AMERICAN DONKEY & MULE SOCIETY - DONKEY AND MULE COLORS

PLEASE NOTE: ALL COLORS ARE DETERMINED BY THE FRESHLY SHED SUMMER COAT. WINTER COATS,CLIPPED COATS AND FOAL COATS WILL BE DECEPTIVE AS TO COLOR. Please note U.S. terms differ from those in the UK or Canada.

SLATE (GRAY-DUN) This is the most common of the donkey colors (especially in smaller animals). It is closest to the original "wild" color found in the ancestors of the domestic donkey. Body color is some shade of "gray" or tannish gray ranging from very light oatmeal or light silver color, to a very dark charcoal color. Cross, dorsal stripe, ear marks and often leg stripes (garters) or black dots on the lower part of the neck below the jowls (collar buttons) are found. Slate animals may have black muzzles and no light points (belly and legs as well as muzzle are usually lighter than the coat in all donkeys) and still be the gray-dun color. The original name of the color, gray-dun, was coined by the ADMS registry at its founding. It was at that time taken from the fact that the body color is a visual gray of some shade, but the whole color is a probable genetic dun. (Also, most lay-persons when asked the color of a donkey would term it gray.) There is still the possiblity that there are two coat colors which appear visually similar, a self-slate, and the dun-dilute Grulla. Foals and winter coats are <u>often</u> reddish/ brownish but will shed off to some shade of gray. This color differs from other types of gray colors because the hairs are all gray, not mixed with white. Horse terms tend only to complicated donkey colors, but for horse-minded breeders, this color would be equal to the horse terms grulla, mouse or dove dun.

In either form, (self or dun dilute) slate appears to be a dominant color. Slate x slate will produce every range of colors (depending on the hidden recessives) but if you breed slate (SS) to black (bb) the foals will be slate (Foal: SL/b). Since other colors are recessive to slate, the Slate animal would have to have a matching recessive for whatever color you are breeding for. If you want sorrel (so/so) and breed a Slate with no sorrel gene to a sorrel (SL/SL x so/so), you will be disapointed in the first generation, as they will all be slate (SL/so). (The secret is, to keep on with the second generation and use animals you know carry the recessives you are breeding for.)

ROAN (GRAY, BLACK, BROWN & RED ROAN) Roan is a color which is defined as a dark color of hair coat mixed with a moderate to large amount of light or white hairs. The hairs of the body color can be slate, gray (blue-gray in Mammoths with no cross markings), black, red, red/gray, brown and occasionally (especially in mules) other colors, mixed with white hairs. Roan donkeys usually have lighter faces and legs. (Roan horses & mules often have darker faces and legs). If the colored hairs in the coat are black the donkey is a black roan (very uncommon) if gray a gray-dun roan, if red/sorrel a red roan, brown - brown roan, etc. The roan color is very common in mammoth jackstock, fairly common in standard donkeys and seen only rarely in miniature donkeys. NOTE: Donkeys which appear to be dapple gray are almost always a dappled pattern of gray-roan or black-roan. Dapples will appear "reversed", that is, dark dapples on a light coat. Roans may darken or lighten in winter coat, but will return to a shade similar to the previous year each summer. Mules from dappled-roan jacks have not been seen to turn roan or gray, but may have the dark reverse dapples on the summer coat. (see "True Gray" for more details) Dappled roans are dappled over the body, Frosty Roans are commonly seen in miniatures, but only the face and legs will be roaned. Some roans may also have the frosted gene as well and may appear as white with faint dark dapples over the body and flank. Miniature donkeys that appear roan may be FFSW if the presence of pink skin is seen. See FSW.

TRUE GRAY True gray is a color which is documented in an unusual form in donkeys but is still under serious study. An aging gray gene in donkeys does not act like that in horses, or Mules. The aging gray in mules is common in animals which have been bred from gray horses. "Gray" donkeys are often born with very light coats,and extensive "roaning" about the legs and face. Because donkey gray does NOT act like horse gray, the ADMS registries do not use horse terms. "Aged gray" donkeys are listed as Frosted - the term Fully Frosted (followed by the base color) will appear on certificates. To be a true horse or mule gray an animal is born a solid dark color. This color progressively lightens with age, often going through a dapple gray phase (rose gray is a horse term for a bay or red animal in an intermediate reddish-gray stage), until the animal turns pure white with age. The skin is dark. Graying donkeys do not dapple, unless they also have the dappled roan gene. Very early in the lifetime of a gray animal it will look almost identical with a black or gray roan. The difference is that the roan color stays the same (from year to year) while gray lightens with each passing year. Some Frosted spotted animals that have very minimal white spotted may appear to have more dark areas that appear roan instead of becoming nearly white.

BLACK Black is sometimes a difficult color to determine Three appear to be two kinds of black, a jet (raven) black which is easy to determine and a duller black, which often could be a very dark brown. If the donkey is "jet" black or "raven" black with no visible cross and stripe, it can be listed as Black. This is common in the larger animals. If the coat appears black, but the cross, stripe, and lower legs are visibly darker black, it is termed SMOKY BLACK There are very few jet-black miniature donkeys, most that appear to be black will still have some faint markings of the cross/stripe and even garters.

Black/brown is the term which should be used on animals whose coats are very dark brown in appearance with darker *black* cross, stripe and lower legs.. (This terminology is short for a "Dark brown or black" as used in the thoroughbred industry.) Care should be used in listing dark brown animals as black if it is not felt there is a true black gene present so as not to mislead future breeders. Charcoal is not a shade of black, but instead is the very darkest shade of slate (gray-dun). These colors should all be updated at maturity, in the short summer haircoat. In horses the determination is sometimes made by the fact that a black horse will have a black muzzle not a brown one--but this does not hold true for mules and donkeys. Most black mules do have brown muzzles, sometimes up to the eyes, and lighter flanks. They are still black, as the modified point color is typical of mules. The color must be determined by body color.

It is possible that the genetic control for the cross and stripe (aka primitive marks) has nothing to do with the body color, and even animals which are true, genetic jet-black do have a cross and stripe. However, observation shows that the animals which show a cross and stripe pass it along to offspring. If it is desired that dark animals not have a cross, then those with visible crosses or other markings such as garters be avoided in breeding.

WHITE /IVORY   Due to many factors, "white" is not always snow white. Often it is yellowish. If an animal has blue eyes and pink skin it is registered as an Ivory (Blue-eyed white) . Although there is no true pink-eyed albino in equines, the term albino-white is accepted in equine circles. In fact, according to Dr. Phillip Sponenberg, there are no pink-eyed large animals. Genetic albino large animals will always have bluish eyes, as the thickness of the iris can no longer maintain the non-pigmented pink color as it increases in size.

Contrary to popular belief, albino animals do have markings - albino snakes are pink with yellow markings. *Leucistic* animals are white with blue pigmented eyes, and no markings. "White" donkeys appear to be closer to albino than leucistic, as they often have faint cross markings. These Ivory animals are more probably white-phase or "pseudo albinos" (like white tigers, where the base color is washed out but markings are still seen) than cremello or perlino as in horses, which are diluted colors. No evidence has been seen to show that the white gene is a creme-type dilution. However, this is a difficult test to prove, as the dilution gene (in horses) has no effect on the black coloration, and since many donkeys are slate based, the dilute might not show up in the coat. The best test will be to breed Ivory to Sorrel and see what results.

Ivory has thus far pointed toward being a recessive, although anyone with an understanding of genetics can plot the pedigree with colors and come to the conclusion the gene is either a dominant or a recessive. Known ivory bloodlines at this time have come from slate lines, but Ivory does breed true (Ivory x ivory = ivory) The foals have creamy or tan/yellowish coats at birth, and the shorter muzzle hair may look lighter against the buff-colored long body hair. As they shed, the coat appears white, although a cross may be faintly seen. Most Ivory adult donkeys look White at first glance and are often called that by breeders and horsemen alike.

Dark-eyed white animals with mottled skin are spotted and not true white. These may be either Fully Frosted Spotted white, or Spotted to an extent where they are mostly white with no visible large dark spots.

F F S W - Fully Frosted Spotted (white) - Formerly Few Spot White. This is an apparent genetic cross of Frosted (Aging-Gray) and Spotted. The eyes are dark. The skin (especially around the eyes, muzzle, and genitals) is spotted pink and black. The body may actually show mottled (patched) gray & pink skin, but the color does not appear on the coat. A dark or partial cross, colored eartips, tail-tip, striped hooves, dark spots may be present in the foal coat, which fade out in the adult coat, leaving the spotted skin as the only indicator of the spotted pattern. If a breeder want white animals but dark eyes, they should not use Ivory, but FFSW instead. FFSW can occur over any base color, but since slate is the most common color, most FFSW animals are probably slate based. However, the FFSW will not breed true for white. Since these animals carry the genes for : Frosted/non-frosted, Spotted/non-spotted and various base colors, the resultant foals may get all, some or none of the "modifying" genes. This results in a variety of colors from FFSW bred to solid, or even FFSW to FFSW, ranging from FFSW, spotted, roan, or solid.

SORREL   Because even in horse circles opinion is divided on what separates a sorrel from a chestnut, the ADMS uses sorrel for all the red shades which are *not bay, red roan or reddish brown*. Sorrel is a red color of the body in which the legs are the same color or lighter than the body. They can also be darker if they are a darker shade of the *red* of the body. If the legs are black or dark brown the color is red/brown or bay. (Due to the extensive amount of research needed to test for genetic factoring, the the horse terminology of black chestnut, or sooty chestnut is not used in donkeys. If it exists in donkeys, it has not yet been proven. Red animals with black on the cross or lower legs will not be classified as sorrels - chestnut with black legs/mane and tail is BAY. It is the presence of black in these areas which separates the sorrels from the other red terms. If sooty is suspected, it will be listed under description.)

Sorrel is a recessive color - that is, the sorrel coloration is cause by inheriting one sorrel gene from each parent. Breeders of Mammoth jackstock have found this to be true; cross two black mammoths, and all of the sudden you have a sorrel jack colt! How did that happen? The recessive sorrel is hidden, or masked, by the stronger colors, and can lie hidden for generations until a pair is made.

Miniature donkeys sometimes have a pinkish/gray color which is hard to define. Summer, adult coat photos are necessary to classify these animals as they may be light sorrel, roan, or frosted.

In rare cases some donkeys may be labelled as **Rose Dun** when both sorrel and gray tones are reflected. Some Rose Dun donkeys do appear to be a blend visually of both slate and sorrel, and many will have one sorrel and one slate parent. Foals in heavy coats may appear to be brown/sorrel Foal Coat or Possible rose dun if the color is not absolutely clear. Another possibility is that some Rose Dun donkeys may also be slate with a brown-based dilution. If registering animals as sorrel, please list all colors of parts - legs, Cross & Stripe (especially) , eartips, eyelashes. This may help to determine the overall color of the animal. Again, photos MUST show the correct color or the animal will be listed as the color seen in the photos, as photos are used for identification of the animals. See also, Russet.

LIGHT SORREL/"PINK" - Pink is not used as an actual color, but may include it in the Description of the animal. Pink may appear in several different ways. "Pink" donkeys may be dilute sorrel, the donkey equivalent of Palomino. Others appear to be sorrel with roaning all through the coat (similar to a strawberry roan) Breeding trials are still needed to confirm this genetically. Please note if there are white hairs mixed in with the red hairs (sorrel roan) or just light red hairs and pink skin anywhere, especially on the muzzle (an "apricot" coat all over, a possible dilute). Be as detailed as necessary as to the colors of the body hair, cross & stripe, upper leg, lower leg, and the lips and muzzle.

BAY Bay is very common in mules but rare in donkeys. It has been recorded in Mammoth, standard and miniature donkeys but is uncommon. *The body is some shade of red, the mane, tail and legs are some shade of black.* In donkeys this is usually a rather dilute black, in mules it can be very dark. Some slate and brown donkeys have darker legs, which is either an Extension Gene or a dun-type dilution (where the body is lightened but not the extremities). Unless the body color is a definite red and legs true black, this is not defined as bay. The terms bay pattern may be used under the Description field if the red tones in the body warrent. ADMS has noted that even apparent bays have more brown tones than seen in horses, the deep RED of horses is not apparent in donkeys. Bay has different genetic factors that must be proven to show that it is a separate genetic factor and not a visual color caused by other genes. In horses you can get bay by breeding chestnut to black. You can aso get black or chestnut back out of breeding two bays. Until this can be proven in breeding donkeys that look bay, the term bay should be used sparingly. See also, Russet.

RUSSET Russet is used for those donkeys which are not a clear shade of "bay" (that being red/brown bodies with black legs), but are not true sorrels. Light red animals with black manes and tails (but usually having light legs) were previously classified in with sorrels, or as light browns. Research is showing that they may be a form of bay, but the color does not act like horse bay. This may be due to a roan factor paired with the bay (thus the roan or light colored legs) It is the presence of black paired with the red coat that separates the russets from sorrels. Although there are red tones in the coat, the shade is often not deep enough to carry the term RED, which has been suggested for donkey-bay. If the coat has light sorrel shadings, a black/brown mane and tail and light legs, the animal should be listed as russet. Animals with the above coloration and true black legs may be listed as bay. Further research should determine whether or not the russet animals are true bays with extensive white points hiding the black legs, or another color unique to the donkey. If breeding for sorrel is desired, russet animals shoudl be avoided, as foals by russet animals often come out russet. Russet may also be used in with sorrel or bay as a modifyer, such as sorrel/*russet (* then defined under Description field) or russet/bay if exact shade is still undetermined.

BROWN Brown covers all shades of brown from very light tan to very very dark brown/almost black. The legs are the same color or may be darker, even black. It includes the color known commonly as "chocolate" (a term not used in registrations.) The principal reason for this is that observers are unable to agree what color should be designated as chocolate - Hershey Bar or 3 Muskateers?. In all colors adjectives may be used to describe the colors. In brown the usual descriptions are light brown, medium brown, dark brown, very dark brown (usually used for chocolate) and if unsure whether black or brown-- black/brown. Caution must be used not to register a brown donkey as black since this will deceive future buyers. A few of these "chocolate" Brown (red-brown with true black legs) may be bay and can be listed as brown/bay. If the legs and cross are true brown, the animals is Brown. The registries currently do not use the term Liver Chestnut or Chocolate Chestnut. Some of these brown animals may be genetic dark chestnuts, but more breeding trials are needed to prove this. If it can be proved these animals are genetic chestnut and not Brown, chocolate Chestnut would be the trem of choice to adopt in the ADMS nomenclature.

SPOTTED Donkeys in the US are not listed as paint or pinto, leaving this up to the horse world. Mule owners may do so, or may adopt the donkey term which is "SPOTTED". The spotting pattern in donkeys is unique and follows a distinct pattern, as do horse pinto patterns. (For more information about spotting patterns, request the article "Seeing Spots"from the ADMS, which covers horse patterns and their workings as well.)

In the UK or Canada you might see donkey termed Pinto, broken-coloured, skewbald, piebald, or Paint. The term Pinto could be applied for donkeys, as it must measns spotted that is not appaloosa. Broken-coloured means white breaking up the base color of the animal, but is not used in the US. Piebald is a European term for "patched black and white", skewbald is "any color other than black, and white". Paint should not be applied toward Donkeys or Mules, since the Paint Horse is a distinctive breed registered by breed type and bloodlines. To be a Paint, a horse must have Paint, Quarter Horse, or Thoroughbred breeding. No other breeds are accepted, so donkeys are definitely out.

The spotted donkey may have only a little white, or may be mostly white with only a few dark spots. Some may have three colors, black, brown (or gray) and white. (These colors do not include the colors on the cross or dorsal stripe. These are assumed to be black unless is it noted otherwise.) Donkeys are considered to be spotted if they have even one of the dark type spots on a white background (spotted, mostly white, or also see FFSW) or if they have a lot of small black spots. Please note that animals are always listed as "color & white" and not as "white with (color) spots". There is one rare type that resembles the leopard appaloosa, but this is registered a spotted with the pattern of spotting listed in description (aka Tyger spotted). Donkeys do not show the true tobiano, overo, or tovero horse pattern, and these terms are not used on donkey papers.(Note - a solid foal from two spotted parents does not carry a spotting gene and will not have spotted foals unless bred back to a spotted animal. A blaze faced foal from two spotted parents is still spotted, see below).

MASKED SPOTTED Blaze faces with no other spots anywhere on the body are genetically spotted, but do not have body spots themselves. One or more other spots must be present on the neck/leg (not a sock) body to be classified as spotted. This is taken from the ACOSA rulings, requiring a body spot. (This is similar to the AQHA and Paint Horse rulings that state Paint horses must have a spot above the knees and hocks and past the line of the lip on the head.) Blaze faces (not a star) are the minimum expression of the spotted gene. These animals usually have extensive white points as well as the blaze face. The blaze may or may not actually extend down onto the lip, but since donkeys usually have white muzzles, it will make the face and muzzle look white in most animals. If you look closely at the blaze, you can see where the pink skin is (the actual blaze) or where the dark skin is (the light points). Masked Spotted will breed as any other genetically spotted animal, throwing spotted, blazed, or solids. Minor white leg markings such as low socks, stockings, or flashes of white on the legs are indicators of spotting and are not random as in horses. If an animal has a blaze over the flat of the face and minor white on the legs, it is genetically spotted, just without a body spot (genetically spotted horses of overo and sabino types that do not actually have a body spot are fairly common). Donkeys of this type are NOT solid, they are masked spotted factor.

Papers with ADMS will read Slate(or other color) */MSF to indicate the spotting factor in the Color section of the certificate. The description field will specify the location of the white markings. Please turn the face toward tha camera, as the blaze may be combined with a snip (pink between the nostrils) or other white markings on the muzzle (indicated by pink skin).

UNUSUAL COLORS Donkeys can come in some very unusual colors. We have one registered donkey named *Neopolitan* after the ice cream. Her body was 3 distinct areas of roan, front nearly white, barrel darker roan and rear black roan. She was one of the most unusual colors in our records. Unfortunately, she produced no offspring before she died. There are also animals with "displaced" dark spots where the pigment is not in a normal position. In these cases, the animal may not be genetically spotted, it may be more like the way color is deposited in a "Birthmark".

The "black muzzle" or "no light points/NLP" is a recessive gene, meaning each parent must contribute one dose for it to occur. NLP x NLP should always give foals with NLP. This pattern has been exhibited in spotted animals (appearing with odd, dark muzzles) and in at least one sorrel animal. It is also possible the gene could be present in the rose, pink or ivory animal, however, not enough generations have been specifically bred for this trait to show progress in these colors.

For animals with No Light Points, there may be varying degrees of total dark on the head (eyerings and muzzle) or the muzzle may just have a tiny patch of tan color (not the usual bright white). These animals frequently have one parent who has No Light Points. The genetic control for this variants may be due to a number of factors, or similar to those that control Shade (light, medium, dark).

BRINDLE - There are several donkeys in the ADMS books that appear to have brindle-striping over the body. Whether this is a true brindle or merely extensions of the primitive marks is still unknown. The brindles so far have been Miniature Donkeys, and none of the parents have shown visible markings that appeared brindle. One animal with the brindle patterning is also spotted! The lines of the brindle marks also extend onto the light color of the belly, which may be the key to unravelling the genetics of these markings.

MARKINGS Markings (other than the cross and stripe) are often overlooked. Small markings such as "collar buttons" and garters, zippers and ladder marks should be mentioned as they are very useful for identification. Garters is our name for the leg stripes (rings) and collar buttons are small black spots on the neck near where the jaw joins the neck which are usually seen in the gray-dun color animals. Collar buttons are often overlooked in fuzzy foal coats. Check the throat of mature animals carefully. Some animals have only one button, or they may be of unequal size on each side.

Stars are fairly common in donkeys, but the usual white leg markings seen in horses are equated in donkeys with the Spotting Gene. A donkey with a white blaze and leg marks is Masked Spotted. There is one known bloodline of Miniature Donkeys who have a star and a white snip between the nostrils. This particular bloodline is not spotted, and to make it more unusual, these donkeys usually have No Light Points!!! It may be that donkeys still genetically a more primitive animal than the domestic horse, therefore the occurance of random white is less frequent. This is true of the known populations of Przewalski (Mongolian Wild) Horse also.

DILUTIONS - There is much research being done as to the occurrence of a dilution factor in donkey coloration. In horses, the creme gene causes a bay coat to dilute to buckskin (yellow with a black mane and tail) and a chestnut to dilute to palomino (golden body with light or white mane and tail) with a single dose. Two doses (one from each parent) causes the bay to become Perlino and the chestnut to become cremello. Both of these horses are pale creme, with blue eyes, but markings can be seen. The best way to produce palomino horses is to breed chestnut to cremello. All of the foals will then be palomino. However, if you breed palomino x palomino, you will get ¼ chestnut (no creme gene from either parent) ½ palomino (1 creme gene from one or the other parent) and ¼ cremello (creme gene from both parents). Cremello x cremello should always produce creme colored horses only, as each parent will always contribute one creme gene.

There are no records of either buckskin or palomino donkeys, although blue-eyed white donkeys do exist. This causes the question to arise as to whether the Ivory (blue eyed white) donkey is the same as a cremello or perlino horse. Ivory x ivory in donkeys will always produce ivory foals, but this can be either a true recessive, or a dominant creme. Breeding trials of Ivory to sorrel donkeys (and the resultant offspring) will be the key to unlocking the Ivory color.

"Pink" donkeys may be the equivalent of palomino, if they produce both sorrel and pink foals when bred to sorrel. If Pink x pink produces sorrel, pink, pink or creme, then the pink color can indeed be labeled a dilution. However, there are some colors, such as rose dun, which may show other dilutions exist. One rose dun donkey jennet recently researched has no sorrel in her background, and instead appears to be a dilution of brown.

FOAL COAT COLORS In all equines, but most especially in donkeys, foal coat colors can differ from mature, summer coat color. The summer coat color is the one used for identification of an animal's true color. When the color is doubtful, the ADMS will register a foal as "Slate" (or brown, or brown/slate, etc...) (foal coat) and will change the color along with the height and mature photos when we reissue the certificate after the animal's third birthday. One fairly reliable way of telling mature color is to shave off a patch of hair (usually on the neck) and see what the hair beneath it looks like. However a drawback to this is that shaved hair is often much lighter than properly grown out hair.

FULLY CLIPPED COATS - may be useful in determining markings hidden by heavy winter or baby fuzz, but the clipped hair is often different from the naturally shed hair. The freshly SHED Summer coat color should be used as the color for the adult papers for accuracy. Colors may always be listed with the time of the coat shown in the photo (winter coat, foal coat, clipped coat) and updated at a later date.

Brindle-like marking over the body of a slate Miniature donkeys.

Displaced dark spots on a Frosted Dapple jack.

IDENTIFIERS IN THE DONKEY

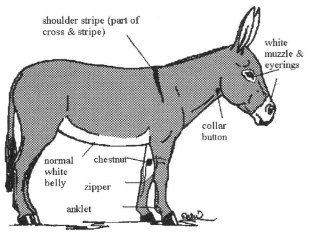

shoulder stripe (part of cross & stripe)

white muzzle & eyerings

collar button

normal white belly

chestnut

zipper

anklet

These specific points labelled on the donkey may not appear on all animals, but all are important in identification of individual animals.

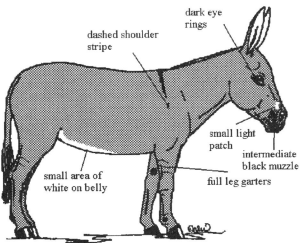

dark eye rings

dashed shoulder stripe

small light patch

intermediate black muzzle

small area of white on belly

full leg garters

The Intermediate Black muzzle usually has only a small patch of light on the top of the nose, dark eyerings, and little white (or tan instead of white) on the belly. Other markings are examples that may occur in all or part.

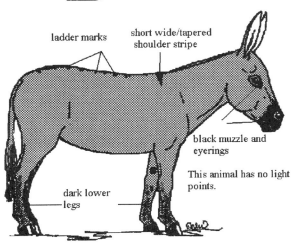

ladder marks

short wide/tapered shoulder stripe

black muzzle and eyerings

This animal has no light points.

dark lower legs

This is what is visually closest to the Grulla (Grullo) coloration in horses. Often, but not always, the head is black as well on Slate donkeys. This color pattern may also show the most prominant Primitive marks (such as the ladder marks) and darker legs or full leg garters.

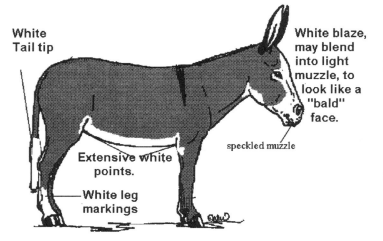

White
Tail tip

White blaze,
may blend
into light
muzzle, to
look like a
"bald"
face.

speckled muzzle

Extensive white
points.

White leg
markings

This is the Masked Spotting Factor - no actual body spots, but a white blaze and various leg markings. One leg is usually dark or has dark markings on it in spotted animals.

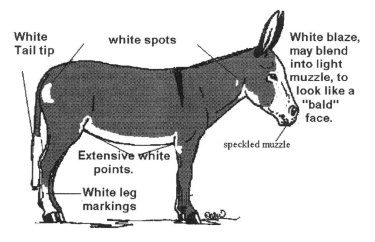

White
Tail tip

white spots

White blaze,
may blend
into light
muzzle, to
look like a
"bald"
face.

speckled muzzle

Extensive white
points.

White leg
markings

The minimal expression of the spotting factor is the Masked Spotted, where there are no actual body spots. In accordance with ACOSA, one body spot must be present to be listed as Spotted.

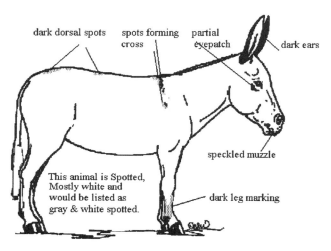

dark dorsal spots

spots forming
cross

partial
eyepatch

dark ears

speckled muzzle

This animal is Spotted,
Mostly white and
would be listed as
gray & white spotted.

dark leg marking

This animal is spotted, mostly white. The eyes are dark, and there is spotted skin on the muzzle, eyelids, and genitals. A number of small dark spots can be seen, usually concentrated on the head and along the topline. Also, the hocks or cannon bones may have small dark areas.

FAQ (Frequently Asked Questions) about Donkey Color.

Please realize that color research is ongoing in different fronts. The ADMS is conducting in collaboration with Dr. Phillip Sponenberg, DVM PhD. Our work is not complete, but there are some aspects which have already been proven. If we can't answer one of your questions now, please feel free to contact us at the office and discuss it with us.

This information packet it copyrighted by the American Donkey and Mule Society and may not be reproduced in part or in whole without permission of the ADMS. © 1998

Can we use horse colors to describe donkey colors?

Horse colors and donkey colors are similar in many ways, but they are not the same. In order to understand donkey colors, we need to understand how horse colors work, and then how the donkey colors are similar or parallel, or totally different. Some horse terms can be used, others must be found that are unique for the donkey.

Horses have no exact equivalent for the Slate (gray-dun) color. Dapples in horses have light centers, in donkeys the dapples are "reversed". We seem to have a true brown in donkeys, while brown in horses is usually modified black, chestnut or bay.

What are some of the distinguishing marks of the various colors, ie eyelashes, hoof color etc.

The areas that should be looked at first in distinguishing the colors are first the **body**, for the base color. Then the color of the mane, tail and cross (the **trim**) should be noted as modifications of the body color. Lastly, the color of the **lower legs** is important. The lower legs might be covered up by the frosty pattern, in which we have to do a closer examination of different areas of the legs and also the trim to determine color. If we are dealing with a true dun factor in the Slate coloration (Grulla pattern) then the color of the face, (darker than the body or the same color) is important. This is why we use the different descriptions on the registration certificates. We use the trim color and the lower leg color to help give a more complete color overview. A red body with black trim and roan legs is listed as *russet*, because the roan on the legs covers up where you might normally see black. A red body with red trim and roan legs is *sorrel* (and probably *frosty roan*). A red body with red trim and dark red or brown lower legs is *sorrel* or the *red dun pattern*. All three have a red body. Two have dark red trim. The combination of all of the parts has to be used, not just one main area.

How do you identify colors for registrations?

Again, we are referring back to the ADMS color guide. We must rely on both the breeder's observations, and *also the color photographs we are sent*. Unfortunately, it's hard to get photos with good color. However, **foal coat color is the absolute worst indicator of adult color**. We have records of donkeys that were *pink* in winter coats, but just as dark a *Slate (gray-dun)* in their shed summer coat as you have ever seen. Genetically, the animal was *Slate (gray-dun)*. It may be that all *Slates (gray-duns)* have some degree of red in the coat. *Black* certainly bleaches out to red in the sun, and many *brown* foals have a gorgeous "redhead" foal coat that they loose as they mature. Actually, the notion of having one color in a baby coat that is lost at maturity is not at all farfetched. Zebra foals have red stripes at birth that darken to *black*. Lion cubs are born with immature rosette markings that fade out in the adult animal. The red color in donkey coats may be of a similar nature. Donkeys are probably less removed from their primitive roots as wild asses than are horses, so the red color may be a "wild" protective coloration leftover.

Should one breed for color?

Conformation, and temperament should always be the first concern of a breeder. Size is of concern only when you are trying to make sure your animals fall within a LIMIT (use donkeys under 34 inches if you want 30-33" donkeys, or make sure that the difference in height is not TOO great between the two parents (such as using s 34" jack on a 28" jennet) but color should always be considered a bonus. Use the best jennets and especially the best jacks you can find of the particular colors you are striving for. For the betterment of the breed as a whole, it is better to use a 36" *gray-dun* jack with perfect conformation than the brightest of *sorrel*s that is 30" tall but has dwarf characteristics or is roach backed and bow-legged.

How do you determine which cross will produce what color?

First, you must look at the visual color. Although some coat colors can fool you, most are a pretty good indicator of what **dominant** genes you are dealing with. To be able to project what combinations you would get from a pair, you would need to know their genetic makeup. You can tell some of this by looking at the pedigree or background. But the best way is to see what other colors those animals have produced. There is no absolute way to be able to look at an animal with no background, or one that is untried, and be *certain* what colors it will throw, even if is one of the darker colors, which are usually recessive. Too many factors may be masked or covered up. We have dark brown animals with recessive sorrel, and black/browns that seem to have a brown and black gene. You can narrow your chances down somewhat, but 100% certainty is difficult.

Explain Dominant and Recessive.

There are basically two types of genes - **dominant** and **recessive**. Dominant are the strongest. They win - they get expressed. Recessive are "weaker". They keep their head down and hide. They can hide for many generations. In order for a recessive gene to be expressed, it has to team up with a partner from the other side (the other parent). Once the recessive finds his "twin" on the other side, Recessive is now "stronger" than dominant and pushes dominant out of the picture. The color expressed is the recessive, and the dominant color gene is no longer present in the make-up for that animal - it gets left out entirely, just a memory.

We can use slate and sorrel as an example. The jack is slate, but he has a recessive sorrel gene - let's say his mom was sorrel. (He has one dominant gene - the slate, and one recessive, the sorrel) You breed him to ONLY slate jennies. If these jennies have *no sorrel gene*, you will only get slate (dominant color from the jennies, or even from the jack). But, if some of these jennies also have the recessive sorrel, you have a *chance* of it pairing up with the jack's sorrel gene. If this happens, and you get a sorrel colt, that colt will ONLY have the recessive sorrel gene to pass along. The slate in this case is out of the picture. The same with spotted. *Once the recessive Non-spotted animal jumps out, it won't matter how many spotted parents there were in the background. The dominant is lost and is not recoverable.*

Dominant colors can be **homozygous** (meaning the same, or one identical gene from each parent). This means that every foal from that parent will have at least one Dominant gene. If that foal has a recessive gene, it's not from the homozygous dominant parent. Gray-dun can be dominant. If a jennet is homozygous for gray-dun, ALL of her foals will be gray-dun no matter what she is bred to.

Dominants may also be **heterozygous**, meaning different, or mis-matched pairing of the genes (like that gray-dun/sorrel jack above). Each of these foals has, theoretically, a 50/50 chance of getting either the dominant or the recessive gene.

Recessives that are paired with a heterozygous dominant are passive. They are not expressed, but can be passed along.

True paired recessives are the "surprise" colors that pop out of nowhere (like two gray-duns having a bright red sorrel foal). The animal is then homozygous for sorrel, it can only give a copy of the sorrel gene to it's offspring.

How easy is it to get color?

Well, in a sense, every animal has color. "Color" means something different to everyone. There are breeders who LIKE *gray-dun*s - getting a good *gray-dun* foal to them IS getting color. If we are asking how easy it is to breed for a dominant color - it's a roulette game. If that dominant color has an underlying recessive, you have that chance of it pairing with a matching recessive from the other parent, and then you get a surprise. **If you are trying to get recessive colors, the only sure-fire way is to breed**

ONLY like color to like color. *Sorrel* is recessive and can only contribute *sorrel*. So breed ONLY *sorrel* to *sorrel* and you will come up with *sorrel*s. Once we get past the point where many animals of confusing tones were inadvertently labeled as *sorrel*, (where their records have proved them to be *brown* or *rose dun*, etc) and these are NOT used to cloud the *sorrel*s any longer, then you will eventually have true *sorrel* bred to true *sorrel*, and you will have tons of little red donkeys everywhere. Just remember, if you continue to breed for a recessive, you have blocked off all outside color, and you will end up with a gene pool that has only that one color - they can't contribute any other color factors. If everyone ignored *slate* and tried only for *sorrel* you have to imagine this scenario. *You breed a* slate *to a* sorrel *and get a* slate *that has a recessive* sorrel *gene (it has to, the* sorrel *parent can only give* sorrel*). *You take this number-one foal and breed it to another* sorrel *(again, remember you only have* sorrel *genes coming from that* sorrel*). *So the number-two foal has the chance of being the dominant color, the* slate, *or the* sorrel. Itss a dice game, and dice don't always roll the way you want. By chance, you get the *sorrel* you wanted. Again, you take this *sorrel* to a *sorrel* and get *sorrel*, and so on, ad infinim. If you never bred any of the *slate* into the herd again, you would only ever get *sorrel* forever (okay, you could have a mutated gene, but that's another research project).

Is there such a thing as a jack or jennet that is a consistent color producer?
This is really an interesting subject. You have a spotted jack that manages to throw 75% spotted foals instead of the projected 50/50. That's a color producer. Why? Are the odds just good? Or is his spotted gene just "faster and stronger? And gets used more often? We don't know. However, if you are dealing with a straight recessive gene (like dark *brown*) there is really is no such thing as the animal with the recessive being a color producer. If you are getting a dark jack throwing dark foals, it's because the jennies also had the dark gene. *Sorrel* jacks can't contribute anything else, it's up to the genetic background of the jenny (is she slate with a recessive *sorrel*, recessive brown, or straight *slate* across the board). She (the jenny) has the key when you are dealing with a recessive color from the jack.

Please explain how to get spotted donkeys.
The Spotted gene so far has proven to be a Partial or Incomplete Dominant, more properly termed heterozygous (meaning different, homo meaning the same). This means is takes only one dose of Spot to get the spots. We have not yet found any animal that is for certain Homozygous (two doses) for spotting. Research is being conducted to see if this means that the homozygous spotted is a lethal - meaning you won't find a 100% color producing donkey, one with both parents spotted, because the gene combination is no viable.

    Although donkey color doesn't act the same as horse color, we need to look at one horse example to clarify. In the Paint horse industry, owners with *tobiano* horses have found that their horses can be homozygous for *tobiano*. *Tobiano* is dominant. If their stallion is homozygous for tobiano, ALL of his foals will be tobiano marked, no matter what the color of the dam is. (and yes, even if the mare was solid or appaloosa. There are such things as pintaloosas). The paint horse breeders are now marking in their stud advertisements if their horses are Tt or TT markered. This way, if a breeder wants to make sure his *sorrel* QH mare has a paint foal, he goes to a TT stallion. Now look at it this way. That foal will be tobiano, but since the mother had no matching tobiano gene, the foal will be heterozygous (Tt). All of it's foals will have one chance to be spotted, and one not. That's the way it works in our spotted donkeys. Even using a spotted jack on spotted jennies sometimes results in the foal getting the short end of the "t" from both parents and coming out solid. You can't choose which gene they'll get, unfortunately, although we all wish we could. Take your best spotted jacks and put them to good solid jennies and you get a 50/50 chance of a spotted foal.

What crosses produces *black, brown*, and *sorrels*?
    We are dealing with two types of color that are straight recessives and one that is a partial dominant. Black and sorrel are true, paired recessives. The genes for either one will hide under slate or brown. Of the recessives, brown is "stronger" than sorrel,

and you can have a brown animal that has one *sorrel* gene and one *brown*. Therefore, *sorrel*, *black* or *brown* can "pop up" out of *slate*, but if you breed *sorrel* to *sorrel*, you should only get *sorrel*. *Brown* can hide the *sorrel*, so *brown* to *brown* matings should give *brown* or *sorrel*. (More on color projections can be found in the Appendix.)

Is there a deep red *sorrel*?

There is a deep red in donkeys, but it is not the rich, blood-toned red in a horse. Donkey red is different, and always seems to hedge toward the brown or mousey tones. The *sorrel* colors of Mammoth donkeys seem more red than those in the Miniatures. Breeding paired-recessive *sorrels* (and not *browns* with one recessive *sorrel*) might be the answer to producing a more clear, rich red tone.

Why only Sorrel and not Chestnut?

Even in horse circles, the line between *chestnut* and *sorrel* is blurred. You will never see an Arabian listed as *sorrel*, but Suffolk Punch horses are always *sorrel* and never *chestnut*. Yet if you stand the two up against each other, the visual color may be the same. Some say if the animal exhibits several shades of color on the body, it's *chestnut*. No shading, it's *sorrel*. Others go by the amount of brown or red in the coat. You may see "red sorrel with flaxen mane and tail" or "light chestnut with blonde mane and tail". Are they the same? It's a matter of opinion at this point. The old-time Jackstock breeders called the red ones *sorrel*. ADMS stayed with that term. Many *sorrel* Mammoths have a lot of *roan* on the face. Some *sorrel* Minis do (it appears to be in certain strains) while others are closer to what horse people would call *chestnut* or even *red dun* - no *roan*, with darker heads and lower legs. Right now, the ADMS feels it is best to list all red donkeys (just red, not with black) only as *sorrel*, and then use modifiers to describe the *roan*, darker legs, etc.

What Miniature colors were the original imports, and are "pure" colors, not bred-in colors?

The original Sicilian, Sardinian, and Ethiopian Miniature sized donkeys that were imported to be the original gene pool were visually *Slate* (*gray-dun*) and *brown*. They had both the familiar light points and the dark muzzles. We now know that Luigi 95, a prominent jack in many pedigrees, was the source of red (*sorrel*, *russet*, *red dun*, etc). in most of our pedigreed donkey population. There were obviously other donkeys with the recessive red as well. *Brown* is a recessive, and it's easy to see that the recessive for black came in the original imports. If you are asking if spotted is an "original" color or bred into the current population, there are two answers, Neither can really be proven so far. No spotted animals are recorded in the original registry records, BUT white blazes are often overlooked in donkeys! *(IVORY (Blue-eyed white)* is also an apparent recessive, and can lie hidden, as can any recessive, for many generations. There is no reason to believe it was not carried in by one of the original donkeys. They were closely inbred for several generations, and inbreeding is one way to see the recessives start cropping up.) Also, there is some scientific proof that if you close-breed animals for enough generations, a mutation will crop up. Spotted hedgehogs, and spotted pot-bellied pigs are just two examples of inbreeding causing the partial-white mutation. The Przewalski horse, the last true "wild" horse now has such a small gene pool they are being very closely inbred. There are reports of animals with white stars, white faces, and even white body spots beginning to show up. So are spots bred in from Standard donkeys, or did we really have some minis with a crop-out spot pattern? We don't know.

What is the foal coat color of *Slate* (*gray-dun*), *black*, spots and *sorrel*s, and can foal coat determine color?

Dr. Sponenberg states that foal coat colors are the worst indicator of color. Foal coats can fool you. Have you ever heard of leopard appaloosa horses that are born dark, then turn into leopard spotted? Guess what!!! That's foal coat and that "protective coloration syndrome" we discussed earlier. Foal coats and winter coats are fine as descriptions for what the animal looks like at that stage. The freshly shed adult summer coat should be used as the true coat color. Freshly shed, because the sun can bleach colors. Even with the summer coat, we have some donkey colors that just won't be defined one way or the other. We have *smoky blacks* (because you CAN see a cross) and *brown/slate*, because they show both mixed together. We can do breeding trials to see what colors they throw when they are adult.

To answer the question *slate (gray-dun)* foals may have dark charcoal coats, *gray-dun* coats, *brown* coats, *brown/tan, rose*, or *pink* hair. *Black* foals usually have dark hair, *black*, although *black* Mammoth foals usually have red/brown winter coats their first year. Spotted foals will keep the spotted pattern the same as the when they were born - the spotting doesn't change, but the base color (the dark hair) will act the same as if the spotting wasn't there - the slate-and white spotted foal could the foal coat in the spotted areas any of the color we just mentioned (such as dark *slate* (gray-dun), *brown, rose*, etc). If the animal is a *frosted spotted white*, the colors may be dark and will lighten up. The *frosted spotted white* foals you can sometimes tell when they are born because even though they have spots, they already have lost the color around the eyepatches, with only dark "mascara" showing. Other frosted foals are born with the dark patches already gone. (ADMS is researching to see if there is some other factor that makes them fade faster - and will publish when it is known.)

Why are black and white spots so rare?
We're dealing with a two-strikes against situation. *Black* is recessive. This means both parents have to carry *black* or be *black*. Then you have to get the spots, which, as discussed earlier, you are getting 50/50 chances. If *black* spotted animals are only bred to *gray-dun*, then you have taken away the necessary factor to match up the black. If you want to try for *black-and white spotted* (or dark *brown*) you have to take your *black and white spotted* (say a jack) and breed him to a select group of jennies. This is your grouping: **Group 1** - *black* jennies (in which you have a 50/50 chance of getting *black* solid or *black* spotted)- all foals should be *dark* unless both sire and dam have recessives for *sorrel*. **Group 2** you should use spotted jennets - they need to be black and white spotted (you have a 50/50 chance for each of the parents to give a spotted gene) and *all of your foals should be dark*. **Group 3** - the jennies should be *slate* with one *black* parent. They should be carrying a recessive for dark (we'd rather say dark than *black*, or *black/brown*, or *smoky*, because of all the other factors on top that might cause *black* to come out looking *brown*, etc). If you take these black-carrier jennets and breed to your black spotted jack, you have the chance of *slate* (since it's dominant) in both solid or spotted, and *black* if the recessives pair up (in both solid and spotted, that 50/50 chance). The same thing applies to your *slatn* spotted jennets - if they have a *black* parent, you've got those chances for *slate (gray-dun)* or *black*, spotted or solid. You just have to hope that the genes pair up right and you manage to get the dark spots.

Is black with /black points more dominant than black/light points?
This is a two-part question. The point color (the muzzle, eye rings, belly) color is totally separate from the body color. *Black* body color is recessive whether the points are light are dark. Are dark points recessive or dominant? They are recessive to the white points. The white points are dominant, which is why you see them more often. The donkeys with the dark points (termed no light point) have two recessive genes for the dark points. The donkeys with light points can carry one recessive gene for No light points. You get the two recessives together and the surprise black-muzzle foal pops out.

Are there any health problems inherent in various colors?
We need to break this question down into parts. They question most important is that of *the lethal white gene*. This is a complicated subject, so bear with us. In Paint horses with Overo patterns (see Appendix for explanation of Pinto Patterns) there is a gene defect, now discovered to be a recessive, that causes foal death. The foals are born *white* or nearly white , with blue eyes (with spotted parents) and are either stillborn, or die shortly after birth because a vital part of the colon is incomplete. Researchers have now located the gene in the overo horses. The question has been asked if we have this gene in donkeys. We will say this simply, but the statement is very important. **We do not know if we have the lethal white gene because no one has reported any such incidents in donkeys**. The only way we will ever know if this fault

exists is for people who lose foals at birth to keep records of the foals' color, to have a post-mortem (Necropsy) done on the foal, and to record the parent color. A dead foal from two spotted parents - but you have no idea what it died from and therefore no way to help any research team find out if the flaw exists. We know it's embarrassing to have foals die - from whatever cause - but until we - or any researcher - are given some kinds of figures on foal deaths, then no one will ever be able to determine if these deaths are accidental, or due to some genetic factor. We'd love to be able to know if this is a possibility or if we can say it doesn't seem to exist in donkeys, but until we have numbers from breeders, no one will ever know. Please remember it is for the donkeys, and encourage everyone you know to keep records and report incidents. (There is a sample sheet in the Appendix of this book)

There are horse diseases that are just being discovered and researched. One research group is conducting breeding trials to see if a CIDS (Combined Immune Deficiency Syndrome in Arabian Horses) like disease exists in donkeys. Again, until more hard evidence and facts are reported by breeders, this will be a long time coming to a conclusion.

Although deafness is also a factor linked to blue eyes or spotted genes in other breeds (Paint horses, blue-eyed white cats, Dalmatian dogs), again, no one has reported any such occurrences in donkeys. More information from breeders is needed before these statements can be answered.

Other health problems? There are genetic health problems, but more are conformation-related than color related. Since we can't say anything about lethal *White*, the only other real color-related problem is sunburn on pink skin. *Blue eyed whites* and spotted donkeys with lots of white may get badly sunburned on the pink areas, especially the nose. Sunscreen! Are light hooves (like those on some spotted animals) softer than dark? That's an old debate, and since most miniature donkeys do not wear shoes and work on hard surfaces, probably not as much of an issue as they would be in a work horse or mule. Does white line disease affect one color of hoof more than others - this is probably related more to outside conditions than to hoof color.

Do ALL donkeys have a Cross?

Not visually. Some donkeys appear not have a cross, in others, the shade of the cross is so close to the shade of the body (as in some *sorrel* Mammoths or in some very dark almost *black* animals) that it is hard to tell. There is one, complicated breeding trial, involving horse mares, that MIGHT prove yes or no to this question. For now, we have to say, you can't see a cross on all of them, and ADMS lists this on the papers as No visible Cross and Stripe. However, sometimes a cross can be seen in winter or baby hair and not in the slick summer coat. If there is a visible cross in the heavy coat, it should be noted for the sake of future offspring.

Is the demand for certain colors cyclical and/or regional?

Regional, we don't show any evidence of. Cyclical, definitely. Brown was first, then spots, then black, and now *sorrel*. We know that some breeders would eventually like to come up with a true *sorrel* spotted donkey, but so far, that elusive bright red-and-white hasn't shown up.

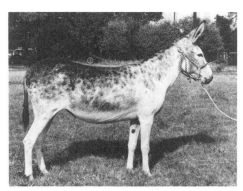

The dappled roan pattern in donkeys is reversed from horses - instead of lighter circles on a dark background, the dapples are dark against the lighter body coat. They are most visible across the barrel, with less contrast over the forequarters.

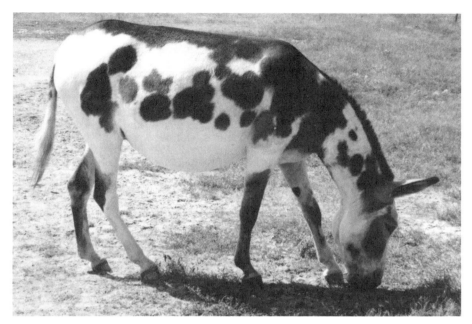

The typical spotting pattern of the donkey. The spots are often small and overlap each other along the line of the barrel. Even though this jennet has white leg markings on all four legs, the portions around the knees and hocks are still dark.

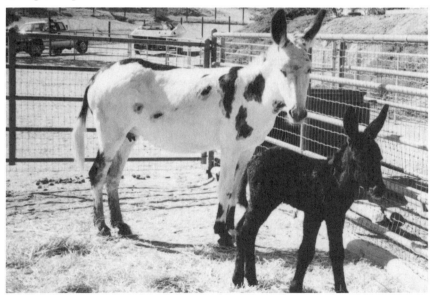

The lovely solid black (no light points) jennet foal was a surprise to her owners, since both parents were loudly marked black and white spotted themselves. She simply got the recessives - for non-spotted and No Light Points both! Her little sister the next year was black and white spotted, though! This is *Asspecial Maggie* and foal *Asspecial Gypsy*, owned by Tom & Jane Sauers, Hemet California.

SELLING DONKEYS

All that research and hard work has paid off. You have settled all of your jennets, made it through that first year, and now your foal crop is on the ground. (You may even have gotten the colors you wanted!) Whether you have one or 50, are you going to keep every foal you have? No, although many of you are in it just for fun and will only raise one a foal a year, others may be in it as a business venture.

While most mule breeders experience less and less trouble in selling the mules they raise, people who wish to sell donkeys often have problems. Since in our experience, there are a good many people out there who would like a donkey if they could find one, we think that the main problem is twofold: 1. Letting people who want a donkey know that you have one for sale and 2. Letting people know that they want a donkey! There are some people who have never thought of it - but would realize that they would like one if they were put in mind of it.

Of course different people have different problems. The problem of selling one trained gelding perhaps, or a single foal, is considerably different from selling foals from a breeding establishment. We will try to handle the problem by categories to make it easier to see some solutions.

MAMMOTH JACKSTOCK

The breeder of true Mammoth Jackstock (jennets over 54 inches and jacks over 56) is the one ass breeder who will have no trouble selling stock. These animals are much sought after and most of them sell by word of mouth. If however a mammoth breeder lives in an out of the way place or has a good deal of competition some well placed advertising will get him all the business he can handle. We are not speaking here of large Standard (48" to 54") but true breeding Mammoth Jackstock. Prices for Mammoth stock usually start at $1,000 and the breeder of these animals will be the only donkey breeder to make a really good profit usually. However, the initial cost of breeding stock is extremely high, and should always be the best available, as quality is much desired, so it will be some years before the beginning breeder will break even and make his profit. It is extremely important to have the jennets vet checked and cared for because each foal lost or jennet barren is a year's profit lost. Therefore feed bills (because of their large size) and vet bills will be high compared to other breeds, the best reward the Mammoth breeder has is the market which is constantly improving both for large jacks and large jennets.

MINIATURE DONKEYS

We have had Miniature breeders who also breed Standards tell me that "the miniatures pay the feed bill." We think that this is true. As a general rule there is a steady if not bullish market for good Miniatures, especially the jennets. However an excess of jack colts may produce a problem. One problem some Miniature breeders have run into is that of buying their original breeding stock at extremely high prices and being led to believe that they can get the same price for the foals. We know one woman who became so bitter when she found out that she couldn't, that she had her three jacks gelded, refused to sell anything and just kept her whole expensive herd as pets from then on. Hopefully most breeders caught in this bind would not do this, and would sell the foals at reasonable prices (say $500 to $800 for a jenny) until they caught up with the original break even point.

Some breeders of miniatures will geld the excess jack colts and sell them at very reasonable prices as pets. This depends on advertising which we will discuss later. If people are going to keep miniatures as pets, the males should be gelded anyway, as they think they are as big as a mammoth jack when you leave them entire, and entire jacks do not make the best pets, especially for children. A good many miniatures sell for breeding stock and of course people want jennets, as you can have one jack and several females for him to serve. It sometimes pays to sell your jennets only as breeding stock at good prices and sell only your very best jacks in this way and advertise the rest as pets. Some people however want only a female, not even a gelding as a pet, and if they are willing to pay breeding stock prices then they should have one. If you offer geldings at very reasonable prices (say $250.00-$350.00) you will have more luck at getting rid of those excess jack colts.

If you are just starting into the business of breeding miniatures, keep in mind that they are not as hard to find as you might think (ADMS has a list of breeders) and don't buy the first one you are offered if it is not good. Miniatures often have faults such as very crooked legs with too light bone, slab sides and roach backs. Look for animals with proper donkey conformation. Good miniatures are almost small draft animals and should have good heavy bone and straight legs for their size, well rounded ribs and well shaped backlines. There are also some bloodlines which are dwarfy, and although they seem cute to some, they are not good breeding stock The miniature horse associations have gone through that stage (they had little "sausage horses" or Dachshund-types) and they have managed to get away from that type - donkey breeders should too!!

STANDARD DONKEYS

Many people would prefer to raise standard donkeys. There are good reasons for this. The breeding stock is easier to find and less expensive to buy. There are different colors and sizes enough to please any taste. And, of course, there are many more uses for them than for the other two breeds.

With standard donkeys, perhaps more than the other two the beginning breeder must first decide what market he is aiming for. There are many ways to go. If your area wants pack burros, breeding small, light boned driving animals is a waste of time. Of course your own taste must prevail, but you must have a common sense idea of what will sell best. If one is just beginning in standard donkeys, a good start can be made by buying donkeys of good conformation, with enough size and ruggedness to ride, drive or pack, with good looks and then buying the finest spotted jack you can buy to go with them. This way, your young stock will be of all colors, but the spotted ones will begin to sell better as they are a novelty. If you can afford it and like spots, you might try a whole herd of spotted stock but the expense is higher, they are harder to find and you have less choice in conformation because of less animals to choose from. Another alternative might be raising a herd all of one color. People are quite impressed by a herd of all black, or all gray-dun or all sorrel shades or all white. When picking for color, again, you may have a hard time getting the conformation and looks you should have, and may end up having to breed for them, so always get the VERY BEST HERD SIRE you can find!

Again, you may prefer to breed for some function and not bother about color. We have already mentioned pack burros. One of the most famous breeders of standard donkeys ever, FARVIEW FARMS of Carmel, Indiana, built its reputation on donkeys suitable for light harness pleasure driving, and beautiful animals they were. In other areas, people might want donkeys only as pets. In this case you can afford to buy smaller animals, making sure they are nicely built and good looking and sell only for pets and children's riding animals. If adults may wish to ride you should breed larger more rugged animals, but never coarse!!! About prices, a good standard jennet should never sell for less than $300 and a jack or gelding for less than $200.

SELLING IDEAS

SELLING ONE DONKEY

If you just have one donkey to sell, or a jenny and foal, chances are the price you could get would not be worth a big advertising campaign. The best thing to do in this circumstance would be first to put ads in the classified sections of the newspapers in the towns around you, not neglecting the big city. Frequently these will sell your animal quite soon, and you might try just one town at a time to save money. Also if there is a regional club near you, an ad in its newsletter is an excellent way of letting the people you know are interested, about your animal. Failing this, a classified ad in THE BRAYER is quite cheap and reaches other people not reached by the other ads or in horse magazines. Also you can put up photos - preferably cute ones - in color - in local places where people come. Feed stores, saddle shops, auctions, etc. Please do not sell them in an auction, they will probably go for dogfood and I know no ADMS member would do that to their donkey! Auctions can be good, but they can be bad too. Flood the market, animals end up at auction, the price goes down, and auction animals get bad reputations - it is a nasty chain.

THE BREEDER, SELLING FOALS

The first thing you must realize as a breeder is that QUALITY SELLS. You have to be able to state things in your advertisements that let people know you are offering quality animals. Such adjectives (and they must be TRUE) as REGISTERED; TRAINED; GENTLE; FRIENDLY; FANCY; FANCY COLORED; TINY, PETITE, RIDING; DRIVING; PACKING; PET STOCK; REGISTERED BREEDING STOCK; SHOW QUALITY; etc. are invaluable in advertising donkeys. Ordinary "burros" will not sell like these animals. Just the fact that some of these things are applicable and that YOU BELIEVE IN YOUR MERCHANDISE will raise the price 100% sometimes on these good animals!

If you can't buy registered stock, have it inspected as soon as you start to breed it and register it with ADMS to help KEEP PEDIGREES! A pedigreed animal, even with only one generation is worth more than a non-pedigreed one. On a pedigree do not just put the name and registration numbers of sire, dam, grandsire, grandam, but put their color and size and other distinguishing characteristics. No donkey breeder should be using unregistered stock. Remember that if inspection is a problem, once the foundation stock in inspected, all foals born from registered stock need not be inspected.

ADMS registers all sizes and types of donkeys, as long as they meet minimum conformation standards.. Spotted animals should be registered with the American Council of Spotted Asses, and then may be registered with ADMS in order to follow some of the continuing award and other programs available through that registry. Miniatures, spotted, and mammoth can all be double registered which raises their value in the eyes of the public. Register your foals before you sell them, this gives them much more quality and value in the eyes of your potential customers. BE SURE TO TRANSFER all registrations OR register foals at the time of sale in the name of the new owner - but insist on this - don't neglect it.

Even though stock is inspected before registration, some is better than others. Try if you can to get breeding stock with the best possible looks and conformation for your breed and type. If you are not sure what to look for, review the Conformation Charts and the Buyer's checklist in this book (Also see appendix) and learn before you buy! Visit some shows if there are any in your area and see what wins.

When people come to look at your stock they will be completely turned off, if the animal they want to see takes one look at them and runs for the bush! Handle all your stock, especially the dams and foals, take treats to them every day and walk among them petting and talking to them. If people walk into the pasture and the babies gather around in a friendly manner, you will sell those babies, if they run away people will decide against buying a donkey for a pet. They had heard they were friendly - so why do they act this way? It pays a million percent to halter break and gentle each baby before it is sold. They should be halter broken and their feet should be trimmed starting in the first month. (If you have read this before it's because it can't be stressed enough.) Crooked legs all too often come from untrimmed feet on foals. Each weanling should lead well, allow his legs to be picked up and allow himself to be handled all over and should stand tied. If you sell older animals, break them to ride and drive in a basic manner so they will be started for the customer, and charge extra for the work involved. They are worth more. Make sure the buyer understands this. One way to do this is to make up an inexpensive information sheet on your donkeys. Put all the above in it in some form, explaining about registration, vet care, handling foals, training of older animals, show quality conformation, anything unusual, the uses they were bred for - and on the other side, how to care for the donkey, clubs and groups the buyer can join, address of HEE HAW BOOK SERVICE etc. All this will PAY OFF. If you don't know what to write just ask for the Donkey information packet from ADMS - you are quite free to use any of this literature in your own leaflet, indeed we hope you will do so!

ADVERTISING YOUR HERD

Now, how do you get those people to actually come and look at your stock and get your leaflet in the first place?

Well, first you can spread those leaflets around. Have a good large batch made at the nearest Print Shop (there are some of various sizes on every corner now) type of place. Then put them anyplace in the surrounding towns that will allow you to put them up. Bulletin boards in feed stores, saddle shops, and other places that you would not ordinarily expect livestock owners to go, most donkey owners are beginners and pet owners, not livestock owners or farmers -put them EVERYPLACE! This leaflet is super free advertising as well as telling people how to care for their donkey after they get him.

If you plan to sell donkeys you must find ways of letting people know you exist. A breeder should always be present in the minds of other breeders and buyers. This doesn't just mean people in your town - breeders will buy good stock from the other side of the country! This means keeping an ad, large or small, in your own breed magazines. Many farms have built whole reputations on just good stock and ads in the proper publications. If your name is kept before your own kind in this way people will soon begin to think of you as that "famous" donkey breeder so and so. And you know, that no matter how wonderful your animals are, if they aren't "hyped" a bit, nobody will know, and if they do know, they won't believe it. So take ads in your local club's newsletter, in THE BRAYER and other magazines. And, if you are smart you will have a small display ad (or business card) made up and ask the other club newsletters if they will accept it also, all the time, all year long.

Be sure you have business cards made up. They usually average around $20 for for a thousand of basix design, and you can spread them around lavishly, as well as using them for ad copy. Be sure when you make them up ask the printer if they will print well as camera ready copy, as you wish to use them as ad copy for newsletters. Some colors of paper and some photos and cuts don't work as well as others. A business card ad in THE BRAYER for instance is only $48.00 a year (as of 1999), a real bargain for keeping your face in front of the public all the time, and the same goes for the other publications mentioned. They reach YOUR people, but the prices for ads are not high.

If you reach a point in time, where you have a lot of foals to sell at one time you may want to take out more far reaching ads. Ads in local and city papers near you as well as in horse magazines help. You may want to use national horse magazines such as the WESTERN HORSEMAN, or state type horse magazines, or your state horsemen's association magazine or newsletter. In all of them, assert the QUALITY of your animals, and if you can put registered, and some suggested uses in the ad it will sell them much better. If people just want a burro for a pet they may adopt a wild one, but if they want a quality animal with breeding, registration and hopefully a pedigree, they will choose yours if your ad is convincing.

One of the best market creators for donkey people is to start a regional or local showing club. This isn't as hard as it sounds and it is incredible how donkey sales go up when people know they can SHOW AND USE their donkeys! This really cannot be emphasized enough, and we hope a word to the wise is sufficient. If people can actually win blue ribbons with their donkeys, they buy more and better ones and start promoting them themselves. When new breeders start the established breeder of good stock is there to supply them, and you won't suffer from new breeders, as long as you educate them about quality stock, and promote that local club! Even a show once a year is better than nothing, but a series of 4 shows with a year end high point award does WONDERS for the donkey business!

Also, get out and show yourself locally. Have a wagon, or cart made up with advertising for your place on it and show your donkeys to people in parades in towns around you. If you get out and do these things with registered donkeys you can also earn hall of fame points at the same time. If you ever get a hall of fame donkey on your place it will be wonderful advertising - such as **Triple D Donkey Farm: Home of "Lester"- Hall of Fame Versatility Champion Donkey** - or some such. If your animals win such awards or classes in shows, keep track of them and use them in your advertising - don't just forget it after you hang up the ribbon or dust the trophy. The more you take your donkeys to public functions in the area and make it known (TASTEFULLY PLEASE) where they come from, the more buyers in your local area will appear. However, if you use show titles won (Champion High-point All-Around....) make sure they are accurate! People can and will call to check on this, as it is important to some but not to others.

CASTRATION

Castration of male equines is so routine that it is often passed over with a simple mention. However for beginners it merits a word of explanation. If you are uncertain whether to geld your young jack, please read the section on handling uncastrated jacks before you decide.

Age: Donkeys are best if not left to develop a thick neck, so castration may be done at any age. Sometimes the testicles are descended for a few days after birth, and the vet may be able to do it at this time - sometimes not. If he can, this is ideal. Later the testicles will retract, only to "drop" again later when the animal is older. This can happen as early as 1 month or as late as 2 years. These are extremes of course. From personal experience we can say that if they haven't dropped by the age of 18 months, have the animal checked. One of our young jacks had a retained testicle which was up in his abdominal cavity. This had to be removed surgically which was more than twice the expense - but if it had not he would have been what horsemen call "proud cut" (which simply means some of the hormone producing tissue is left somehow) and would have acted like a jack with no ability to breed for the rest of his life! A highly undesirable proposition!

Studies have shown that if the testicles have not descended and stay down at most times by age two, the inguinal ring (the band of muscular tissue that keeps the testicles down and away from the heat of the body) will close up. If the testicles are not dropped, they will no longer be able to after the ring closes. Cold weather is of course, not a good indicator of whether they are down are up - the animal can retract them up closer to the body for warmth! But if you don't see them if you casually check (while he is eating, playing, etc), then you need to check several days out of a week, for several weeks, to see if they are dropped.

Please have a qualified veterinarian castrate your animal. The expense for a normal castration is not great, usually under $100.00 (average is $75.00) , and the safety factor is much greater. It is cheaper if done at the vet's office, but can be done at home also.

When you get your colt home the vet will show you the surgical wounds. Ask him for specific treatment instructions. You may be distressed at first because the wounds are left open for drainage and really look large and gaping! The best way to examine is to stand behind the animal (carefully) and look through his back legs, if possible partly lifting one leg which will open the wounds for examination. A good reason for having your animal well trained and tame if at all possible.

Many people have their own treatments, diluted peroxide wash is good - but we have found that a commercial wound spray (check the brand with your vet) used once a day works fine. Also if their are flies be sure to spray AROUND, the wound not on it, with a good quality commercial fly repellant and use a wound spray to protect the wound. It is best if gelding can be done when there are not any flies around, but it is not always possible. It may take 2 to 3 weeks before most of the healing is accomplished. If the animal walks normally and eats you have few worries. If he seems very stiff, refuses to move unless he has to, goes off his feed - CALL THE VET IMMEDIATELY. It is probably nothing much, but it may be infection, which is very dangerous.

It is up to your vet whether or not he does a standing castration, or puts the animal under a general anesthetic. Whichever way, the dosages for anesthetic are still determined by body weight. Don't let the vet tell you the procedures are different because you are dealing with a donkey instead of a horse. Donkeys are still equines and not alien creatures!

LIGATION

The consulting vets of the ADMS recommend only one thing differing from horse castrations. The blood vessels in the jack tend not to constrict as well as in the horse. The tool used in castration, the emasculator, crimps, and then cuts the cords and vessels. For some reason, about one in a hundred castrations is on a jack that bleeds heavily. Sometimes they are young, others are older. To prevent the episode of a bleeder, **have your vet tie off the blood vessels** while he has them in hand. Most vets are reluctant to do this - and they are the lucky ones who have never encountered a bleeder jack. Those who have seen what can happen will be far less inclined to argue.

It takes only a moment longer, and a short bit of surgical silk. The alternative is having to use a general anesthetic to put the jack back down, go fishing for the bleeder vessels, and tie them off anyway.

A BLEEDER CASE IN POINT

From Leah: We had a bit of a horror story when we took our donkey colt, Rabbit, and our mule colt Curly, in to be gelded. Both were about 12 months old. The vet had no problems with Curly - he did a standing castration, and it was his practice anyway to put clamps on the vessels. Curly dripped for a while, but recovered just fine.

Rabbit, however, was a bleeder. After 45 minutes in clamps and still dripping, we were starting to get alarmed, and were suggesting the vet do something ELSE to help the donkey. The amount of blood the poor guy lost was alarming to us, and we were afraid it was going to get desperate soon. After over an hour, the vet finally agreed he had to go back in and tie off. This meant leading the staggering little fellow out onto the grass, laying him out, fishing around, and tying off. After all that, Rabbit decided he'd just as soon not get up. Can you blame him? The blood pooled where he had been standing was substantial - don't let your colts go through this. Show this chapter to your vet and insist he tie off. If he refuses - talk to another vet. Hopefully you will never have to go through this kind of nail-biting, edge of panic feeling at seeing this happen to your animals!

"*Lucifer*" (aka *Lickety Split)* is a fabulous Mammoth Gelding. He is a top performance donkey in the South and many times over a Champion. He is ridden by youth and adults alike, and is the perfect example of what a good gelding can achieve! *Lucifer* is owned by the Teel Family of College Station, TX

Training The Donkey

CHAPTER FIVE

AN INTRODUCTION

It is our philosophy that a donkey can do anything a horse his size can do if properly trained and conditioned. He probably will not, however, do it in exactly the same way. The conformation and temperament of the donkey are considerably different, but if properly bred, nourished, trained and cared for, donkeys can be excellent riding and driving animals.

In this book we present some general principles, specific methods and a few individual tricks. It must be emphasized that there are as many ways to train as there are trainers! Experienced trainers have their own methods and short cuts. This book is intended for beginners with donkeys and for people who have little or no experience in training them, even though they may have trained horses. If some of the methods go against ones you have previously used with success, by all means use your own knowledge and tricks! You will learn to use these suggestions as a basis for developing your own training methods.

Please keep in mind that donkeys are extremely individual animals. What is a problem for one is simple for another. What is a vice in one, may be a virtue in another. When training your donkey, use this book for a guide, but put your own common sense to work at all times, and if necessary, think something out and devise your own method. If you are PATIENT, KIND AND FIRM, your donkey will stand for a lot of improvisation and probably enjoy it. Remember a donkey that loves and trusts you will actually like the attention you give him in training and will strive to do his best most of the time.

Contrary to what a horseman will tell you, you can and should make a pet of the donkey you are training, both before, and while you do the training. The crucial problem here is that he must NOT be a spoiled pet! Love and discipline go together, and he should be a properly disciplined pet.

Let us compare your donkey or any animal you may set out to train, to a child. A child who feels confident in your presence, whom you comfort if it is in pain or afraid, who knows you are on his side, and who loves you and receives love in return, both physical and mental is a happy and cooperative child. He understands the rules you have made and knows he will be brought up short if he breaks them and will be allowed freedom if he does not. An undisciplined child or donkey is an unhappy and insecure child or donkey - even if it does not show in an obvious manner. The happiest people or animals are those that have the security of knowing what is right, and what is wrong, and who know that if they obey the rules they will be treated fairly. Now, punishment does have a small part in discipline, but in reality it plays a small part if discipline starts early and continues in a human and sensible manner. Both children and donkeys will continue to test you and your rules as a part of their growth, and you must be prepared to go to the lengths necessary to enforce them, but no farther!

Unlike children, disciplining donkeys usually means having some way of controlling the physical actions of the animal. You ideally should stop bad behavior before or just at the time it begins. For instance, if your donkey lays back his ears, glances behind and threatens to kick the animal behind him, a timely jerk on the halter may stop the bad action while it is still in the planning stage. This is far better for discipline than punishing after the act. If however, the animal gets his kick in, he must be smacked sharply on the legs which hurts enough to get the point across without causing damage. If you are going to discipline you must do it THE SECOND THE BAD ACTION HAPPENS!!! This cannot be stressed enough. Animals are not good at associating acts with results and even a few seconds later he will not associate punishment with the crime. Punishment must come almost simultaneously or you are simply being cruel and hurting an animal for no reason it can understand and it will simply resent you for it. Wait for the next time and be sharper, punish it as soon as it happens, or actively prevent it happening. One well-placed and firm, loud smack is worth a hundred late taps.

Use your voice all the time. Donkeys are very sensitive to the human voice and learn voice commands for many thanks. Never underestimate the voice for punishment or reward in animal training. A donkey will soon learn your "love" voice and your "angry" voice.

CUES and AIDS

One thing you need to be familiar with are Cues, and Aids. Both are used in training, and in riding, but they are different things. Cues are some sort of signal, visual, through the reins, a clicker, a voice command, that the animal will make a response to - a cue makes the animal use the brain. An Aid is an implement used to produce a cue - your voice is an aid, your leg, the halter, a crop. You may have heard the term - "Between the Aids and On the Bit" - meaning the animal is collected and balanced between the bit (an aid) and your leg (an aid). You may have your animal collected, between the aids, and then give the vocal and pressure Cue (clicking and touching your heel to the side) to move on. Both Cues and Aids are essential to training, regardless of the method of training you use. The newly revived fashion of "Horse Whisperers" rely on the cues given by the animal, while using visual body cues themselves, and the aids of a whip and/or long rope as an extension of the hand and body.

Meredith Hodges, well known author and trainer, and her jack *Little Jack Horner* demonstrate that Donkeys CAN do dressage!

TRAINING THE FOAL

CARE OF THE DONKEY AT THIS STAGE

Keep in mind that no animal can perform properly unless it is properly nourished and in an optimum physical condition. With this in mind, start conditioning your foal before it is born. Feed the jennet hay, good quality grain ration and plenty of free choice salt. Pick out a supplement recommended for pregnant mares with the proper balance of vitamins and minerals and feed according to weight. Be sure she has plenty of clean, fresh water at all times. If she can get grass that would be ideal. Make sure she doesn't get too fat and see that she takes plenty of exercise. Do not work her too hard during her last trimester. Keep her feet trimmed and keep her on a suitable worming program for a pregnant jennet. After the foal is born, supplement its milk with a grain mixture made especially for foals (these come in grain and pellet form). Take proper care of its physical surroundings to prevent injury from fences, trash, other animals, disease, weather etc. Watch the jennet to make sure she is milking well. She needs more feed while milking than she did while pregnant and plenty of clean fresh water to make all that milk. Be absolutely sure from early foalhood on that you do not OVER FEED OR OVER SUPPLEMENT the foal. You can simply destroy a good foal by feeding him tremendous amounts of rich feed. Current research recommends feeding a foal a high protein balanced feed, good hay and mothers milk in moderation only according to age and weight and NO more. This is true throughout the growing period. A surfeit of rich feed in an attempt to make foals and youngstock grow faster causes serious imbalances in their body and serious damage to growing bones and joints. FEED YOUR FOAL AND YOUNG DONKEY ALL IT NEEDS **BUT NO MORE**!

BUILD TRUST

Remember, when you approach any donkey for the first time, that your first task is to build a relationship - to establish ties. Then, you build slowly, step by step, using that good relationship to TEACH the donkey, not force it to your will. If you have a setback in training, just forget it. Do not think it is the end of the world. Go back to a place that you both understand well. Then start again allowing you both a little rest and calming down time. Also don't fall into the "I've got to make him do it" trap. This is very easy to do, and completely untrue. Instead of forcing the donkey to do a difficult or frightening thing all at once, go at it a little at a time. Sometimes added maturity is needed and will solve the problem almost by itself - so go slow and careful on these things. I am sure that my harshly forcing one of our donkeys to cross a white curb as a youngster implanted a fear of curbs in her that still endures today. If I had not fallen into the "make him do it" trap she could have been led to lose her fear of curbs with greater maturity and more experience of them. Remember, the donkey CANNOT READ YOUR MIND, so don't expect him to do so - that is truly cruelty. Also, please do not give your donkey, or any other animal, credit for human motivations and reasoning. He reasons, but it is donkey reasoning not human, so don't penalize him with that type of muddy thinking on your part. Keep in mind that donkeys act for very simple reasons, food, avoidance of discomfort, desire to please you, etc. Work from the point of view of the donkey, get "into his mind" if you can, and your training will be more successful.

TRAINING THE FOAL: EQUIPMENT

10 to 15 ft. soft rope, home made or commercial, well fitting foal halter (see the chapter on Equipment, halter fitting)

If you have a secure place to work with your jennet and foal it will make training easier. A box stall or closeable shelter is best. A large open pasture is just about the worst. If you have a foal it needs shelter from the weather so you might consider fencing off a corner of the pasture and building a shed. Be sure the small area is kept clean and sanitary.

The first thing to keep in mind when handling a young donkey from birth to 4 years is that you are dealing here with children. They can be very playful and will probably try to treat you like a donkey playmate by kicking or biting or rearing at you. This is not a vice, but cannot be allowed after a certain point. Until you are able to catch, halter and control the foal you just have to try to avoid its antics and discipline it with a loud "NO". Do not use physical violence on a foal. For example; if the foal or young donkey nips at you, which is a natural thing for him to do, do not slap him. Instead, grab his upper lip with your fingers and pinch it, meanwhile saying "NO". If you can do that when he bites, he will soon learn not to. If the foal rears at you, give it an unbalancing push on the shoulder, making it stagger but not fall, (too dangerous) meanwhile saying "NO" again. Rearing won't last long that way. (Just remember that is a natural play behavior, and a stronger tendency in jack foals that in jennets.) Kicking has to be avoided when the animal is loose, but the "no" command doesn't hurt.

Just do NOT make the mistake of encouraging any of this "cute" behavior. It may not hurt other donkeys but it sure can hurt people, and especially children. Watch the dam and foal--she disciplines him when he bothers her too much. She usually will bite him across the tops of his front legs. This is a good place for a small switch to be used on youngstock as it mimics the mother's discipline practices--slightly if necessary--don't beat him. Also, boys will be boys, and until you have the jack gelded (as early as possible will be fine with donkeys - the sooner the better) he will be rougher than a jennet.

THE FIRST STEPS

To begin training the foal you need a physical and mental relationship. If you are able to lift the foal and carry it around at first this will be a big help. It knows then that you can control it and even lift it off its feet but will not hurt it. If the foal has grown too big to carry, try to ease up to it, perhaps while the jennet is eating or tied up. If it is newborn be careful because for the first two or three days, many perfectly gently jennets turn into tigers because of the many hormones in their blood and will really fight and even injure you or the foal to "protect" it. Keep one hand behind the rump and the other in front of its chest to restrain the foal. Try to get it to allow you to pet every part of its body, including between its legs, under its tail, belly and legs. Find its favorite "itch spots" and scratch them. Two favorites are the top of the rump just where the tail joins on and backs of the thighs. Another may be gently rubbing the inside of the ears. This especially will come in hand later - it will help make your donkey less ear shy if you start with ears early.

When the foal is a week or two old, and used to being handled, fit a small, well fitting halter with a long soft rope onto the foal. Now you can use the halter to restrain the foal for petting. If at this time you can get him to let you lift his feet without a gigantic struggle you will have taken a giant step. You should have been handling the feet while he was small, but restraint with halter is somewhat different. At first it will scare him so restrain him with your hands as well until he calms down and gets used to that nasty feeling thing on his head. Be careful to not lift the feet too high or throw him off balance and scare him. You want him to feel safe on three feet. A foal that will allow its feet to be freely handled is almost never a kicker later in life.

Once the foal will stand still to be petted and handled all over, you can begin teaching him to lead. Remember, he doesn't have the foggiest idea what you want, and besides he doesn't want to follow you--he isn't too good about following his mother when she wants him to-she would tell you that he is a naughty boy about that and much too independent for a staid old jenny to put up with! Your task is to teach him that he can, should and will, follow you on command. Halter him and see if you can get him to take a few steps--perhaps following his mom. Stop, and scratch his favorite spot and tell him what a good boy he is. Have your beginning leading lessons inside a small enclosure---the sight of freedom may make him try to run and start a fight that is not good for either of you.

Have a helper lead his mother a few steps at a time and you follow her with the foal. When he tries to go off in another direction you will appreciate the small enclosure you are in, and you can restrain him as gently as possible. The first few days, when he fights, stop his mother and him and soothe him by talking, scratching and perhaps letting him nurse. The idea is to be persistent but not to tire him by more than a few minutes twice a day with these lessons. Small foals are only babies and they tire easily both mentally and physically. When he is following his mother well under halter restraint you may repeat the lessons outside. When he is calm in the wide open spaces you will have to try to lead him for longer and longer distances. At first lead the dam away and bring him up to her, later lead him even a few steps away and then make it longer and longer distances. If he will tolerate having mom shut up in a stall for awhile it will work even better, but some foals and dams just have to see each other very minute or they get too upset. You may have to put a long, soft rope around his haunches (not under his tail) to get him to come along, but only for the first few times, please. If you must use it all the time, he will become reliant on the butt rope and not move willingly without it.

Be sure that the foal halter fits reasonably well. Many breeders do not keep a lot of different foal halters around, but you may be able to borrow one that fits. Donkey foals have larger noses and deeper jaws that horse foals. Use a soft nylon halter if possible, it is easier to make adjustments. The crown piece (the piece that buckles behind the ear) should be snug enough not to slip down on the neck. If it skips down, it can apply pressure on the nerves of the neck due the the way the vertebrae are placed in the neck structure.

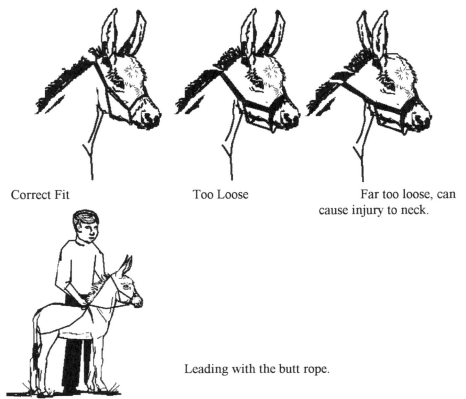

Correct Fit   Too Loose   Far too loose, can
                                                            cause injury to neck.

Leading with the butt rope.

You may need an assistant at any time so be sure to have one handy. Sometimes the foal may try to run sideways or in front instead of pulling back. Brace yourself and stop him at the end of the rope as gently as you can. Make him turn around and face you (give you his head) then walk up to him hand over hand of the rope, stand next to his shoulder, face front and try again. NEVER LEAD BY GETTING AHEAD AND PULLING, stand by the side of the neck and lead that way. Only get ahead to lead in an emergency or tight spot. If you can stay up close when he misbehaves, you will do better than letting him fish around on the end of the line. Putting an arm around his neck when he settles will help to calm him down, too. His mamma would cuddle him up like this with her head, and he will feel less inclined to struggle and jump around.

Standing in front and pulling will cause the donkey to set back on the rope.

Never stop a lesson on a bad note if you can possibly help it. Have the donkey do something right even if it was not what you were trying to teach him before you put him away. Also if you think you are losing your temper--STOP right there, you can't train animals if you are not in full command of yourself!

When you have the foal leading well, teach him to stop each time you say "whoa". You just cannot teach this too soon. All donkeys should know the meaning of the word and have it ground into their reflexes so much that they will stop automatically upon hearing it. Never use it to mean anything but a full stop. You can now teach the foal to stop on command, stand fairly still for a short time, turn right and left, lead in patterns such as figure eight's and to back up. At this age it is easy to accomplish backing with hand pressure on the chest and nose pressure on the halter. If he gets used to backing during his first leading lessons you will have less trouble teaching it later.

Work with the foal only about 15 minutes once or twice a day and don't neglect his mom, she may get jealous. When teaching anything use appropriate voice signals. Short and firm for WHOA, sharper perhaps for BACK and drawn out and soothing for WAAALK. Any voice cue will do as long as it is consistent and the donkey hears it every time. Later add the cue for trot and canter. Your donkey will understand a surprisingly large vocabulary of these signals as long as you are consistent with them. They will make training easier for both of you!

From foaling to the end of the donkey's second year is the optimum time to teach him all the important basics of ground work. These are the building blocks upon which stand the rest of the training, so at any age, this work is very important. It is also important in itself since it is used in showing and in any basic everyday handling of the donkey.

Using a "butt rope" on a foal and help him move forward when asked. Always lead from the head and shoulder of the animal.

WORKING THE YEARLING

CARE

Your donkey should be on a prescribed worming program, and probably will be wormed at weaning time at 4-6 months. Put it on a balanced mixed feed with vitamins and minerals included - or on oats, hay and a supplement. Of course the donkey should have hay or grass with its grain at all times. If he is not gelded and is ready by all means have it done at this time. Unlike horses donkeys do not have to wait to "develop", they can be gelded as early as they are ready. ("Developing" in horses refers to letting the male get some muscling up through the chest and neck. Some feel early castration in horses makes geldings that look feminine, others feel it makes no difference in age, it's just the genetics for that animal. Donkeys don't develop arched crests, so it makes no difference if you leave him entire longer in regards to his muscling.) If you do have a male, and he is not gelded, this next year will be harder on both of you. Keep his feet trimmed level and at a proper length. If you want them rasped between farrier's visits ask him to show you how. Be sure the feet are kept properly at this age so that the legs will grow as straight and strong as possible.

TRAINING THE YEARLING: EQUIPMENT

1 standard, flat nylon halter. The kind that is put together with rings, not a rope halter.

1 Standard flat nylon lead line or braided cotton lead with chain end.

1 very strong, unbreakable rope lead, at least 10 ft. long.

1 long buggy whip, or slender stick of the same general length.

Close-fitting leather gloves (like driving gloves) - optional

A designated work area. A corral, arena or breaking pen is best of course, but you can make up a ring with barrels, or other obstacles if you need to. He will soon understand that this is the place to work in.

If you have been training your donkey since it was born, further work will simply be a natural extension of previous work. If not, you must cover all the previous steps before you can go on to the ones mentioned below. Older donkeys or Wild Burros, can be harder to deal with than foals because of their increased strength and independence.

To start, get the animal tame, so that it will eat our of your hand, and hopefully let you pet it. Somehow, get a well fitting strong halter on and leave it on if it can be done safely (*see the chapter on equipment) , so that you don't have to wrestle with that each time you want to work with your youngster. For this period try your best to have the donkey in a small enclosure, preferably away from other donkeys, because if he is in a large pasture he will be able to stay quite wild.

Follow the directions on teaching to stand tied and break the yearling to stand. Then start petting it slowly and bit by bit, until it will finally allow you to pet it all over its body. Do not skimp on this lesson because you are setting up trust. If it fights your hand to a dangerous degree, pet it with a stick or some object (really and truly, we used to use a new, clean toilet-brush, as it has rough bristles you can rub with, and a handle for extending your reach...) , but make it a good experience - not a bad one, you are getting the animal to be unafraid of being handled - you can progress from the stick to the hand when the donkey is calmer. If it will eat while you do this so much the better, but a really frightened one will not.

If the donkey is very wild just have it stand there with feed in front of it - for an hour or so each day while you walk around it, work around it, etc. but don't do scary things, talk quietly to it all the time and show it by example that it has nothing to be afraid of. Go to it about every 5 minutes and talk to it and try to pet it. Do this until you can get to the petting all over stage and the donkey stays calm and friendly. This may take one day or one month, depending on whether you have a gentle, hand raised weanling or a wild burro, or something in between.

When the donkey will let you pet it all over you and an assistant must teach it to lead and obey the signals given by halter and lead rope. You use the same general technique as you did for the foal but you have to be more strong and resolute. The rump rope will help some, but there will probably be a lot of heel digging and stopping at the end of the rope before he learns to "give you his head".

When you finally have him gentle, and leading more or less as the case may be, you may proceed to the next steps.

The worst problem for the home trainer is if the yearling has his mother or his friends in the pasture with him. There are extremely strong emotional ties between donkeys, and getting the donkey to concentrate on his lessons instead of his friends will probably take about half your lesson time at first. If he can be kept alone, or with animals he is not too fond of at this time it will make your work much easier. If this is impossible, be firm about taking him away from them. Even if you don't have time for a lesson try to lead him away from them every day and keep him away for at least a few minutes. He will finally catch on that he has to do this thing in life, and will begin to be more cooperative. He should always be taken out of sight (if not out of earshot) of his friends and on no account worked in his home pasture. Your work-spot should always be a place where the donkey is not usually found. It might be a good lesson-time for him mom as well - she gets to stand tied outside your work pen (use a safety knot) or work elsewhere with someone else while you work with Junior.

One requirement of training at this stage is a designated area that both you and the donkey know is a work area. We do not have a fenced training ring here, but we have had remarkable success by creating a "closed" space by setting up large oil drums and garbage cans at long intervals in our field. They do nothing at all to physically hold the donkey in, but after he knows the area they seem to have a strong psychological effect. You should choose a "gate" on the end that is away from the donkey's home and always enter and exit there, When you end work in any arena, stop for a few seconds at the far end. Then walk calmly to the gate and out, never stop next to the gate, then turn and go out, that is asking for bad trouble!

When leading, always lead from a position beside the neck of the animal. The traditional side is the left one, but all animals should learn to do everything from both sides. Always face ahead, look where you are going and step out as though you meant to get there. Don't stare at the donkey and walk backwards or sideways! It looks terrible, has a bad effect on the animal, is incorrect and DOES NOT WORK! You should lead from a point about the middle of the neck between the head and shoulders. The only time you should go ahead and lead is in an emergency or a tight situation.

To get the donkey to walk briskly, on a loose lead, beside the handler, you can use the buggy whip or long stick. If your donkey, is leading, though erratically, he needs to become smooth. If he is just in the first stages of being taught to lead properly this is also the technique that will prove most helpful.

If your animal is very headstrong at this age about pulling away or running ahead you may have to run the chain on the lead strap from its clipped position on the right UPPER ring of the halter, through the right noseband ring, under his chin, and out through the left noseband ring and thence to your hand. This is a good disciplinary and control method but must be used with humanity and discretion, and you should check to see that the chain is loose again after you have had to tighten up on it. Do not use this

Getting in front of a reluctant animal and dragging will only result in the donkey propping back and a tug-of war ensues. You could drag a smaller animal, but you are only training it to resist.

method unless you have to, but it may come in handy under many circumstances, especially with a jack or a pushy donkey of any sex or age.

Lead your donkey from the left side (the Near side) , just behind the head area. It is customary to work with equines from the left side, but after your donkey is leading well, accustom him to be led from the right side (the off side), mounted from the right, etc. It is no fun to be on a narrow mountain precipice with an animal that cannot be mounted or led from either side! (Other places too are narrow and troublesome - not just mountains!) To start the donkey with the leading training method, stand in proper leading position facing front, don't stare at the donkey. Hold the lead close to the head in your right, and fold the excess lead in your left, with the whip. Hold the buggy whip so that it is stretching out behind you toward the donkey's rump. This is so that you will be able to sneakily tap him with it, while looking innocently ahead. The less he associates you with the whip the better - so act accordingly. NEVER wrap the lead around either hand, and DO NOT loop your fingers into a chain!!! You may end up with serious rope burn, crushed, or missing fingers!!!!

People HAVE been seriously dragged when they wrapped lead ropes, lunge lines, or reins around their hands. It just should not be done. One may think you have a firmer grip and can keep a hold of the animal if they bolt, but you are more likely to lose your balance, definitely some skin, and possibly more (teeth, fingers, etc) if you hit the ground and he's running. You can try one method of BRACING the rope if you practice with a human volunteer so you understand the principle. Hold the lead as usual with the right hand. Take the lead behind you across your own rump. Hold the excess lead folded in your left hand.

Now if he starts to run, gets around in front of you, you can sit back a bit and keep your feet under you. Instead of being out at arms length, you have a better maintenance of the rope. If, though, you cannot keep safely onto the rope, turn AWAY FROM the donkey as you DROP IT. The excess lead will fall to the ground, and you can then recapture the animal. It's not worth being yanked off-balance and injured trying to hold a real fighter. Just be sure not to use a very long line when using this technique, or the whipping line may still wrap around your legs. If you have problems coordinating this technique - then DO NOT TRY IT with the animal.

Properly leading at the shoulder, lead rope folded and not wrapped. The whip is used as an extension of the hand. You might consider sturdier shoes instead of tennis shoes to protect your feet from a wayward hoof .

You may need an assistant to start the donkey moving the first few times. The idea is to teach him to walk briskly along beside you. Every time he pulls back or slows down, TAKE A STEP OR TWO BACKWARDS, towards his rump, and tap him with the whip. You may have to walk backwards all over the place with some donkeys but never step out front and pull! Just stop and start over if necessary, after scratching his special spot and soothing him with your voice. Try not to make a war out of this, after all you are teaching, not forcing. The idea of all this is to make the locomotion come from the hindquarters instead of dragging him along on his front feet. If you ever want to train a donkey to be stubborn, just get out in front on the rope, face him and haul!

Don't Drag!   Face the same as the donkey.   Tap &cue,   and step out!

This facing ahead and walking backwards when necessary method will finally give a brisk, willing walk with the animal looking collected and alert, not strung out and pulling back. When he is fully trained with this method you will have the additional advantage of the "step back". That is, when he slows down or tries to pull back for some reason, all you have to do is take a step or two backward even if you don't have a whip or stick, and he will automatically move forward faster. In the show ring for instance this is almost unnoticeable, where if you pull it will look really terrible! This method works on all donkeys from Miniature to Mammoth and is more psychological than physical. However you must explain the step back to strangers who are going to lead him because ignorant people (and that includes many horse owners) always tend to step ahead and pull, which will slow the donkey, not make it move faster.

Another good reason to use the step back method on youngstock, is that pulling on the neck time and again could possibly cause damage to the neck. You might watch them pull back and set back when tied, but they will soon pop forward and quit pulling. A person pulling and heaving on the other end of the rope might not quit when it begins to hurt, or might just get the rope pulled through their hands (which if you don't have gloves on could be painful!).

This method will take a while with some animals and be almost instantaneous with others. but in any case just persevere and be patient. Sooner or later you will come out the winner. When the donkey has caught on to what is wanted work more and more on walking at a brisk gait on a loose lead, and stopping just as briskly on the common "whoa". Saying his name in a low voice before any command is a good idea, as it will give him a cue so he has time to get all four legs and a big body ready to perform your command. Remember, you already know what you are going to say, but it takes him by surprise! You don't have to yell your cues and commands, he has big ears!

If he tries to go too fast, tell him to walk in a soothing, long drawn out tone. Gently bumping on the line to get his attention is better than a solid pressure or a sharp jerk. At first only practice on straight lines (turning him away not towards you at the end) and large circles. Then go to figure eights, various patterns etc. Eventually try to teach him to stop and turn almost on his haunches and go directly back the other day, first at a walk, later at a trot. This is what most judges will ask you to do in the show ring in halter classes.

TEACHING TO STAND TIED

Standing tied with patience is the first lesson your donkey should learn when he is a weanling, but it may be taught along with the walking and trotting lessons. If you have a gentle animal he may learn it with no special effort on your part, but you probably will need to teach most donkeys. One of our colts was taught by the simple expedient of tying him when he ate. He was close but outside the fence to the other donkeys. By feeding him and then leaving him tied for varying amounts of time, he was able to get used to the idea by degrees. Then we started feeding him farther and farther away, until finally we worked up to feeding him out of sight of his friends. It worked quite well, and is a good example of the gradual, "coaxing" method of training.

It is extremely inconvenient and dangerous to have a donkey that will not stand tied for any length of time without pulling back and breaking or fighting the rope. There are two main methods for teaching, both of which may have to be used if you can't use a gradual method from foalhood, but the gentle one is preferred where possible.

Take the young animal, making sure the halter, lead rope and rope snap are too strong for him to break and tie him to a tree or post with no dangerous obstructions around it, by means of passing the rope around a time or two and holding the end so that you can let it go and get him loose immediately. When he gets restless let him loose, scratch and talk to him, lead him around and do it again. (But make sure you untie and release during a calm moment and not when he is prancing or fighting the rope. You may have to distract him from fighting in some way, but don't scare him into fighting worse. If he lets up for a moment, count ONE, move quietly in, praise and RELEASE.) If you do this frequently, for longer and longer periods, he should have the idea in about a week. Then tie him with a type of knot which you can undo instantly, but which will hold until you undo it. Tie him fairly short, as a long rope is dangerous and will cause more fighting than a short one, just make sure he is comfortable. Put his feed in front of him and walk away. From now on, take him out and tie him up to feed him. After he is through eating leave him tied for 5 or 10 minutes longer each time up to an hour. He may get impatient and fight the rope. If the halter, hardware, rope and post are unbreakable, he will soon learn it is not worth it and quit. Donkeys are very, very sensible animals, however, they are also very smart. If he does manage to get away from being tied by fighting the rope it will take many sessions with unbreakable ropes before he realizes he won't be able to do it ever time! You may talk to him and pet him during this waiting period, but don't do anything to upset him yet, like sacking or handling his feet. Most donkeys, young or old, will learn to stand tied with good manners by using this humane and fearless training.

If however, you get an older or wilder animal who just insists on pulling back and trying to break the rope you may have to use stronger methods. Tie the wilder animal with the usual unbreakable gear. Tie him short remember, as long ropes promote fighting. Then run a rope with a knot that will not tighten up around his belly at the girth area. This should be a soft cotton rope. Run it between his forelegs and fasten it to the post, up high. Make the tie rope on his halter a bit longer, so that when he runs back against it he comes up against the belly rope first. There may be some spectacular acrobatics so be ready, but about 3 lessons will teach most any donkey to stand tied patiently. They have a great facility for accepting what cannot be changed. Be ready with a SHARP knife to cut rope, and also tie both ropes to the post with a quick release knot. You can forgo the belly rope and just tie him hard and fast by the halter, but he could hurt his neck badly this way so be careful.

You should practice tying the quick-release knot over and over, before you start training. You should be able to do it quickly and correctly each time. You can use the "Breakaway" or panic snaps (like in trailer ties) as a permanent fixture to your tying rail, but know how to tie a quick release.

There are also some Houdini's of the donkey world who will learn how to pull the end and release that knot. A different method of tying must be used, but the animal should already have learned to stand tied quietly. He will untie the quick-release out of boredom, not by fighting. You can tie his rope back to his own halter ring (and there use the quick-release) but don't hard-tie an animal that is still in intensive training.

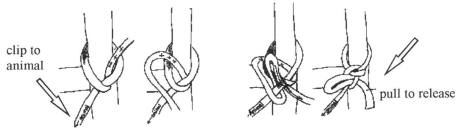

clip to animal

pull to release

GENTLING

If your donkey has not been previously handled from birth on, the time to start "gentling" him is when he has learned to patiently stand tied. You do this by getting him accustomed to being touched all over his body. To handle him, start with the neck and shoulder on a really wild donkey, or with his favorite scratch spots on a tame one. (usually the root of the tail and the backs of the thighs) Then bit by bit, and it may take days with a wild one, work your hand all over him, scratching and patting GENTLY, and talking in a soothing voice all the while. It won't hurt to give him treats to eat from your hand at this point if he will take them. Most really wild ones won't at first. If he objects at one place, go back to a place he is calm about and start again until he gives in and relaxes. In other words, just persevere and go at it slowly and a little at a time until you can touch him anywhere including inside his ears. Take special pains to stroke and pet his ears gently, because sensitive ears can cause a jumpy donkey. Normal donkeys love to be scratched gently on the inside of their ears with the flat of your finger, if however he has had his ears mistreated it may be very difficult to get enough trust to do this. It is important that he allow you to handle his ears however, so work on this as long as necessary.

HANDLING LEGS AND FEET

This is sort of a "special department" but the same tactics apply. Start by stroking down his legs, from the shoulder, down farther and farther. When he objects, go back up and start down again. Sooner or later you will get to his ankles. Work them over well so that he is unafraid of being touched anywhere on his legs. When you first try to pick up a foot, it will startle, even frighten the donkey. All equines feel safe when they have full control of their own feet, preferably with all four firmly on the ground. However, he must be made to understand that it has to be done and that it won't hurt him or make him feel completely insecure. To get an idea of what is involved in this venture, kneel down beside a small child and telling him to stand still and hold on to something, then try to pick up his foot! You will see for yourself that it isn't only donkeys that object! To pick up a hind foot, stand facing the tail at about the level of his leg. Run your left hand down the left leg, lean very slightly against him to put his balance on the other hoof and cupping the hoof in your hand lift it a few inches above the ground. Be sure when lifting feet that you notice in which direction legs do bend! Some people seem to think that donkey's legs bend in very odd places. Unless you bend the leg in exact line with nature's method of bending, you and the donkey are in for a lot of wasted effort and probably pain too.

When you can get the hoof off the ground just lift it longer and farther every day. If the hoof you start with is firmly planted in the ground try another one until you can at least get one up! It is probably easier to start with front hooves. If the donkey pulls a kicking spree the first few times you pick up his hind feet, and most of them will, just put it down firmly (preferably YOU put it down not him). But don't give up. Just keep at him until he becomes resigned to this ignoble treatment! If he really fights it and plenty of perseverance and patience won't do the trick it is time for that final lesson - that you INSIST. Get a farrier or a strong and accomplished horseman to come and hold that animated tootsie until he just gives up. This is perfectly possible and can even be done with big horses, but it takes someone who knows how and has the strength for it. The technique is to follow the kicking with your arm, not fight against it - but don't give up the hoof until the animal tires out. It may have to be done several times and on both feet but if the animal has been handled sufficiently before, and knows perfectly well you aren't planning to hurt it, then it will give in when it realizes that the "jig is up". Reinforce your control of the legs with voice commands - he should understand the meaning of "NO" by now. If you can get him to stop fighting or pulling for a moment when you command "No", then this is the time to wait a second past the stop, and then release. That's your positive moment.

One problem with animals that try and pull feet away and humans that hang onto them is usually the foot is extended out too far, or lifted past the balance point for the animal. Handlers think they can make the animal stand still be holding the leg stretched out, or by picking it up higher to "show who's boss". The usual result is causing the center of balance to go off to one side. Thus the donkey (or mule or horse!) will try to reclaim it's foot and also move the leg it is standing on to keep from falling over. Only lift the foot as high as needed, and be careful of the balance of the animal. Many people complain the donkey will lean on them - think about it - they are missing a leg, and you are standing in the place where the leg would be….and you become a literal "jack stand"!

When you finally have the donkey lifting his feet properly, clean them each day with a hoof pick and tap them with the handle to prepare him for the farrier. His first visit from the farrier will be a bit upsetting, and it is much better if he is prepared ahead of time. Better for him and better for the poor long suffering farrier who will probably resent having to trim a donkey because he has to bend over so much farther than he would with a horse.

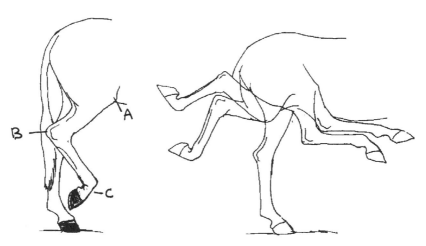

Observe where the leg bends. The parts of the leg are the same as your own! A. Your knee, B. Your heel C, the top of your toes! The leg has a limited range of motion, so don't try to pull it up too far. You will overbalance the animal or strain the leg.

BACKING

Each time you take him out for his lessons you must give him a short lesson in backing. Stop two or three times during the lesson and ask him to back. Use a different sounding vocal signal, meanwhile pushing on his chest with one hand and pushing back in a give and take motion on his halter with one hand. If you do this several times a day with a young donkey he should catch on. The trick is to use a series of short pushing motions, not a long steady pull. Watch a rider ask his horse or mule to back, and he will drop the reins low, use his seatbone to urge the animal back while using a give-and release motion on the reins. Use the same cues on the ground and you will be that much further when it comes to asking your donkey to back under saddle.

A trick that was given to me by an old time mule man should only be used on a tame donkey that refuses to back, but it is humane and works. Have the donkey in his usual harness or bridle. Blindfold him and take a blunt pencil and while an assistant reins him back (properly, in a give and take motion) tap, tap, tap, him with the blunt stick on the soft part of his nose. After 3 or 4 of these lessons you can do it a few times un-blindfolded and he will have caught on. If he ever refuses to back you have a lesson you can perform again to refresh his memory, all without hurting or scaring him in any way. When training to back, exert every effort to make him back in a straight line. Three steps in a straight line is better than ten in a zigzag one!!!! Backing on command is necessary in the show ring, and may save your bacon in an emergency so be sure every donkey is trained to do it well.

SHOW STANCE

One important aspect of ground training which is difficult for both animal and handler is the teaching of the donkey to take a show position and stay in it on command. Unless you are sure you will never show your donkey, he should learn at least the basics of this. Proper show stance for donkeys is: standing square on all four feet with the head up and alert. Ears are another matter and have to be left to chance most of the time. Your main problem will be getting the donkey to stand in a foursquare position for any length of time, as donkeys tend to get thoroughly bored in the show ring and want to relax. Experienced handlers say to set the back feet up first, then put the front ones in place. You can do this by actually picking them up and placing them, but the best method is to lift and pull front and sideways on the halter so he takes each set-up naturally. To change position, walk him forward, never back him because this causes a sway backed look. Work on getting him to set his back feet evenly apart, sraight down from his rump and flat on the ground. When he finally does this, hold him still with the halter and try to nudge his front feet into position with your feet or an assistant can help. You can also move his front feet by subtle halter pressure later when he is more used to this. Hold him there with the halter for a few seconds. When he looks like he is going to move despite you, move him yourself instead of letting him do it.

Try to think up another special command and sound for this exercise. After each try it is a good idea to do something else as it is a hard bit of concentration for both of you and a good reward afterwards is some brisk action. One day he will suddenly take the stance and hold it and you will probably faint and ruin the whole thing! Then of course, he will apparently forget how to do it for a full week, but don't let him bluff, donkeys are expert bluffers, you have him now! He knows what you want and practice makes perfect. Do not make him hold the position too long it is not natural. Even in the show ring only "set him up" when the judge gets to the animal next to you and is almost ready to look at your animal. Do not however, let him slump completely in the show ring, but don't keep him at a total pitch of alertness at all times, it would be nearly impossible.

TRAINING THE TWO YEAR OLD

During this third year of life the donkey should not be carrying any real weight on his back but he can work longer than he did as a yearling. Half an hour to 45 minutes a lesson is enough unless you are taking a relaxing walk or doing some other non-strenuous activity. You don't want to work him too hard, because besides "souring" him mentally you can cause him joint and muscle pain, as well as permanent damage to growing bones if you aren't careful.

CARE OF THE DONKEY

At this stage the donkey may need to have his grain stepped up. It is hard to say how much grain an individual may need. Go by the basic rule of 1/3-1/2 lb. for each 100 lbs. of body weight, and don't overestimate his weight, which many people tend to do. He should be in good flesh but not showing a big roll of fat or even a moderate one, and not too fat PLEASE! At this age he will become sort of gangly and "teen age" looking and may look the worst in his second and third years than he will ever look in his whole life. Do not despair, keep him in flesh but not too fat and close your eyes, a swan will develop out of your ugly duckling a bit later. If your grain ration does not have all the vitamins and minerals in it, give him a supplement, but do not overdo it, remember too much grain and too much supplementation are BAD FOR HIM! NOT GOOD!

LUNGE LINE TRAINING

Training on the lunge (long or longe) line can be very effective for donkeys. The donkey may tend to be a bit sluggish on the long line, or he may not, depending on character. Donkeys tend to see lunging as a "been there, done that, got nowhere" type of exercise and quit after they understand they are only working in a boring circle..... This type of training is not absolutely necessary, as you can go direct from ground to harness work, but the best trainers give it as their secret for turning out really superior donkeys, trained to do anything a horse can do. By lunging young donkeys, they can be taught to do all the basic gaits in a very efficient way. Once the donkey has been taught that he must do all three gaits, walk, trot and canter, he is much less sluggish about cantering and taking correct leads in the show ring, or on the trail. Also at maturity the unruly animal may be toned down a bit before riding or toned up a bit after a time of idleness with the longe line. You do not have to be an expert to teach an animal to work on the longe, but you must have patience and be willing to discipline both the animal and yourself. The lunge line is an exercise in discipline and in learning and should be approached as such.

Lunging is a procedure in which the donkey travels around the handler in a large circle on a long strap or line. Lunging can be started after weaning, but be careful not to let a young animal be injured by too much work or by being jerked off balance by the line. The major equipment needed is a halter, a long whip, a long line and halter lead shank. A special lunging cavesson is not necessary, but can be used if you find on that will fit your donkey. A well fitting halter to which the longe line can be attached on either side of the animal can be used by anyone. Web or nylon lines are desirable and inexpensive. They are lighter than rope or leather and can be bought as "lunging lines" at any equine supply store. Fly repellant spritzed at his shoulder or rump helps to keep the animal's attention on you. (So will a water spray bottle, and it is less expensive.) If you can lunge your animal in a small pen from which he cannot escape you will be much better off. If you don't have such a place, try to find a semi-enclosed space perhaps in a fence corner or some similar place.

If you are using a lunging cavesson, set your line to the top ring first, as it will lessen some degree of the tangling that is bound to occur as you start. As you progress, you can move the snap to one of the side rings. If you are using only a halter, you should run the line through the nearest side ring, under the jaw, out through the opposite side ring, and up to the jaw ring. You will reverse this when you reverse side. You can snap into the bottom ring if necessary, but it tends to twist the halter around the face.

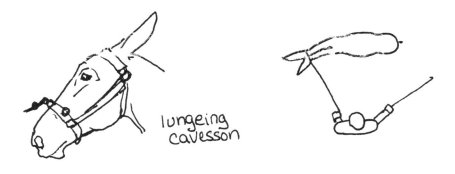

lungeing cavesson

Do not use a bridle to lunge in unless you are lunging a trained animal, and are experienced with training and lunging. If you must lunge in a bridle, you should never snap directly to the bit rings. (We are referring to a snaffle bridle here.) You should rig through the ring, under, out and up just as with the halter. Preferably, a halter should be placed over the brid¹e, and the line attached to the halter. If the animal pulls away (in fighting or even falling) you can seriously injure the mouth with direct bit pressure, or scare them and they will refuse to lunge in a bridle. To lunge in a halter over the bridle, take the reins over the head, twist them a few times, then put them back over the neck. Place the halter on over the bridle, so that the reins come out the back of the throatlatch. The reins will now stay over the neck and not slip down and cause a tripping hazard.

run up to browband or buckle

lunge

under chin & up through other side

The donkey should be leading well and be tractable and tame before being taught to lunge (or longe - we have to laugh, at times the spell-check has changed this word to Lounge - yep, donkeys would prefer to lounge!). Begin by walking in circles with the new equipment adjusted on him. Although expert trainers usually prefer to work alone, most beginners find an experienced assistant a big help in starting the training. The assistant works from the opposite side away from the trainer with a halter shank to help start and control the donkey. Most trainers prefer to start circling to the left, which allows them to handle the line with the right hand at first. The assistant should eventually release the shank from the halter and drop back while the trainer urges the donkey forward in a large circle. This maneuver is accomplished by keeping the donkey positioned between the longing line in front and the whip behind. After he has circled a few times, the trainer should start to drop away from his close position behind the shoulder, keeping the donkey moving forward by tapping the ground lightly with the whip. You will find that the regular long "longing whip" is much more suitable than the regular buggy whip for this. The lunge whip has a longer lash, the buggy whip has only a short lash and is supposed to reach to the shoulder of the animal when hitched. In lunging you may need those extra two feet of reach to urge the animal forward by touching it on the hocks with the lash.

The trainer should drop toward the rear of the donkey while the assistant falls back toward its shoulder. The assistant should take off the halter shank and gradually drop backward as the donkey continues walking forward. To keep the donkey moving forward, the trainer should stand by the donkeys left leg and hip as the circle is gradually made larger. Hold the whip near the hind legs of the donkey. If he stops ask him to move forward and hit the ground lightly with the whip. Be sure to use any voice commands he already knows from his ground training.

If the animal faces the trainer the process should start all over again, also the same applies if he panics and tries to run or get away. Donkeys that are tame will usually drive the trainer crazy by coming up to him and obviously asking, "what it is that you want me to do? - and wouldn't you rather pet me?" In this case, start all over again. The trainer should still make a small circle himself as the line feeds out. The whip is to be used to keep the donkey from stopping or closing the size of the circle. The donkey will have to learn to stop and stay, facing the way he is heading, on the perimeter of the circle. In later lessons he should stop in place on the perimeter until commanded to face inward and come to the trainer. If you have trouble with this point, walk to him instead. Do not allow the donkey to anticipate commands and make his own decisions. When the donkey is stopped, whether at the center or at the perimeter he should be taught to stand in place. Don't allow him to stop briefly and then come into the circle. If he is stopped on the perimeter make him stay there. Vary the amount of time he stands so he will not anticipate and move out too soon. Work the donkey in the opposite direction with the assistant. It is a good idea however not to dismiss the assistant too soon because you may need emergency help.

Enlarging the Circle: It sometimes helps to use the butt of a whip as you circle the donkey and drop away from his shoulder. If he tries to follow you as you move back, move him to the perimeter with the butt of the whip against his shoulder. Don't allow it to jab him in the ribs or flanks. Continue intimidating him as the size of the circle increases. This procedure should continue with the donkey increasing the perimeter of the circle and the trainer decreasing it, until the trainer is standing in one spot and the donkey is moving in a large circle around him. Some donkeys keep the line tighter than others. It is undesirable to keep a tight line or one that is so slack it drags the dirt. It should be just taut enough to feel the contact between you and the animal. Short pulls and releases should be used to restrain him. When the donkey is going in a large circle around the trainer with the correct tension on the line the trainer can stand in one place and effect the lesson with minimum effort.

Changing Direction: Change direction with the donkey by the same procedure. Many are definitely one-sided and you must work the weaker side more than the stronger side, although the temptation is to do the opposite. Donkeys are often frustrated with a direction change and may attempt to escape, run backwards or come in to you. Be patient and start again. Keep lessons short, 15 to 20 minutes, but stop on a positive note.

Potential Problem.: A donkey may want to run while being lunged. Use your voice to reassure him. Get him used to your voice for future riding lessons. When a donkey has confidence and know voice commands the trainer can often talk him out of unfavorable responses. If the donkey panics stay cool. A handler can jerk an animal sideways too sharply and possibly cause him to strain a leg or fall. For this reason, weanlings and yearlings are usually not allowed to canter on the line. If the ground is slick, do not longe. Getting the line tangled happens to everybody. The main thing is not to get it around your feet or body and not allow the donkey to get tangled in it. If something really goes wrong, it is best to let the line go altogether. Remember to teach the walk, trot and canter as well as backing, and remember PATIENCE ALWAYS!

What to do with the excess line? Always coil it up and hold it in your hand. Never let it get strung out on the ground beside you. Sooner or later, you will have it wound around you, and that's trouble. Don't wrap the lead - whether lunging or leading - around any part of your body. Always coil or fold excess line and hold it off the ground.

ASSORTED GROUND TRAINING TIPS

Clicker Training - Fashionable for dogs and Hollywood animal actors, clicker training can have a positive place in training equines. Find a good book on the subject at your local bookstore and see if it is for you. The basis of clicker training is to reward positive movements and behaviors, associating the good with the sound of the click. Stop on whoa, hear the click. Step forward when asked, click again. This can come in very handy with ground training, and later for more advanced training. If your colt understands "Stand up" means - stop fidgeting and stand still" - give the command when untied, and click to reward. When it is time to stand tied, he fidgets, shakes his head - you command "Stand up" - he does, you click, you release. Positive rewarding, less fuss, quicker understanding.

Gates: Do not let him barge through gates with, or ahead of you. Always make him stop, let you go first then come through and turn around to face you while you take your time shutting the gate. If he barges past you, crook your arm around his nose and brace your feet. Letting him run into that a few times will stop him. The flight response of a horse is "up and away", the donkey is "down and away". You will note he ducks before running. Take control of that downward movement and move it "in", to your advantage.

Circling: This is good discipline if a donkey is acting up, either in hand or under saddle. Make him turn in several very tight circles to either, or both sides. Then head him out briskly going straight. This is a method of many uses and comes in quite handy.

Outside Work: After your yearling is trained "in hand" so that you can control him, get him out of the work space. Take him for long walks into places that frighten him. Don't force him, just endeavor to show him everything you can think of and get him unafraid of them by experience. This is very important for your safety in later riding stages. Be sure he gets used to all kinds of traffic and is so unafraid that he will not shy away even from sirens, motorcycles, big trucks or screaming kids. These long walks are an essential part of the training and you will do this in harness and under saddle as well. Remember on these walks that the idea is to get him over his fears, not to force him into places he is afraid to go. Approach everything gently, but repeat and repeat until he loses his fear. Let him smell things and see them from different angles because an equine's fields of vision are different from yours and greatly depend on movement of the head and neck. He simply may not see what you do.

Halters: Do not turn your donkey out to pasture with the halter on if it is not absolutely necessary. It is dangerous. (See more about halters and Halter Turnout on page 109)

Smell: When you handle your donkey make sure your hands are clean. Smells he will hate are petroleum products, meat and perfume. Do not come to him smelling of horses if he is not used to them, and NEVER APPROACH A JACK IF YOU SMELL OF MARES, JENNETS OR A RIVAL JACK.

Stepping On Things: Give up on manhole covers, he has more sense and so should you! Donkeys are extremely cautious animals and have a great fear of stepping on strange things which might be dangerous. This includes water, and water may take a lot of work. It is very important to get him used, on your walks, to white lines, black spots, etc. on streets. Let him walk over shallow water at every opportunity, or make opportunities. One thing to remember, though, is no matter how much you school over an obstacle at home, it's different in the show-ring! It's not "his" blue tarp (even if you supplied the props for trail!) and many donkeys (and horses, and mules) will act as if they have never seen a tarp, or flowerbox, hula hoop ring, or sheet of plyboard in their life. Don't get mad, just sigh. It's part of owning a donkey.

Nipping: One good punishment for nipping is to grasp the upper lip and tweak or twist it firmly meanwhile saying "NO" sharply. After a while a normal donkey will give up. Youngstock and jacks are natural biters, older geldings and jennets rarely do this unless they are spoiled. NEVER DISCIPLINE OR CONTROL A DONKEY BY HOLDING HIS EARS!!!!!!!!!!!!!!!

Move Over: To teach your donkey to move over for grooming etc. tie him up and push his hindquarters over with your hands or the butt end of the whip while saying "over". He will probably push back to your hand and if he doesn't give in, use the end of a blunt stick or the whip. When he does move, praise him and he will soon catch on.

Weather: If the weather is oppressive, stormy, lightening or high winds just forget the training session for the day or make it short and simple. The same if the footing is slippery. And do not work him on ice, or you may frighten him of smooth surfaces forever. When he is mature, and used to it, is time enough.

Temper: If you are going to lose your temper, WALK AWAY IMMEDIATELY. Go kick a fence post or something. You can undo weeks and weeks of careful teaching if you lose your temper with your donkey so try your best not to. If he loses his, do some work which is calming and which he already knows how to do and after he does it well, quit for the day. There are bound to be some lessons which are difficult and make one or both of you mad, so take them in short and hopefully easy stages.

Punishment: Yes, sometimes he will have to have a quick, severe punishment, when you know that HE knows perfectly well he is doing wrong, and is testing you. When you must punish, you must do it that moment, and make it count. You aren't beating and abusing, this is not a whipping. A couple of sharp pops with the whip, on the quarters, body or legs as the case may be, but NEVER NEAR THE FACE OR EARS, will be enough for most donkeys. DO NOT punish by striking a bony part of the animal with your hand - you will hurt your hand far more than the animal, and if you don't strike quickly and MEAN it, they may take it as play. This is not time for a love tap - swat him and let him know he's WRONG. If he just took a chunk out of the right portion of your behind, are you going to shake your finger and scold, or pop him one so it won't happen again?

Early halter training is beneficial if you plan to show your future herdsire. This jack colt is only 2 months old, but stands quitely in the ring. Owned by Bess Jackstock.

TRAINING FOR HARNESS AND RIDING

STEP ONE — GROUND DRIVING

EQUIPMENT

Bridle with snaffle bit (may or may not have harness blinders) two long driving reins or 10 ft. soft ropes, harness girth or saddle pad and blanket.

DONKEY NATURE:

The nature and usual temperament of many donkeys is placid, and as such, they may let you put all of the equipment on them the first time and never bat an eye. **This does NOT mean, however, that just because they will wear a saddle, or let the cart be placed behind them, or let a person sit on their back, that they are broke or trained.** They must have experience working with the equipment and getting used to it, with instruction, not just intuition.

GROUND DRIVING

You can go right into ground driving instead of longing if you prefer, although that means that you must teach the canter much later when the donkey is under saddle.

Now is the time to fit him with bridle and a small saddle or saddle pad. Put a simple bridle with a simple snaffle bit — broken or bar but not a shank snaffle, on the donkey. Be very careful not to hurt his ears. To bridle him, do not fold his ears or bend them in half. Swivel them around and put them through the bridle by pointing them forward. OR, if he is not perfectly sure about his ears, unbuckle the bridle and put it on buckling the cheek strap after it is on, thus avoiding the ear question altogether. A snaffle bit, fitted properly will just barely wrinkle the corners of the mouth. Put this outfit on without reins and leave him to wear it 20 minutes or so at a time, preferably free in a paddock or pen for several days to enable him to come to terms with this disgusting thing in his tender mouth. Think of how you would feel and be patient with him. He will get used to it, just the same way you would get used to a set of dentures.

Since your donkey is quite tame and used to being patted and touched all over, the feel of the saddle and girth should not bother him. (If he is not tame, then you are not anywhere near ready for saddle training. Go back to the previous section and teach him the basics.) The unfamiliar weight on his back is what will make him jumpy at first. Make it a light saddle. Put the blanket on his back, and when he is used to that ease the saddle on. At first just walk him around the place with the girth and stirrups tied up on the saddle. If he gets very upset you can just lift it off. When he is used to that, girth it up well enough to hold but not tight enough to frighten him.

When placing the saddle and pad, it is preferable to put it too far forward and slide it back, rather than trying to push it forward. The hair of equines grows from front to back, and if you slide the pad back, it runs with the hair. Pushing a slipped saddle forward pulls the hair the wrong way - it pinches, pulls, and makes for a sullen or angry donkey. Later, when actually riding, if you know the saddle has slipped back, stop, get off, and lift and reset the saddle - don't push. You could possibly get a wild ride otherwise!

An assistant should be used rather than tying him up hard and fast. If you want to tie him, take a couple of wraps around your tying post and have the assistant hold the rope. Do this for two or three lessons, girthing the saddle tighter each time, then walking him around until he relaxes, until you finally have it girthed up to normal tightness. At this time you should be able to insert two or three fingers flat between his body and the girth. A saddle should never be girthed tighter than that under normal conditions anyway. Also if his coat is long make ABSOLUTELY SURE that hair and skin are flat under the girth, especially under the metal rings. If they are not, hideous sores can result which may damage him both emotionally and physically for life. To make sure the skin is not pinched, girth up, then lift the foreleg up and front, gently stretching. This is pull any wrinkled skin out from under the girth.

If you are an advocate of clicker-training, this can be a good time for it's use. Clicker training is used to give a reward (usually just the sound of the click and praise) when a correct response if given. Clickers can be combined with giving a treat as well, but this can be awkward for the saddle animal. As the donkey relaxes, stands still, or moves correctly as you ask, the click is a reassurance that he will remember from his ground training.

When the donkey is used to wearing both the bridle and saddle and will walk around with them in a relaxed manner, you can start ground driving him. Each driving line should be attached to the rings of the HALTER at first then run back through the stirrups of the saddle, which are brought up as far as they will go, and back to your hands. Always stay a donkey's length behind for safety's sake and be careful not to let your hands or feet get entangled in the driving lines. If you must use a Western saddle to ground drive, then leave the stirrups down, and tie them together under the belly with a shoestring or other such cord. A children's western saddle or saddle where you can run the stirrups up is best, and helps to keep the reins in the right position.

Diagram running stirrups:

Use your usual working area and have an assistant lead the donkey. Have him led around the ring while you walk behind him. Work the lines gently against him so he will know they are there. After a few times around, have your assistant gradually get away from the donkey. If he stops, use your walk command and flip the reins a bit to startle him into walking. Be patient, as this is entirely new to the donkey. (If you are starting a foal, you might "play" at this with him from time to time as he grows up and he will be used to this sort of thing.) When he does move, he may want to come toward you which will really mess your lines up! Try to avoid this by pulling on the outside line and moving rapidly to stay behind him. If he is faster than you, keep relaxed., get things straight again, and start over. When you get him around the ring two or three times without too much trouble, praise him and put him up for the day. When he has caught on to having you behind him, start on some turns. When turning, make your pulls on the reins as easy as possible, and be sure and use a give and take motion, not a steady pull! Beginning sessions should be no longer than 15 minutes, working up to 45 minutes later.

Most of what makes the animal jump and run with the lines behind them is a) the lines on their rump and b) you being in their blind spot where they can't see you. Donkeys like to see exactly where you are, it takes some time for them to stand quietly with a person right behind them. Draping the lines over the rump, haunches, and hocks while they are standing calmly (with that helper) will get them used to the feel of the harness, lines and shafts over the body as well.

After the donkey has learned to walk well both ways, and stops on command and you have done turns, figure eights etc. with him, he can be worked at the trot. Since he already knows the voice command "TROT" from ground work he may pose little problem with the trot with you behind him. Sometime during all this training use your judgement and when he understands what you are doing, change the reins over to the bit. Take it easy the first few lessons to avoid hurting his mouth, and do only simple things. You should start each day with backing lessons also. At first work with an assistant and with the reins on the halter, and later with the reins on the bit. Remember the blindfold and pencil trick if he just sets his feet and refuses to back up, but keep his backing straight, even if it is only a few steps.

When you have him walking and trotting on command and calmly, around the ring and in figure eights and other designs and when he stops and backs readily on command your ground driving is finished and you are ready for harness training. Remember that some donkeys catch on quickly, others may take several months. Just make sure he is reliable on one thing before starting another, but don't bore him to death with the same old stuff every day. Vary the routine enough to keep him looking forward to his lessons.

Radar, a 2-yr old Large standard gelding, first time hitched to cart. The cart is actually an old Bentwood racing sulky from the early 1900's, with an added bench seat and footpan. It was rescued from an old barn about to be demolished. *Radar* showed no hesitation in stepping out in only a halter and lines pulling the old sulky.

STEP TWO — HARNESS TRAINING

EQUIPMENT
Two wheeled cart, breast collar harness, Bridle with snaffle or driving bit, Halter with long reins, strong assistant, buggy whip and perhaps a "popper" (noisemaking bat).

The Whip
The Whip should be a buggy-whip. A long snake whip is great for the experienced teamster driving a 6-up or 20-in hand, but you just need the short, flexible type. They are make of a flexible rod, covered in nylon braid. The length of the whip and lash together should be just long enough to reach the shoulder of the animal. If you are driving a unicorn hitch or team, you will need a longer lash. Check the rulebooks for shows as to lash length. The whip is an aid and must reach the forward (front) animal. Buggy whips don't really "pop" or "crack" like a blacksnake whip (shades of Indiana

Jones) and you don't really use them for this. They are a reminder, not a punishment. Learning to use a real drovers whip or lash like Indy will get you punishment of a certain kind - you will whip yourself unmercifully while learning - takes time and practice - AWAY from the animals. Once you have mastered it yourself, you can develop the control needed to actually use such a whip around your team.

CARE OF THE DONKEY

Care is the same as before, remember to have him on a good worming program as well as feeding him his grain, hay and clean water ration. Remember to let him have "growth breaks" during the winter months (and check to make sure everything still fits!!!). You can however, do ground training work about twice a week in the winter when weather allows to keep him refreshed in his memory and under discipline if you would like to. His mouth should be used to the bit from ground driving, but keep the bit as mild as possible. Make sure it still fits width-wise, and that it is not hitting any teeth.

CART TRAINING

If you can't find a cart and harness through ads in your local papers, consultation with horsemen and riding clubs, most horse magazines have ads for them. Also your tack store probably has a catalog to order from, or a local welder can make you a good sturdy one also. Be sure if you have one home made that you ask to have motorcycle wheels instead of bike wheels put on. Even if you have a factory made cart, a time may come when you want the extra strength of motorcycle wheels. A local man might even be able to fit a brake on your two wheel cart. Even this cannot not stop a donkey that really wants to leave, but it sure slows him down until he gets tired out! Pulling wheels that don't move is much harder than puffing ones that roll! Also you can buy nylon or leather harness.

First fit the harness on the donkey until he gets used to it. Keep all the ends tucked up. Big clothes pins might be helpful here. Ground drive him until he relaxes in it. This is usually at least a week. Drive him first in the halter, then in the bit, but place the halter on over the bridle.

Let the donkey, see, smell and investigate the cart thoroughly, then ground drive him while an assistant pulls the cart **behind you** to get him used to the noise. REMEMBER the noise the cart makes on a gravel road for instance, is a lot louder than in your pen — many accidents have happened on this account, so get him used to the cart making ALL KINDS of noises!!! The first time you trundle the cart along, use the halter or halter/bridle combo - you don't want to punish his mouth trying to stop him from a very natural action - running from the monster behind him!

Trainers Tip - Leah Patton:

A note about your assistant pulling the cart. Some people have tried having the assistant pull the cart alongside the donkey, to see that it can travel with him without hurting him. This may work for some animals, but it will backfire on others. Our donkeys thought it was quite amusing for a person to pull a cart, and took to it with no problem. They had to show us how it was done *correctly*. However, our Mustang mare, Myryha, took one look and said, "Yep, you go right ahead pulling it. Why should I bother?"

PUTTING TO

What is known in fancy circles as "Putting To" is called hitching up by most of us. It means attaching cart to harness in order to make the donkey the motivating power —hopefully under control! When you first do this, the control part may be in doubt. When the donkey is used to the cart have one or two assistants to help you. Three people make things easiest, because when you start fooling with harness you find out quickly that a donkey has TWO sides and things ought to be done together on both sides, which is quite impossible for one person. Speak in a calming manner to the donkey, but have a good, secure hold on him. **DO NOT** tie him up for this procedure. Hold the donkey with the halter over the bridle unless you find you must use the bit for emergency control. If he tries to run away from the cart you don't want to hurt his mouth if you can help it. Have the harness on, and all loose ends except the shaft **loops securely tucked**

away. Speak to the donkey while the assistant brings the cart up behind, slips the shafts down over the donkey's back and puts them is the shaft loops. At this time it is handy to have someone on both sides of the cart for this operation. The shafts should be put in firmly enough so that they will not pull out with normal walking forward with no weight in the cart. They should remain unfastened to the cart itself, so that they can be pulled out without undoing anything in an emergency.

Then, have an assistant come to the donkey's head, each one of you take a lead rope fastened on each side of the halter (not the bit, remember) and start leading the donkey slowly forward. Some donkeys take it all perfectly calmly and you can be driving them from the seat of the cart in half an hour. (Just remember, they don't have "power steering" and "brakes" at this stage - they are just more comfortable with the cart behind them.) Others try madly to run away from this horrible thing behind them.

Many donkeys go forward rather well but panic when they try to turn and find themselves confined by the shafts. A donkey trying to spin in the shafts will wedge in tighter and tighter and become more frightened unless you can quickly straighten him out. This is the time when two strong people controlling the animal's head for a little while make all the difference. Straighten him up, pet and calm him. Have him take a few steps forward, whoa on command, (stopping on a good note) and try again later.

If you can't get a helper and your donkey is nervous, take it very slowly, one easy step at a time until he gets used to the whole thing. If you can do these first lessons where the donkey will not have to make any tight turns-only very large circles, it will be MUCH better for all concerned. If you can get him calm in the shafts this first time then lead him in large circles, both directions, praise him and put him up. He has done plenty for the first lesson. The next day, have him repeat the lesson including having him smell and look at the cart.

When the worst of his nerves is over and he shows no signs of kicking from fright, you can hitch him up properly and have an assistant lead him around the ring while you actually drive, walking BEHIND the cart. When he has that down pat, and has learned to make sharper turns, keep the assistant for safety's sake but actually drive the cart.

When he is completely calm you can practice figure eights, turning patterns and backing in the ring. When he finally works well in the ring, including turning at a trot (not sharp turns, take most of the ring to turn around in) you can take him out in the neighborhood. If possible, have a friend follow you, but not near enough to make him run or rely on them for leadership. Try to stick to places he knows well and is not afraid of. If he should run away and you are in a safe place, take your time stopping him to save his mouth. Donkeys rarely run far and rarely run fast as to injure themselves unless really in a panic. If you can't bring him to an easy stop or run him in a large circle, you do have enough leverage with the long reins and the footboard to stop him. Use a sawing motion, first one side and then the other to sort of throw him off balance in his run, also use **give and take**. NEVER use a straight pull on a runaway.

This step is where you may possibly have trouble because he doesn't want to leave his friends in the pasture. When you feel he is safe outside at a walk you will want to ease him into a trot. Ease him into it with your voice signal and a tap or two with the whip ON THE SHOULDER, not the rump. The best time to do this is on your way home. He will be so busy concentrating on going home that he will probably forget to play up. On the way out he may walk like a snail, and some donkeys shy at everything just as a protest to having to do (called dumb insolence — in the service). Remember to slow him well before reaching home, and to do one more little thing before you unhitch, so he doesn't get the idea he can run home and be   turned loose for the day.

HOW TO PUT ON HARNESS AND HITCH TO THE CART: BREAST COLLAR HARNESS

Putting on a breast collar harness such as you will use with a pleasure cart is relatively easy as soon as you get the hang of it. To start, tie the donkey up by his halter, you will leave the bridle until last. You will find, when you pick it up that a good deal of the harness is attached, and lies down on the top of the donkey's back, and sort of falls into place. At the front is the "saddle" or pad, with the girth attached, and this fits right where the riding saddle fits. It is attached along the back by a long strap that goes down the line on the donkey's back to the crupper and britching. An assistant helps until you can get it all laid on properly. Fit the crupper and making sure no straps on the britching or elsewhere are twisted, the britching under it. Then lie the rest of the harness along the back until the pad rests where it should. Have your helper hold the pad in place while you reach under the donkey's belly and retrieve the girth. Then girth him up in the normal way and most of your harness is in place!

Next take the breastcollar and undoing the lead rope, slip the narrow strap over the top of his head so that the collar fits over the front of his chest, held up by the narrow strap across the top of his neck. Then take the strap that is connected to the britching and either draw it up and put it over the shaft loop strap, or if it connects to the shaft, put it up over the donkey's back to get it out of the way.

Also, put the traces, (lines that come back from the breast collar) and any other hanging straps up out of the way.

Bridle the donkey and hold him by the reins or have your assistant do that.

Ground-drive the donkey up to the cart, turn him and position him in front of the shafts. You can put the halter on over the bridle if you want to and hold him by this means. Bring the cart shafts up over the rump and down and through the shaft loops. You win have to go to both sides or have your helper assist you in this. Then fasten the traces from the breastcollar back to the singletree of the cart. Check them for length, the animal should not be close enough for the cart to hit his legs during the trot or stop, or so far away that he has no leverage, medium is best. If the cart hits him at the stop, he may be startled and run away. When the animal is walking the traces should some tight so as to take the pull of the cart, as he is not supposed to pull from the shafts. The shafts and traces should be fairly in line. If the shaft is much lower than the trace it has to be raised up. To do this you will have to take the young donkey out of the cart, although the experienced one will stand for it. It is a long procedure and there is a lot of tugging necessary to get the buckle of the shaft loop undone because it is on thick leather, and the loop is raised.

Next put the shaft wrap straps on. These must be done properly to ensure their use as BRAKES. There should be a "stop" on the shafts 12 to 16 inches back from the tip. This is usually a loop but not always. The shaft loop should rest firmly in front of and against this stop. If there are no stops you can use "thimbles", which are small leather cups which fit over the ends of the shafts and buckle back onto the backpad via a long strap which act as stops by their bracing action and prevent the cart from sliding backwards.

Bring the wrap strap between the brace and the donkey and wrap over the shaft directly in front of the shaft loop. Keep in mind that your purpose is to hold it firmly on the shaft and against the stop. Make one wrap in front of the shaft loop, then bring the strap back behind the' shaft loop and wrap it around the shaft directly behind the stop. If the stop is a metal loop you can put one wrap through the loop for extra safety. This win result in a figure eight type of wrap. If you have enough length of strap to make two wraps on each side of the shaft loop do so, but try to make both sides symmetrical. Bring the loose end down and buckle it back on to the lower end of the wrap strap ending up with the trace between the two halves of the wrap strap. Be careful that you do not buckle them so tight as to make extra pressure on the backpad, they only need to be tight enough to keep the shafts from flapping. Usually after this the girth, or bellyband will need to be tightened, so check this.

It is time to adjust the breeching (harness). Bring the breeching strap under the brace and through the brass fitting under the shaft, wrap it around the shaft and buckle it back onto the breeching. There should be about an inch or two of slack when the donkey is moving forward. Check that both sides are symmetrical and that the trace runs between the breeching straps.

Now fasten the strap that you found on the top of the bridle between the ears, to the fastener on the backpad — this is the checkrein and is meant to keep the donkey's head up. Do not make it tight, it should exert no pressure if the head is held at a normal level. A donkey normally carries his head rather low and should be allowed to do this.

By far the best way to learn to harness properly is to have someone who really knows how show you. That way you will find that it is quite simple and not nearly as complicated as it sounds in print.

COLLAR HARNESS

This is a little more difficult than breastcollar harness because of the collar adjustments. Entering on the left side of the donkey put on the collar pad if needed. Be sure the actual collar and pad if used are very clean and free from dirt and sweat. Unbuckle the collar. Collars are stored buckled to prevent breaking away in the wrong places. Do not attempt to put the donkey's head through the collar like a noose, but open the top and put it on from under the neck. The large end is at the bottom while the small **end and buckle are at the top.**

Now pick up the harness. If it was stored properly it win fall right into place when you put it on the donkey — if it wasn't we bet it will be next time! The harness should be hung on two pegs. On the right is hung that portion which crosses the rump. Put this piece on your right shoulder. Then pick up the hames. Get in beside the donkey again and place the hame in your right hand over the donkey and down along the collar on the right, and the left hand tight against the collar on the left. Then heave the rest of the harness onto the donkey's back (thanking your lucky stars you are working with a small donkey and not a Percheron), transferring the load from your right shoulder to the donkey's rump. If the harness was put away it should fall naturally into place (more or less). Now fasten the hames under the collar, making sure they are positioned properly in their grooves. On most hames there is a sort of clip at the bottom giving you extra leverage. The hames have to be extremely tight or they will pull off the collar and injure the donkey badly. There is a large strap which passes under the neck, fore and aft. Reach down and pass this between his front legs and up under the belly. Grope around under the donkey until you find the end of the belly strap which goes under the donkey's middle and under the strap coming back from the hames. Snap or buckle this belly strap to the other end of this strap on your side of the donkey.

There are two more straps, leading from the ends of the breeching on either side. Find these and snap them into the ring on the big fore and aft strap held up by the belly strap. Pull the tail out from under the breeching. With some adjustments the donkey is now essentially harnessed. Bridle him and be sure everything is properly secure and fitting well.

When hitching, always fasten the neck yoke first, thus lifting the tongue and avoiding a dangerous runaway with the tongue loose. Hook up the tugs to the singletrees, always using the same length on both sides of each animal. Trees should be as close as possible but should clear the hocks in full stride.

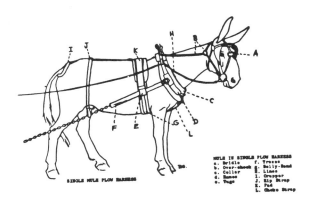

MULE IN SINGLE PLOW HARNESS
a. Bridle   f. Traces
b. Over-check g. Belly-Band
c. Collar   h. Lines
d. Hames   i. Crupper
e. Tugs   j. Hip Strap
             K. Pad
             L. Choke Strap

SINGLE MULE PLOW HARNESS

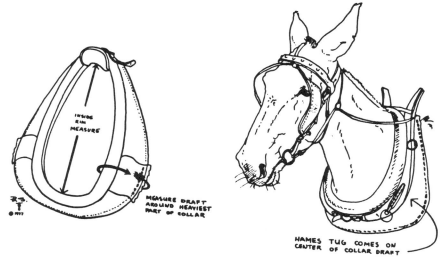

INSIDE RIM MEASURE

MEASURE DRAFT AROUND HEAVIEST PART OF COLLAR

HAMES TUG COMES ON CENTER OF COLLAR DRAFT

FOR PROPER FIT, ONLY ENOUGH SPACE FOR 4 FINGERS SHOULD BE BETWEEN MULE'S NECK AND THROAT OF COLLAR.

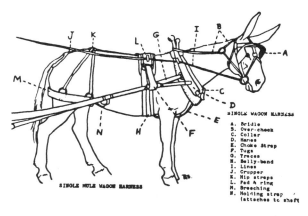

SINGLE WAGON HARNESS

A. Bridle
B. Over-check
C. Collar
D. Hames
E. Choke Strap
F. Tugs
G. Traces
H. Belly-band
I. Lines
J. Crupper
K. Hip straps
L. Pad & ring
M. Breeching
N. Holding strap (attaches to shaft)

SINGLE MULE WAGON HARNESS

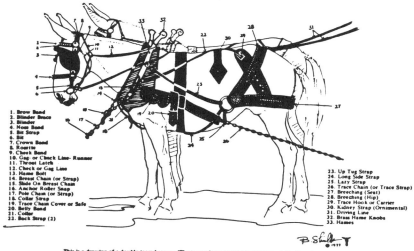

1. Brow Band
2. Blinder Brace
3. Blinder
4. Nose Band
5. Bit Strap
6. Bit
7. Crown Band
8. Rosette
9. Cheek Band
10. Gag- or Check Line- Runner
11. Throat Latch
12. Check or Gag Line
13. Hame Bolt
14. Breast Chain (or Strap)
15. Slide On Breast Chain
16. Anchor Roller Snap
17. Pole Chain (or Strap)
18. Collar Strap
19. Trace Chain Cover or Safe
20. Belly Band
21. Collar
22. Back Strap (2)

23. Up Tug Strap
24. Long Side Strap
25. Lazy Strap
26. Trace Chain (or Trace Strap)
27. Breeching (Seat)
28. Breeching (Hip)
29. Trace Hook or Carrier
30. Kidney Strap (Ornimental)
31. Driving Line
32. Brass Hame Knobs
33. Hames

This is a drawing of a double team harness. (The terms that go with the picture are in list form.)

STEP THREE — FINISHING THE HARNESS DONKEY

GOALS

1. To be able to pull the cart at a trot for a reasonably long period of time.
2. To have style and animation.
3. To have both a slow trot and a "road gait" or **extended trot**.
4. To be able to turn, back and manage the vehicle in tight spots.
5. To be able to pull the cart among other vehicles and in deep footing in the show ring without becoming exhausted or frightened.
6. To stand quiet and alert in the show line-up and to back on. command.
7. To stand tied quietly when asked.
8. To let a child or inexperienced person drive him.

Your donkey is by this time "broken to the cart" but is by no means a finished driving animal. Since we are now going to begin to work in earnest he should have passed his third birthday.

CARE

If you have taught your donkey to lunge you should lunge him at least three times a week instead of driving. WORK ON THE CANTER. If you are driving you should only be teaching the trot, and unless you work on the canter in some way you will have many problems with it later. If you are very experienced with driving you can teach your donkey to walk, slow trot, fast trot and canter in harness, but it is tricky. Be sure he is in good health with all his immunizations, free from worms and has his feet trimmed and in good shape. It is about time you dressed him up a little. If it is spring now, you might want to clip him. However groom him as little as possible unless you are showing. Leave most of the dirt in for protection and just brush off the outside mud he has picked up by rolling.

At this time if at all possible you will need to do a lot of driving over the countryside, preferably on dirt roads. To describe this work I will assume you have them near you although you may have to make your own special provisions for this finishing work. Drive on paved roads also, and through water, moderate driving on them will not hurt his feet and he has to learn to cope with them.

Start slowly, not so much with short lessons, as with a lot of walking, interspersed with trotting, turning, stopping and backing. Gradually increase your trotting periods. The best system is not to force the donkey to trot on the way out from home in the first lessons. Let him trot on the way home for as long as he feels comfortable. If you feel he is going to slow down on his own, you slow him down to a walk first. Never let him stop himself if you can help it or you will be very sorry later.

Then let him walk until you feel that he would like to trot again with minimum encouragement, or until you know darn well he is rested enough to trot with maximum encouragement! In this way you can build up his endurance at the trot. A little later, when you know his strength and amount of endurance and have him properly warmed up by walking, you can start to ask for the trot going away from home. Go only for short periods at first but encourage him first by a touch of the buggy whip at the shoulders. If he doesn't respond and sulks, use the "popper". This is a noisemaking whip made of two flaps of leather that hit together and is used by many barrel racers. It doesn't hurt, just makes noise. You should try to use it on the cart instead of the animal if you can. If it takes a lot of forcing, make the intervals of trotting short when going away from home and build them up longer coming home. Finally you will have him responding to your signals automatically and he will stop worrying about it. However you MUST have him trot **away from home** even if only a little, after the first 2 or 3 lessons.

NEVER USE A WHIP, EVEN A POPPER TO EXCESS!!! You will be teaching the donkey to clench its tail under it like a whipped hound which completely spoils its looks!

Learn to hold the reins AND the buggy whip. One rein in each hand and the whip in your right hand. It is awkward at first but you will get used to it soon. Hold it sticking out over the donkey's back rather parallel or slightly across the back of the animal. At the beginning, start your signaling with the voice and the whip. A finished animal never goes by means of being slapped with the reins — this is NOT the proper way to drive. On a finished animal a light twitch should do the trick. The properly finished harness donkey is guided and stopped by the reins but goes forward by means of the voice, and a slight touch of the buggy whip on the shoulder or by the girth. A tightening of the reins preparatory to taking control is another cue the donkey will respond to. The whip can also be used to help signal a turn. Tickle him with the lash on the shoulder away from the side you wish to turn towards, meanwhile lightly giving and taking the rein to turn him away from the tickle of the whip and into the turn. Soon he will be turning with only the slightest whip signal and small finger twitches on the reins. If you have to beat your animal to make him go, there is something very wrong, either with him, or his trainer.

You will need a great deal of driving, building him up in wind and muscle at the trot, practicing stops, turns and backing and managing the cart in odd situations and using the whip properly. Practice in these things is what makes him a finished driving animal, a first ribbon winner in shows and a great pleasure to drive.

STYLE AND ANIMATION

These depend to a great extent on the animal's physical build, psychological state, physical condition and energy level.

While a great deal of a harness donkey's style depends on its natural ability and conformation, a good deal comes from the development of it's mouth. Never forget that you are making your donkey's mouth all the time you are driving him!

Even though there will be times when you have to pull hard on your donkey's mouth when beginning to drive each time should be chalked up as a minor failure. They won't ruin him, but they should be avoided whenever possible. Rein contact should be light, and turning and stopping should be done by motions of the fingers or wrists, not the whole arm. If your donkey opens his mouth to avoid the pressure of the snaffle bit, fit him with a dropped noseband or some other humane device to prevent his opening his mouth. First, make sure the bit is fitted properly to his mouth, and doesn't pinch his lips at the corners. A dropped noseband fits around the muzzle in the groove where the curb strap would bit and holds the mouth closed. If adjusted properly, there will be room to insert two fingers flat, between it and the nose. After the donkey is trotting well, slight vibrations of the reins may work in causing him to lift his head and thereby lighten his forehand and give him more stylish gaits.

Unless the donkey is in prime physical condition, gained through good feed and much work, he will have neither style or animation when driven. Energy level has to do with good health and nutrition. Don't ask him to do this hard work on low energy food such as grass and hay. Feed him a good, balanced grain ration, hay, clean water and salt, but not so much of all this as to get him obese.

Safety, and skill in managing the vehicle in tight places come with practice. You will find this out especially in that type of rather rough cross country driving that you should indulge in as often as possible to give him a chance to learn to manage on varying surfaces. Be careful when going onto a surface that may prove noisy, as he may panic and run when the wheels make odd noises behind him. If you are not sure, get out and lead him until he is used to the noise. A gravel road caused a friend of ours to end up with a broken neck — We hope it won't happen to you! If he knows the word "WHOA" like a religion it may save you a bone or two someday, so keep practicing with it and enforcing a complete stop every time you use it.

SHOWING WITH THE CART

To train your donkey to trot round and round a ring or arena and to cross it with ease you really ought to practice in one. If you don't have one, then borrow one, even if you have to trailer to one to use it. If you absolutely can't, set up a makeshift one at home. He must learn not to turn right round at a sharp angle, but to cross the ring on a diagonal and end up going the other direction. He must learn that he has to walk or trot around in the circle, even if it is in deep sand until he is sick to death of it, but still obey your commands. He has to learn to go among other donkeys and carts and maybe even mules and horses and keep his head and learn to avoid them without panic. It may be that you will have to go to some shows to get all this experience, but all show animals have to start somewhere, so just take it easy and let him learn the first times.

SHOW STANCE

If you have taught him to stand in a proper show stance in his ground training use your cue if you can and stand him up with his reins from the cart, several times in each practice session. He should stand four square and alert, and not fidget. He may have to relax after a long session in the ring, and wait until the judge comes to inspect him to take the correct stance, but he should never stand sloppy. He should also back 5 steps easily upon command of the judge from this stance.

REVERSING

In the show ring, the reverse should be called by the judge to be performed on the diagonal. The ring steward should stand at the corner of the ring and be the "Guide" to begin the ring reversing. As the steward is passed, the drivers should go across the ring on a diagonal, turning back the opposite way. If all drivers follow in a timely manner, the ring will be neatly reversed with no cramping in the shafts, no tight turns, no breakups. If you do not follow this course of reversing, all sorts of tangles can occur, from running into the person behind you, to the donkey getting cramped in the shafts.

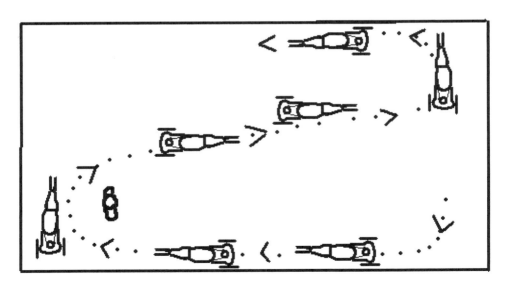

How to reverse properly in the ring.

CHILD TO DRIVE

Once your donkey is as well trained as all this anybody with the rudiments of knowledge should be able to drive him successfully. Sit with the child in the cart and teach him control methods and signals and if possible your vocal signals. The child may not be able to handle the buggy whip at first so the driving will be quite elementary but a well trained donkey should perform anyway. Just be careful to teach the child not to hurt the donkey's mouth and take special care in showing him how to use the reins. Also do not let a child go, where there is any danger such as of traffic, etc. keep an inexperienced person in a safe place or go with them.

FURTHER DRIVING

If you wish to be an expert on the art of fancy driving and showing with teams, or single animals beyond the donkey show point you will have to get involved with the driving clubs and driving magazines of which there are several. Really advanced driving is not within the scope of this book, but it can be done with donkeys if you are interested.

TEAM DRIVING

Donkeys make very pretty and unusual teams for wagon work or for plowing or farm work. Many teams of donkeys can do all the work a light horse team can do for less cost and less work. It is relatively easy to break to team work. As an example we will mention something that happened to us. We had a rather nervous 4 year old jennet. She was finished in single harness but had never felt a collar or worked in a team. She was trying for points in the National Show and needed (a great surprise to us) to go in a team hitch class. Our greatest rival that day, had a beautiful spirited jack that was an exact match for her in looks. He too was finished in single but not in double harness. We decided to do it anyway! My friend borrowed three different harnesses for size differences and a wagon from a brave mule owner! We put Vicks in the nose of the jack so sex wouldn't spoil the whole thing. Then we hitched them up and he drove them out! We ground drove them together for about 15 minutes, then hitched them to the wagon and drove them for about 20 minutes. Then our friend took them into the show ring! They worked like they had been doing this together for years and he won first place. It shows you what you can do with donkeys if you understand them! However, it would have taken them a good deal of work to learn to pull together under all circumstances as a team and work with each other and the driver. They would have learned though, given time.

Team driving is an art, mostly consisting of getting both animals to do the same amount of work together. A team of donkeys is often recommended to practice with before you graduate to horses or mules, for reasons you all know, being donkey lovers!

If you have two untrained donkeys it is best to teach each of them to drive singly at first. If you have an experienced old hand, harness your young donkey to the older animal. If you have a wagon with brakes, so much the better! The brakes and the older animal will effectively check any incipient runaway and a donkey learns fast. Be sure to use your voice and flips of the whip later when he is less afraid, to keep him up even with his teammate and pulling properly. Break him slowly to actually digging in and pulling real weight. If you don't you may hurt him both physically and psychologically. Nothing makes an equine stubborn quicker than being asked to pull a weight that he can't budge. Make sure all collars and harness fit properly and don't rub.

Some people harness a young unbroke team of animals and hook them to a sled (no wheels) with a tongue in it and put some concrete blocks on the sled for a little weight. They then back a tractor up in front of the team and tie them to the tractor. If there is a carryall raise it to nose height in front of the team. Give the donkey about two feet of lead rope. Then have someone drive the tractor at enough speed to keep the donkeys at a good walk, and the trainer can ride on the sled and hold the reins (called lines when you are driving a team). After you have gone a ways and they are settled, lengthen the rope a bit and actually start to drive the donkeys. Do quite a bit of stopping and standing to teach them to whoa while you are behind the tractor and under good control. After two or three days you will have the young team pretty well green broke to drive and can begin working to finish them. This method is used often by a well-known mule trainer.

Don't overwork them because they are young and not hardened to work. You can ruin them with overwork. Many trainers never trot a team until they are fully broken to drive, turn, stop and back. Trotting can come later although this is less of a problem with donkeys than with mules or horses. The true way to have a fully trained team is to work them enough so that they are hardened to the work and understand it and your signals. As the old timers always said, "A mule isn't broke until it has been through one crop season."

A pair of lovely young ladies and their team. This miniature carriage and pair of Miniature Donkeys is owned by Carleton and Robbie Crouch.

A beautiful turnout in England. Mrs. Spencer driving *Aphrodite*. Stoneleigh, England. Donkeys can be quite elegant in harness.

GUIDE TO DRIVING FOR THE AMATEUR
FROM THE BRITISH MULES SOCIETY
by Lorraine Travis
BUYING A VEHICLE FOR DRIVING YOUR DONKEY

It is not worth spending a lot of money on your first vehicle in my opinion. If you and/or your donkey are novices, you'll probably damage the vehicle anyway, but it MUST be sound before you try driving it. This is very important, as it is with harness, for safety's sake. If you see a vehicle advertised as "in show condition", this means that it will be expensive and may or may not be sound. I would suggest either a new exercise cart (in the U.S. this is usually called simply a "pony cart") or a home made or second hand one.

These may be obtained several ways. New ones are advertised in horse magazines. Your saddle shop probably has a catalog with harness and carts in it. You can ask around in your area and with your club members, as personal contacts are a good method. Look for newspaper or magazines classified ads or put one in yourself.

1. The New Cart: The cart is very basic. Two shafts, two wheels, a floor and a seat. It may have a rein rail, whip holder, seat back etc. Will it fit your animal? If you aren't absolutely sure and you can't try your animal in it, measure: height of shafts from ground. Shafts must be level, height approximately half way up animal's body. Width required for shafts: Allowing adequate room for movement when animal is wearing harness. It is no good if shafts are pressing against animal or harness saddle and rubbing. Length required for shafts: From front of shoulder level with collar, to rear of animal, plus allowance of 12 to 18 inches so tail won't be rubbed. Some carts have adjustable shafts.

2. Second Hand and Home Made Vehicles: Some measurements should be taken, but exert much more care when studying this type of vehicle, particularly if made by an amateur because it may be out of proportion. I've seen lots of carts like this. Such as, short narrow shafts on high, heavy vehicle, or shafts may be different lengths, or different shapes or bowed out differently or almost any other proportional mistake.

Other Things To Check: If these aren't right, think about whether they can be repaired, altered, improved and what will the cost amount to?

Soundness of wood: Particularly if old, wood is very prone to rot and woodworm. Body can probably be repaired, shafts can be replaced but can be expensive. Finding someone to do it is a problem also. Wooden wheels are very expensive to replace. It is very easy and often done to fill holes caused by rot and paint over them so they look perfect. This is very difficult to spot so beware of anything recently painted.

Metal: If the cart is metal or if there is metalwork on it, check for rust, pitting, cracks, particularly in axle or spring fittings.

Wheels: Wooden wheels should be sound. If the metal or rubber tyres (tires) on the wheels are worn they will be expensive to replace. Car-motorcycle-bike wheels are often old and worn. Bike wheels may be bent, spokes may be broken or cracked. check to see that they run straight. Stand behind while someone draws vehicle forward to do this.

Fittings: e.g. tug stops, breeching, D's, trace hoods etc. Are they there and in the right place? If not, do you need them? They can be moved on wooden shafts but must be welded on metal. Are there cracks, breaks, looseness etc.?

Balance: This is a place where many good looking carts fail. Stand between the shafts, holding them at the tug stops. (the loops on the underside of the shaft), and lift the cart (to horizontal). The shafts should rest lightly and EVENLY on your fingertips. Pull the vehicle empty and then with someone sitting in it. The pull should be even and fairly easy. If it is not properly balanced, is the seat adjustable or is there room for a weight on the floor to alter the balance? Are the shafts the same height? Balance is vital, as the animal should not have to carry any weight on its back, and the vehicle should pull evenly or it will cause severe strain on the animal's back and legs.

SOME TIPS ON TRAINING FOR HARNESS
by Allan Griffiths and Lorraine Travis
A. Training, early breaking in
1. General points about training: Never go on to the next stage until the present stage is perfect. This is particularly important with the mule. This is especially

so when getting the animal responsive to the bit - neglect at this stage is what has given the donkey the reputation of being hard mouthed. Short, frequent lessons are best, donkeys are very intelligent and soon get bored; always let your donkey know you are in charge, but without breaking his spirit.

2. Treat your animal gently, kindly, consistently but not too quietly or he won't be prepared for the unexpected. Talk to him all the time, particularly when he is encountering strange objects or noises. This will give him confidence and you rapport with him. Also donkeys learn easily to obey vocal commands which is a great help, almost a necessity when driving.

3. Do as much as you can to get your animal used to strange noises and objects, let him look at, smell and touch harness, cart, plastic bags, buckets, dogs and anything else you can think of. There will still be things he doesn't like, especially flapping things. On the whole though if the animal trusts you he will not be bothered by most things if he has encountered them several times before.

4. If your animal won't do what you want, think what his character is like. He is proud, easily hurt, hates being ignored and wants to trust you if he can. Plan on these facts, e.g. if he won't come when you call, ignore him and make a fuss of the other animals, or investigate his cart, he'll usually come to you unless he is older and really spoiled. Don't force anything on him or he'll never cooperate.

B. Driving: Before setting out to do anything check everything for safety and comfort, both yours and the donkeys. If you are going far, take a spare strap in case anything breaks, a knife to cut the harness in an emergency and of course some baler twine in case of absolute emergencies.

1. Concentrate all the time. He won't necessarily go straight like a car, be prepared for the unexpected. Look ahead but keep an eye around you for disturbances and for those which are about to happen. Talk to him to keep him calm.

2. Watch out for other road users, show consideration to them, use clear hand signals, and watch closely for the silly or sometimes malicious things they may do.

3. Slippery road surfaces and steep grades need care, hold your animal back if necessary to help him. If he slips once it may put him off driving or off roads for life. Donkeys, like elephants, never forget!

4. If the animal is 'green' or nervous, have a passenger who can jump out and get to his head quickly in an emergency. If you have to stop for more than a few seconds it is safer to have someone at his head, never leave him unattended.

5. If properly trained a donkey should need only the lightest touch on the reins and vocal commands to control him. In a show ring, a whip is necessary, but this should not be used except on the shoulders mostly to guide, never beat an animal with a whip to get him to move!

6. Walk your animal the last mile home so he can cool down. Don't turn him out hot, don't give him cold water when he's hot, some are not as sensible as others and may drink too much and this can kill! Clean your harness every time and store it carefully, preferably in a harness bag (a laundry bag win do) or hung on PEGS or shaped harness holders, not NAILS! Be sure you hang up your tack in a dry place.

For a good book which details breaking and training to drive you can buy BREAKING AND TRAINING THE DRIVING HORSE by Doris Ganton, from HEE HAW BOOK SERVICE for $13.00 post paid.

A nice spotted Miniature Donkey moving out willingly in harness. Roseburg OR, ADMS Nationals, 1995. Photo by Juanita Snyder.

LIGHT HARNESS WORK FOR DONKEYS

We will change now from recreational driving to doing light tasks around the farm or homestead. For instance, you can bring in wood with your donkey, and you can do it with harness or a saddle, but lets look at harness now. Try not to "overdraw" your animal, that means do not match it with a weight that is above it's reasonable strength for its size. Remember we are not talking about logging, that takes a big draft mule, here we are thinking about bringing in firewood or hauling out brush to clear land. We also are working with already cut wood. If a tree needs to be hauled out be sure your animal or team can take the weight. It should be completely trimmed of limbs and not more than 10 feet in length, for a saddle size mule or a team of donkeys. If you can pick up the front of the tree to your knees your animal can probably haul it without injury. Remember it is better to make too many trips than to strain your animal, perhaps for life! The woods are a place where you have to be very careful. Always work with somebody, but handle your donkey on your own so he won't be confused. It is best to have large trees cut into firewood length and put on a skid which can easily be made at home. Remember woods are rough and usually rocky and the animal has to haul a good distance, so remember this is no pulling contest on smooth ground where the animal only pulls 10 or 12 feet!

Harness can be a problem for donkeys. You can sometimes buy one the right size at auctions and from dealers or you may have to buy a new one that is too large and work it down for your animal. The collar is the most important part and must fit right. After a collar of the right size and shape has been chosen, it must be fitted regardless of whether it is new or an old one to be used on a different donkey. One good way is to soak the face of the collar overnight in a couple of inches of water in a tub. In the morning it is fitted to the donkey, and the hames and harness are adjusted very carefully and the animal is worked moderately. The collar, being damp, willadjust itself to the exact shape of the neck and shoulders, much as a teenager will wear damp blue jeans so they willshrink to the contours of the body. Correct hame adjustment is extremely important. If the hames do not lie in the collar seam for the full length of the collar they do not fit. If the top hame strap is in the shape of an inverted U, rather than lying straight across the top of the collar, the pull of the tugs willspread the hames at the top and cause sore shoulders. If hames are either too long or too short, they cannot be adjusted to fit the collar satisfactorily. The only remedy is a set of hames that does fit the collar. To avoid sore shoulders, the tugs must be attached to the hames at the right point in order to make the pull at right angles to the collar. Watch the donkey's shoulders. If they appear chafed directly beneath the tug attachment, it is likely that the hames are too long or too short. Chafing near the shoulder point comes from hames or collars that are too long. Chafing on the upper part of the shoulder indicates that the point where the tugs pull is too high, due to hames being too short. Sometimes it is because the top hame strap is too loose.

Keep the neck and collar clean. Be sure any mane does not get under the collar, which is the reason some draft horses have roached manes. Stop occasionally at ends to raise the collar away from the shoulders. Wipe off the dust and sweat and give the shoulders an opportunity to cool. It will take a few minutes during the noon hour to remove the collar, but it will pay. Adjust the harness straps so they are neither too tight or too loose. Especially this is important for the back band, belly band, breeching and pole straps. At night, washing the shoulders with a strong, cold salt water solution willhelp keep them in good shape. Wipe the collar faces with a damp cloth and then with another cloth soaked in neatsfoot oil as soon as taken off. If pads are used wiped them clean but do not use oil. Every morning when the team is harnessed, wipe the bearing surface of the collar again and see that it is smooth.

The collar must fit on your animal so that it goes against the shoulders in the area known as the shoulder bed, where the neck slopes onto the shoulders. If the collar is too large it will move around and if too small it will set on the neck muscles. Improperly fitted, the collar will cause bad sores, boils, chafing, pulled neck muscles, fistula, and/or lameness just to mention a few problems.

Use of a collar pad is a matter of personal opinion. Again, if must fit properly and be kept clean. Collars are usually made of leather and some have a canvas backing. They are sometimes filled with horsehair, which can work through the canvas and into the shoulders, causing a boil on the donkey. This leaking of the hair can be very hard to detect, so be careful. The best way to prevent chafing or rubbing is to run your hands over the collar every time you use it, and to wipe it down every time you take it off.

Except for the collar, the working harness is around the body of the donkey, not tightened as in the racing or cart harness. The donkey does not draw the load, he pushes against the collar, tightening the harness and moving the load. The entire weight goes against the shoulder bed. On a small donkey you may wish to get a wider belly girth. As the donkey pushed, the harness may raise off the back if you are using a full work harness. If the girth is too narrow it may cut into the belly. Use a 4" wide strap. Don't pull it too tight, but tight enough to prevent the harness from lifting off the back. Allow a couple of inches under the donkey's stomach. Never use narrow pieces of leather or light, driving harness, which is designed for working with wheels and both pushing and pulling. In working with loads such as wood you will be pushing only.

As for the bridle, that is up to the driver. You may use blinders if you prefer. Some never use them, as they like their donkeys to see all they can. Many have found the donkeys keep better track of the terrain and the driver without them. It may take longer to train this way, but the rewards are greater. Another tip, if the donkey is worked in blinders, then suddenly won't work at all in harness, you might try removing the blinders. The same applies the other way - maybe the shadows and sights alongside are bothering him, and he will do better if he can work with the blinders. Just remember either way to give him time to get used to the different feel and appearance at home, long before you take him out to work or to a show.

The type of bit is a matter of personal opinion, from a snaffle to a kimberwick or anything else. If your donkey works well in just a smooth snaffle, use that. You will be looking for a combination that allows you to control your donkey and to understand each other's signals. If it is only for work and you will never get near a show ring, use what you are comfortable with and don't worry about rule books. However, if you intend to use your donkey in shows with work or pleasure harness, you will need to make sure the animal will perform with the correct type of bit. Bits come from mild to harsh, and you should always use the mildest bit possible and still have control.

If you prefer a head check (may be required in shows), you may find the side check to your best advantage. When fitting the collar, space is allowed for the animal to drop his head and still be able to breathe without interference. A head check should also allow the animal to drop his head to knee height or lower to balance himself against the load. A head check is easy to make if you are using a riding horse bridle. Make a strap to go over the poll, and hook it to the top of the bridle as one would a throatlatch. Sew a loop on each side of the throatlatch strap and attach or buckle it to the cheek strap. You can use this with split ear bridles. Use a pair of reins from the bit up through the loops and back over the hames. Be sure to allow for proper balance of the head. A donkey will naturally travel with the head lower than a horse, and certainly lower than the "gaited" or "carriage" breeds where the horse's neck is up. A donkey will need to reach down and out, so always attach your checkrein when the animal is standing normally. An overchecked donkey will become sore, sullen, and will quit working very quickly.

As for the reins (or "lines" in driving) you can use whatever you feel comfortable with. A pair of soft nylon ropes with medium sized snaps on the ends will do well for lessons or field work. A pair of nylon lunge lines will work equally well and you can work closer or farther from your donkey. Leather driving reins should be used in the show ring, but aren't necessary for your home use. Whatever type of line you use, be careful not to drop them or get them tangled around your leg, the animal's leg, or your wheels, as this is very dangerous.

PHYSICAL PROTECTION FOR THE WORKING DONKEY
TEAMS, PLOUGH ANIMALS, ETC.

If you ever find a working donkey to have a hard swollen neck that is hot to the touch, do not use him, and pay special attention. If he is used just one more time, the neck may begin to have a discharge. This would become quite serious as the neck is injured so badly that the sore portion become necrotic and actually falls out. He must be turned out for complete rest, receive appropriate antibiotics, local medication, and fly repellant. If the wound becomes infected or fly maggots invade the tissue, the donkey is ruined for life. A donkey in regular work will harden the top portion of his neck and rub hair off. This is called a boquet. A donkey with a good neck and collar bed may work best with the use of a full-face collar. Those with thick or wide top necks may need a half sweeney collar, and those with extra wide necks may need a full sweeney collar. Donkey necks are shaped differently from pony or mini-mule necks, so collars have to be watched and fitted very carefully. You must always check the fit of the collar and harness each time you hitch up, as a donkey with a wide neck may lose the fat that makes it wide. After that, the collar will no longer fit. After each day's work, wash the neck with salt water and shampoo. After getting it clean, rinse well and dry. By doing this, many people have been able to work horses and mules hard through the worst hot weather without harming the animals' necks.

Hames that require an upright strap with a center buckle and twin loops can easily cause deep sores. Those that have a flat or lying strap are much better. Make these straps as soft and wide as possible and use a conway buckle on the top half. Lightweight hames help considerably also. Do not use hame housings in hot weather as they impede air circulation and cause local heating.

If you want a pad to prevent sore necks, fold a grain sack in half, and then fold it full sideways. Put this on the neck with the collar over it. Then lay the front half of this over the collar top and put the hames on and you will have a good pad to prevent neck sores. Sweat pads can be used but must be kept CLEAN AND DRY! Sores and scars are a mark of ignorance and neglect, not a mark of a good working animal.

Other problems can be: halter snare wounds, damaged eyes because a bridle blind stay came off or loose and the blinder hit the eye at every step, swollen and draining knees from hitting things, wood splinters driven into the flesh, and ankles mashed by being hit by single trees, eyes knocked out by a blow or thrown rock, broken tongue or jaw from someone standing in front and tearing downward on the bit. You can rip the tongue right out of the head this way.

Do not take a well fed, or fat donkey out of rest and start it fast and hard. Although they are less susceptible to azoturia (Monday Morning Disease or "tying up") than the horse or mule it can happen. Donkeys are less susceptible to heat stroke but it is inhumane to work them through the hottest part of the day without rest, proper watering and previous conditioning. If the animal is not fit and the weather is hot, you can kill even a donkey this way. If working through the heat, the donkeys should be loose and outdoors at night with plenty of salt and water, and they should be in hard condition, neither thin, nor fat.

BLEMISHES

A good working animal may still bear white "harness marks" where the harness rubbed, and the follicles of the hair shaft were damaged. The hair often grown back in white. While this may mean (especially in saddle animals) that part of the equipment does not fit, on an older animal, it may just be "scars of honor" and wear. You can see if a spot is just an old rub, or actually is damaged by gently pressing on it. The animal should quiver the skin, but if they flinch hard, duck away, or act sore, then have it checked out. Scars, rubs, and blemishes are not necessarily a reason to pass an animal up, for work, pleasure or breeding. It all depends on the location and severity of the blemish.

TRAINING THE DONKEY TO SADDLE

EQUIPMENT

Light Western or English saddle which fits donkey, or saddle pad with stirrups. Britching or crupper if needed. Short riding crop or stick of the straight, stiff type, and blunt spurs if necessary Bridle with snaffle bit, and if possible a Western style or English style running martingale.

The Western style is simpler and consists of a strap that loops over the girth and divides at the chest where each half runs up to the reins. On the end of each half is a ring that is placed on the reins before the animal is bridled. The martingale serves to keep the snaffle bit in the proper place in the donkey's mouth and exerts control in a humane way. It aids a great deal in turning. Later you may want to change into some type of curb bit, 4 to 4½ inches is the usual width of a donkey bit.

CARE OF THE DONKEY

The donkey should be at least three years old before you start any serious saddle training, and should be considered to be actively growing until he is at least four. Because of this heavy weight and heavy work should not be done until age four. Care at this time is as described in the previous chapter.

The properly trained saddle donkey willbe a good ride for anyone, adult or child. It will walk, trot, canter and back on command. It willstand still, be calm and be a capable trail mount. Donkeys do not have that capacity for power and speed which cause the rider to choose a horse or mule, neither are they large animals. However, many a long legged or hefty Texan shows donkeys under saddle in our area of the country without feeling out of place, once he has set his mind to remembering he is riding a donkey, not a horse.

Show donkeys should be able to canter in a circle, in the correct lead, for a reasonably long period of time. Lunge training helps greatly with this. They should walk alertly and trot with some animation. They should be willing to canter through obstacles such as poles or barrels and do anything else that may be reasonably asked of them under saddle. We have known donkeys to go through a complicated California style trail course and win, which included side passing over bales of hay. Nobody can ask more than this!

Size is not a particularly limiting factor in who should train the donkey for riding purposes. It is much better for the donkey to be left until mature for riding, then trained by an experienced adult, than to start early and have a child who doesn't know what he is doing train the animal. We have many 44 to 48 inch donkeys ridden by adults in our shows and neither the donkeys or the people show any ill effects. They are ridden in Western Saddles also, which adds weight, but none of them ever are lame or stiff if they are healthy and have no injury. The ideal saddle is probably the army saddle or McClellan. If you have one of these fix it up if necessary and use it. It is made to fit any type of back and also automatically puts one in the correct riding position with the proper center of gravity. Any saddle which willbe used in steep country should be fitted with britching or a crupper (see harness chart). Britching (breetching) goes behind the thighs and crupper is a loop under the tail.

As far as deciding whether a child, teenager or adult should train the donkey, a great deal depends on the conformation and experience of both donkey and human! If you have trained the donkey yourself this far you should go ahead and finish up yourself if you can. If you feel you are too heavy, use this year to have a child ride always under your direction and take up the next year with real training. Or you may keep up with harness work and lunging for one more year before you start to ride. The average donkey, with average to heavy bone can carry you easily provided his back bones and muscles and leg bones and muscles are mature and "hardened". A proper amount of roadwork in harness will help get him "muscled up" also. You can start him weight carrying by putting 25 and then 50 lb. sacks of his own feed on his back and leading him around under their weight first if you don't have any convenient kids to do it with. (Those more familiar with training terms may call this "Backing" - in other words, strengthening the back.)

TRAINING THE DONKEY WITH A CHILD

If the donkey is well trained on the lunge line it will make a great deal of difference in this circumstance. It will be asked to learn to carry weight on its back, but at gaits it already knows. If the donkey has never learned to canter, the rider will have to teach it, and with the unskilled rider or a child this may not be too easy! Trotting is the donkey's favorite and best gait, he does not really believe in galloping unless he wants to. When he does, would rather do it with his nose practically on the ground and only for short periods. This is why it is so important to teach the canter on the lunge or second best, in harness. The exercises described here can be done at liberty, in an ENCLOSED ARENA of small size if the donkey is not lunge trained. NEVER start the untrained donkey in a large open area! Section off part of the pasture or build a round pen of some sort (even using wooden "pallets"). Whether lunge or harness trained the results will be faster and more satisfying for the child than if the donkey has had no previous training in the gaits and backing.

Mount the child on the donkey while it is still on the lunge line. It should be properly tacked up with saddle and bridle with snaffle bit and hopefully a western or English type running martingale. Show the child how to hold the reins properly and sit in the saddle correctly, his back straight and heels down. I am assuming the child has riding experience since it is probable that a totally inexperienced child cannot train the donkey. Explain the voice commands to the child, as well as proper use of rein and leg aids. Do not let him try to neck rein the donkey yet, as that procedure has to be taught by stages.

Tell the child to squeeze with his legs and give the command to "WALK" to the donkey. If the donkey does not understand, and he probably won't because of the difference in voice quality, reinforce it with your own command. You can do this reinforcement when needed, but always AFTER the child has given his own command first. When the donkey is walking quietly on the line, the child can get the feel of it and gain self confidence and the animal can learn about managing with the weight of the child on its back. Explain to the child that if he wants the donkey to stop he must make light contact with the mouth, sit firm in the saddle and give the whoa command. Do not let the child stop until you order it while you have control of the animal. If the child has to pull the reins harder, make sure it is not too hard (if the donkey opens his mouth and turns his head to get away from the bit — it is too hard) and make sure it is a give-and-take motion, NOT A STRAIGHT PULL! You have taken a good deal of care of this donkey's mouth up to now, so don't let lack of supervision ruin all your work and TLC! Give and take can be best explained by showing the rider how to "Squeeze" the reins - Squeeze and pull an inch, release the pull; squeeze and pull, release. An animal with a sensitive mouth will learn that just squeezing on the rein will mean to pay attention.

Explain that when he wants to change direction the child should put more pressure on the rein toward the side he wants to turn, while laying the opposite rein loosely on the neck to begin reining training. (If you want to turn left, pull more on the left rein and lay the right rein over the neck toward the left). For this purpose, heavier reins that the donkey can feel on his neck are convenient. At the same time the child should lean a little toward the direction he is turning and put a little more weight in that stirrup as a cue. If you are working without stirrups, a leg aid can be given by pressing harder with that leg, or moving the leg back slightly (as if pushing the hind end away from the direction of turn.) You may have to help by leading the donkey around the turn for the first few times. Remember it is easier for the donkey to turn while walking than to stop and then turn.

After the child and donkey understand each other at the walk you can just progress in easy stages by going into the trot and then canter on the lunge line, or at liberty in an enclosed area.

When the donkey obeys the child's aids in the circle and seems to understand what the rider wants, encourage the child to ride around in patterns, serpentines and figure 8's and such. Walk well away from the donkey, holding the line but don't take an active part unless really necessary. When they do well in the corral and you think the child has control, let them out in the open, but still tag along, holding that line. Be sure to keep it short enough to exert control if necessary and be very careful not to get yourself, donkey or rider tangled in it at any time. Help with CALM ADVICE and don't help with minor problems. Don't ever yell or be irritable with the child or donkey, just keep yourself under iron control — you will surely need it. The donkey must learn that the rider, and not the person walking beside him is the boss. We have had many donkeys that would behave perfectly if someone walked along beside them, and acted totally puzzled when asked to go off on their own, an obvious effect of training by leading. Stay at the walk and trot for awhile since the donkey has not been asked to canter in the open before. He may decide not to do it at all, or he may think it is a great adventure and take off for the hills!

Finally the day will come when the donkey and child can go off together alone. This may take days or weeks, depending on the two individuals involved. Have them go out first in the ring, later in the open. If another rider can go along on an animal the donkey feels safe with, it is much better. If bad habits develop go back to the ring and if necessary go back onto the lunge line and iron the problem out. Catch ANY problem immediately before it becomes a habit. You may have a lot of trouble at times with the donkey trying to make the rider let him go back to the pasture and his friends. NEVER ALLOW THIS TO HAPPEN. If the donkey does bring the rider home, take them right back OUT!

So far the donkey is still in a snaffle and going by direct or "plow" rein. If your child prefers Western riding and most donkeys are shown Western style, you will have to teach the donkey to neck rein. We have had good success with leaving our mature donkeys in snaffle and martingale, but you may choose a curb bit of some mild type at this time if you want to. Try not to choose a broken snaffle with shanks, this type of bit has a strong "nutcracker" effect on the jaw and can be quite inhumane with an inexperienced rider. Probably a regular pony "grazing" bit is fine.

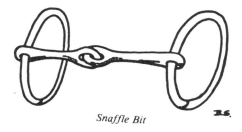

Snaffle Bit

grazing bit.

When the bit is changed, explain to the child that he should ride on a loose rein, but keeps enough contact to feel the mouth by the weight of the reins. The child must be shown the proper way to use the reins for control without hurting the donkey's mouth and be watched to make sure the reins are always even. When teaching to neck rein, do it at the walk until the donkey reins well (whether two weeks or two years after you start!) If the child uses the leg or weight aids which the donkey already knows, he will learn that the rein on the neck and the aid to turn, go together. You cannot force a donkey or horse into a turn by neck reining him, turning by the neck rein is **a voluntary** thing that the animal does, responding to the cue of the rein, weight and legs. Turn with light movements of the direct rein, but lay the neck rein on until he will turn with neck rein signal alone.

Now it is up to you and the child how far the donkey goes in training. If the donkey was only three during all this, you may possibly want to start riding him yourself after he has turned four and seems to be well grown and strong. The child will have given him a good start and you can progress toward more finish yourself, besides enjoying yourself by being able to ride. As far as the child goes, if the donkey is just being ridden for pleasure, all he needs now is time under saddle. If however, the donkey and child will be showing then they both need to be drilled in ring movements, walking, trotting and cantering in an arena, stopping, backing, show stance etc.

SADDLE TRAINING THE DONKEY WITH AN ADULT

There are several delightful things about training donkeys. One is that they are much simpler and easier to train and much more gentle than horses. This may be dull for the horse trainer but is a relief for the amateur. However they are harder to "finish" for really "fancy work" such as reining than any horse — this type of stuff is just not the donkey's chosen style. We have seen it done and know that many donkeys can do it, but their future does not lie here to my mind, but in simple, enjoyable pleasure riding for adult or child. Other things are nice too. If you fall, it isn't as far, and usually the donkey just stands there and laughs or perhaps commiserates with you. If there is a runaway it usually isn't very far or very fast. A standing joke at our house was that our "*Platero*" won't run away with you, he might consider walking away with you..."

We will assume in this chapter that the training methods in this book have been followed. Harness and/or lunge training have been done. However, many short cuts do exist, depending on your own skill and knowledge. If you know good ones that seem likely to work with your donkey, by all means use them! Do not skimp on basic training however; it is like building a house on sand to do that.

If you are small and light and the donkey is big and strong, you can start short and simple lessons when he is three. However if your conformation is hefty or his is light, it is best to start with a child or wait. In any case, don't do any fancy work until he is four, just the simple basics. Remember if you put too much weight on an inexperienced animal he will simply not be able to perform, especially at the canter. Also, if his back gets sore he may very well buck to relieve the pain and thus learn this horrible habit. If he does buck, reduce the weight, or even tie on a grain sack with less weight, but make him carry the weight. However, be careful of his back. If his back is sore, or if he bucks after he is used to carrying weight, reduce the weight, but keep up the discipline! It isn't so much the amount of weight he carries at any one time since you can build that up by degrees, it is his mental state of discipline that counts. Sometimes bucking or other "vices" are simply ways to get out of doing something that he doesn't particularly want to do. If this is so, maintain discipline, but go back one step, to something that he does well and work back up to what bothers him. DO IT AS MANY TIMES AS YOU MUST to get him to accept the thing he doesn't like. PATIENCE AND PROGRESSION BREED FULFILLMENT, that is the motto of the Spanish Riding School in Vienna, and they get horses to do things horses rarely do, so follow that and adopt it for your own! In donkey training you might do well to add persistence, to patience and progression!

If your donkey has been trained by the methods in this book he will be so gentle that unless you hurt him by being on him, it should be no problem at all to mount and ride around, since he trusts you. You could get him ready by having a child or a sack of feed on him first. Remember he is smaller than a horse and the weight on top will cause him to overbalance and overcompensate on stops and turns, and he willbe quite clumsy for awhile. He should know your voice commands, and they will prove comforting to him when you use them, as he will know all is normal even if you are in a strange place! He probably will NOT want to move at first, but use your walk command and squeeze lightly with your legs. If he still does not move, have as assistant lead him until he can deal with the extra poundage on his back. DO NOT get off without him moving at least one step if you have given the command to walk!!! If you think ahead and have an assistant, you can solve this and not let it turn into a problem. Remember that many bad habits are the result of poor training! If you tell him to walk, he doesn't, and you just get off, what motivation does he have to heed your commands?

Once he gets to walking well, have him walk in large circles and figure 8's. If he is used to going outside, take him out after a day or two in the ring. Now, for about a month, if you are not in a hurry, or in between other lessons if you are, take him on long, relaxed, easy trail rides. Use the snaffle bit and martingale and practice neck reining with weight and leg cues on every turn. Go easy on his mouth, but don't ride on perfectly slack reins, you want to educate his mouth, not ignore it! Don't pull or jerk unless you are really in an emergency. Even if he panics and runs away try to stop him by turning him or with firm pulls and releases, or finally by "sawing" the bit, that is pulling first with one rein then the other, to break up his stride and cause him to slow down and then stop. Donkeys don't usually run far, but young ones or wild burros can be just as scared as horses of many things, so watch yourself. The object of these long rides are to get him mentally and physically fit. If he has been used a lot in harness out in the open he will already be a long way toward this goal. A fit donkey can do any work you ask of him. Too many people blame the donkey for faults that come because he was not properly trained, fed or fitted for the work he is asked to do.

After this period of walking and trotting up and down hill with an occasional undisciplined gallop (at least one a ride) on safe grassy stretches, he will be ready for more intensive training. If you are doing the more advanced training from the beginning, make it only every other lesson because he needs to build up his condition and fitness to accomplish what you are asking of him.

MORE ADVANCED TRAINING

The first thing you need to do is set up a program for your work to follow in the work season ahead, and also day by day. Set goals, and try to work up to them, but try not to set a time limit if you can help it, as it will just make you nervous.

The basic work you want to accomplish in the first period of training is arena work: Walk, trot, canter, stop, stand well and still and back on command. Don't forget your ground work if you are going to show him. Keep him refreshed on walking and trotting in hand, and in standing in that elusive show stance. Later you want to trot and canter in patterns, around barrels and/or poles and perhaps work on trail obstacles. You may have special classes in mind for your shows, or special things you want to do with your donkey, which should be rather easy to accomplish when you have these basics down. Be sure to have him backing under saddle, it may take a lot of practice.

If your donkey has been trained on the longe line you will not have as much trouble with the canter as you will have if he is not used to cantering in a circle. Most donkeys find it difficult to canter in a circle at first when bearing much weight. You may have to start by getting him used to cantering out in the open and then by cantering in longer and longer segments in the arena. If you do not plan to show this isn't so important, but if you do, you have to teach him. It may take a long time before he can canter in a fairly small circle, both ways in comfort. Be patient. Just try to make it one step further each time if you can.

It is not so much difficult to achieve these basic goals as it is trying on your patience at times when something just can't seem to get right. The hardest problem of all will probably be getting your donkey to take the correct lead. All equines prefer one lead and are "one sided" about both leads and usually turning and prefer to take that lead at the canter at all times. Well, if you can stand to be 50 % right you can leave it at that. However taking the wrong lead in a turn can be quite dangerous, and taking it in the ring makes you look like a fool who can't train a donkey.

By far the best way to teach leads is on the lunge, just stop and start again and have him take the correct lead each time. You can spend a lot of time and patience doing this. If he is trained this way take him out and lunge him both ways on the correct lead before riding each day. I hesitate to tell you to keep stopping a donkey and trying to start him again as you do a horse, because it will probably make him decide that cantering is just a waste of time anyway, which is what he has been trying to convey to you from the start! He knows that the donkey has a terrifically smooth, mile eating trot which is comfortable for him and his rider — and why do you want to get there in such a hurry anyway! Unfortunately for us sometimes, donkeys are very practical animals. In any case, this stopping and starting again is the accepted way of teaching the correct leads. You will have to judge your own animal and perhaps work out your own methods. Do try whenever possible, not to ride him on an incorrect lead when in a circle, either lead is correct when cantering in a straight line.

The following steps can be used to cue and left lead from the trot, assuming your donkey is used to cantering and will take the canter fairly easily from the trot.

1. Trot in a large circle to the left.
2. Use a light direct rein.
3. Step lightly in the left stirrup and move it slightly ahead.
4. Apply pressure with your right leg at the girth.
5. Urge into the canter.

6. Cuss (it probably won't work) but those are the correct steps so learn and use them!

It may take a while for him to catch on, but if he is going to at all, he should do it sooner later. Obviously the cues for the right lead are simply these in reverse.

For those of you who don't know what the heck I have been talking about — the animal when cantering or galloping reaches out farther with either the left or the right foot, than with the other. When it is the left that is farther when both forefeet are on the ground, it is the left lead. If the right foot is the farthest, he is "on the right lead". If you are trying to train for leads and are inexperienced with them, it would be best to have a horseman give you a few lessons on leads and how to change them first.

Left lead - the left foot is farthest forward, so that if the donkey were to make a left turn, he would not have to reach across his left leg for the farthest stride.

Right lead - the right foot is farthest forward, taking the weight and length of stride to the right. The leading leg should be to the inside of the ring (the donkey would have the rail on his left). To have the OUTSIDE leg farthest forward (not in keeping with the curve of the ring) is sometimes called the Counter Canter and is an advanced command.

Cross-leading (one lead in front, the opposite in back) is also called Disunited. It frequently causes the animal to wring it's tail, and can cause it to stumble if making sharp turns, as the legs cross over and interfere with each other.

If the donkey refuses to take the proper lead, make sure he is not hurting in some way. Then find some variations, such as circling with another animal, or turning against a fence or wall, or turning toward the barn or home pasture. You can also trot into a corner and as the donkey starts to turn, make him start to canter. Sometimes it helps to stop working on leads or other difficult work for a week or so. This is definitely the case if the animal is "sour" or mentally tired of the work, or has developed muscle soreness in the legs or back. Most animals will naturally pick up the correct lead, but some never will. If you have problems with the donkey picking up the correct lead, observe it at play or at liberty. If the donkey still never picks up the correct lead on it's own, you may have a problem in the show ring.

You can make a donkey a really fine and enjoyable trail and pleasure animal. The

JUMPING IN HAND (COON HUNTERS JUMPING) OR UNDER SADDLE

Donkeys can be taught to jump both ways, but it has to be either one or the other. The techniques of jumping are so different that the animal will get set in its ways. Most "coon jumping" is done by mules, but donkeys can do it too, and if it is taught, it can be used over and over to entertain friends and strangers and even put on exhibitions, as it is very impressive and interesting.

If the donkey has been trained on the lunge line this type of jumping is tremendously easy to teach. The principle of this type of jumping in hand is that the donkey walks up to a jump or fence or barrier, stops, looks at it, then takes off from a standing position. He will jump "off his quarters" to clear the jump and then stops. There is no running before or after the jump. It was devised to help hunters cross dangerous wire fences at night, when they were out following the hounds on small mules. The hunter would drape his coat or a cloth over the fence, tie up the stirrups and the mule would jump "in hand". The hunter would then remount and go on his way. In shows this type of jumping should always be done (for mules) with the animal saddled and the stirrups tied up. Donkeys, especially Miniatures, often jump without saddles. Halters and lunge ropes are used on the heads for control.

The basic training method is as follows: Have the donkey on the lunge line and have the lunge whip in hand. Bring him up to a jump pole lying on the ground and ask him to walk, not trot, over it. After he catches on, start raising the pole two or three inches with each lesson. Sometimes you can raise it several inches in one lesson, but sometimes you will have to lower it again. Up to a point he will just continue to walk over it and these lesson win be learned rapidly but thoroughly.

At some point, either by himself or with encouragement, he will hop over the pole instead of walking and this is your first big step. Now your ambition is to get him to hop from a walk or a standing start over higher and higher poles, and not to rush them and jump from a gallop in a flying leap. When the pole gets high off the ground and you have to use jump standards to hold it up, rig a slanting pole so the lunge line will slide smoothly up and over the jump. Some people get in front and pull but it is much better to be where you have control of the hindquarters since this is what he jumps from. Keep walking the donkey up to the pole and urging him to jump until he gets as high as he can. Since you will probably never compete against mules with a donkey, don't force him, just a medium jump will make a good exhibition.

If he proves really talented and you think you can compete, don't jump him over his best height very often, as this will discourage him. Practice it just once in a while to prove to him he can do it. Never beat or scare him, just be firm and persistent. Carrots are a good form of persuasion. If he fails to make a height that you know he is capable of do not lose your temper. Go back to a place where he is confident of succeeding and confirm him on this height. Then work slowly up to the higher bar. The whole thrust of your effort is confidence and developing in him a will to jump to please

you, not because he is afraid of you. This type of jumping is a very handy skill to have when you are riding cross country, since it means that ordinary fences don't stop you! You just go right over them, and it may make a big difference in some trail rides.

Radar free-jumps for carrots!

Lone Pine Taboo - a 37" Standard x Miniature cross jack. This is enthusiasm for jumping in hand! *Taboo* is owned by John and Keith Whiteman, La Jolla, CA.

JUMPING UNDER SADDLE

The whole thrust of this work is different, being as it is a flying leap from a fast canter. Donkeys cannot usually clear much height this way, but a good many can make up to three feet, and it is a lot of fun and very impressive to the general public! (You may not see many donkeys jumping in competition, but there is no reason you should not enter your donkey in the Hunter/Jumper class in an open show!)

Begin by placing several poles in a row on the ground. It is preferable for them to be painted white because of their greater visibility. Now walk the donkey backwards and forwards over them until he walks squarely without hesitation over them. If you have ever seen a horse "refuse" a jump - squirrel sideways and bounce around the side without jumping - watch his next jump. He probably didn't come up square and may even "twist" body over the jump. Some of this is due to not seeing the fence in time, other times it is due to rider error in cueing or control.

Once he moves squarely up to and over the poles, he can start on actual jumps. At first they should be very small, not more than eight inches high build out in the open without wings. Do not expect him to jump any more than two or three jumps. When he can jump these to perfection you can begin to gradually raise the obstacles. Be careful not to over jump the donkey or raise the jumps too quickly as if you do, he will begin to refuse. Then you will have to start from scratch again. Remember, it is always quicker to be patient and avoid setbacks when you can, than to be in a hurry and find you have to start over again.

Once the jumps reach the height of two feet which most donkeys can jump capably with a moderate amount of weight on their backs, it is better not to raise the jumps any higher for a time. Instead make them broader, in order to show him that to jump far out he must also jump higher. This way he learns to jump higher and broader without being "over faced" by a too tall jump. Don't expect him to jump perfectly over the same circuit of jumps again and again because he won't. Transfer the jumps to different positions, vary the obstacles and look for jumps when out riding the trail and you will find that variety win help him a good deal.

You can buy jump standards to hold your poles up, or you can make some. It is best to jump over poles that will fall if they are hit (rubbed) hard, rather than nailed in place. You want him to lift his legs up enough to clear the jump, but not to be injured if he does misjudge and slam into it. Just resting the pole on nails is not enough to hold them, and is dangerous as well if he goes over the jump at an angle. You can make shallow cups with tuna cans, with one half of the rim trimmed away and the edges taped to avoid sharp edges. Another alternative is to use small strips of wood along the inside edge of the jump standard. This will be less steady, but can work. However, you rig your jump, make sure the pole will roll off in the same direction as the animal is travelling if he does hit it.

In-hand jumping for minis is popular at the shows. Cross bars are good for encouragement. Photo by Juanita Snyder.

BUYING TACK FOR DONKEYS
by Cindy Pollock

If you are a newcomer to owning and using donkeys, first off, WELCOME! You have probably had some trouble finding tack to fit, and got a lot of strange looks and even insulting remarks from people when you tell them you want a saddle or whatever for your DONKEY. I have found out through expense and experience that most tack shop owners simply don't know what fits donkeys in general, so it is up to you to fit the animal correctly to ensure its comfort, and a good performance. (After all, the donkey can't learn, or perform, or even act decent if it is in pain!).

STARTING AT THE HEAD

Bits: Donkeys vary so much in size that one make take a full sized horse bit and another fits better in a tiny pony bit. (Editor's note - we have found that a 4" to 4 ½" bit fits the normal standard size donkey.) Both these extreme sizes can be found in most tack shops — although there is almost always a lack of variety and quality in pony bits. If your donkey falls into the in-between size mouth, try looking through used tack, flea markets etc. I have a small bit collection and most of the older bits I have are an in-between size, apparently the size was popular years ago. "Arab" sized bits, although more expensive, are an in-between size.

Bridles: This is not much of a problem. Most donkeys can wear a horse bridle though you may have to punch a new hole or two to adjust it smaller. Donkeys have wide foreheads and large ears. A one-ear bridle is usually too uncomfortable for them, and you may have to buy or make a larger browband.

Halters: If you own several donkeys, you will probably find you need a variety of sizes. Smaller donkeys may take a horse Weanling or Pony size, and we have found that the ordinary horse YEARLING HALTER fits most standard size donkeys with average heads. Large Standards usually do fine in Horse size, while Mammoths may need Large Horse. If you are experimenting with halter size, ask to borrow some if you can, and try them on. Nylon is fine for everyday use. Nylon halters are cheaper, easy to add extra holes in, and come in the most unbelievable range of colors nowadays. Once you have the right size in nylon, if you need a leather show halter, you can go from there.

Saddles: The best fitting donkey saddle I ever had was an old "Mexican" western saddle with a fiberglass tree. Now the fiberglass tree is supposed to be pure garbage from what I've heard, and it may be for horses. However this one was spread out from use and perfectly fit my donkey's wide, round, almost wither-less back beautifully. I am sorry ever sold it but most of the time a wide tree western saddle will fit a donkey. The "quarter horse" tree is wide. Most tack shop owners win never believe that a donkey would need a wide tree, but most of them seem to. They have no real withers and their backs are round and the wide tree seems to fit that type of back best. Each donkey is different — as is each horse. You may have to try several saddles before deciding which to buy. NEVER buy a saddle without making sure it fits your donkey properly. Because of the shape of the donkey back, saddles can slip. The wide tree helps to keep the saddle in place. Also using a flank cinch will help. You will almost always need a britchin strap with a donkey. It is like using a breast collar on a horse, only in reverse! Breast collars can also be used but are not generally needed unless you ride a lot on hilly, steep country.

Editor's note — we have found the army McClellan saddle to be almost ideal for donkeys, although the tree is not wide it fits all types of backs. If you can borrow a McClellan and try it out, see if it fits both you and the donkey. Aussie (Australian) saddles are also coming into vogue, and may do well on your animal. Both the McClellan and Aussie are accepted in most show rings for Western Pleasure classes.

English saddles are another matter. You will probably want to go with an All-Purpose instead of a forward seat, jumping, or dressage saddle. You might need to have a friend who rides English help you fit this type of saddle, as it is important for the seat to be level. The English saddle may ride forward up over the shoulder more readily than the Western saddle, but it all depends on the width of the saddle and the conformation of your donkey's back.

Cinches: Oh-boy! Try to find a really quality cinch that is short enough for a little donkey. You nearly always have to buy pony cinches for donkeys and cinch makers must assume that ponies don't need good safe cinches. If you can, buy a wide, soft cinch or cover the more common narrow one with the fleece cinch cover material sold in tack stores. You can cut it with scissors to shorten it. I've had pretty good luck with cotton strand cinches but "they" say mohair is best. Whatever you use, keep it clean or it will cause sores. If you wish to ride English, have your saddle shop "take up" a regular canvas English girth to your animal's measurements. It is easy and inexpensive and works beautifully!

Ending at the Tail: Although I've always used a breetching or "britchin" to keep the saddle from sliding forward you can also use a crupper, which is used on some ponies and on most driving harness. It must be clean, soft and adjusted comfortably and the donkey has to be used to it. It should be better suited to riding on the flat or in gentle country as it might rub the tail in very severe country — in the mountains use a britchin. One of the advantages of the crupper is that it is easy and convenient to use when saddling up and most saddle shops can make one up for you easily. Also most shops can easily put the small ring it attaches to on the back of any type of saddle, western or English or Army. The crupper also looks less cumbersome in the show ring.

Someday someone may make tack especially for donkeys! But until they do, it only takes a little looking and some minor adjustments to adapt horse and pony tack. You may learn to make or modify small pieces, such as brow bands and curb straps, which is a hobby in itself. Or you may start a bit collection as I did, searching for just the right size or type.

Author's Note: We have had good experience with using a snaffle bit with a Western style running martingale on a child's donkey that did not want to turn well. This worked better than both the broken shank snaffle or the regular curb bit — the donkey stops and turns well with this rig. Just an example of using trial and error to come up with a working piece of equipment.

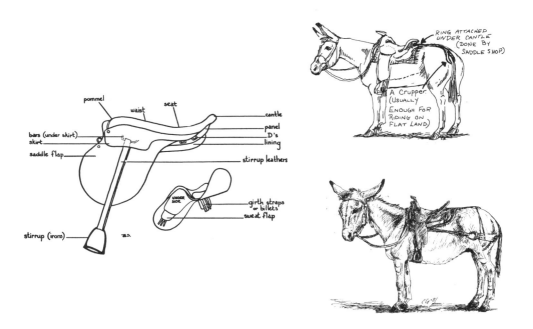

HOW TO SADDLE AND BRIDLE

To put the bridle on a donkey, present the bit in front of his mouth in your left hand, while holding the bridle upright with your right. He should accept the bit, but if he doesn't, insert your thumb into the mouth on the space bare of teeth, called the bar. Press the bar and he will open his mouth. Try to do this smoothly and with no fuss. When he accepts the bit, pull the bridle up and GENTLY over his ears with your right hand. You should always have the bridle loose enough so that it will pass easily over his ears without injuring them. If you ever have to put a tight bridle on him, never bend his ears. Rotate them at the base and lay them either forward or back on his head as necessary, very gently. Finally pull the straps all around to their proper fit (snug but not tight) and check everything on both sides of the head to make sure it is in place. This is very important because straps can be over an eye, or twisted and cause intense pain and danger to you and the donkey. This double checking will soon become second nature with you, so don't neglect starting the habit. Do not let the reins drag during the bridling operation, put them over his head before you start. If you cannot trust him to not walk away, tie him by the halter. Take the halter off his head and rebuckle it around his neck. Keep him tied this way until he is properly bridled then unbuckle the halter and control him by the reins. Don't forget when adjusting the bridle to buckle the strap that goes under his jaws, the throatlatch, and to unbuckle it before you try to take the bridle off.

Get into the habit of placing all ends into their keepers. This includes fully doing up buckles - not just placing the tongue in the hole - place the leather end under the bar of the buckle also. It is not only sloppy looking not to have the keepers in use, but will help you in checking that all pieces are fastened properly. It might save you from a bad accident, in the saddle or in harness, if a piece of harness or bridle were to come undone.

NEVER tie up your donkey by the bridle reins. Always use a lead rope snapped on to the ring at the mouthpiece of the bit. Do not put the snap on the ring at the lower end of the bit shank, as this could cause serious injury. Tying with the reins can result either in broken reins, an injured mouth, or both some day when you least expect it.

Fasten the halter back around the neck.

Put ends in their keepers!

SADDLING

To saddle your donkey, first put the saddle pad or blanket on by starting some way up the donkey's neck and sliding it back to the proper place on the back. This is to avoid ruffling the hair under the pad or blanket, since the hair grows from head to tail in direction. Place the saddle on the pad just behind the cross on the donkey's shoulders, where it seems to fit comfortably. The saddle pad should be thick enough to protect the donkey's back, not just a towel or cloth. Some English events call for no pad, in these cases the saddle fit is ABSOLUTELY essential, and then the rider will still use a pad in practice to save wear on the saddle.

The girth and stirrups should be laid over the seat of the Western saddle at this time, so that it presents a compact object, not a mass of flapping straps. On an English saddle, the stirrups should be run up and the girth laid back across the saddle. Do not heave the saddle on, but set it on gently. This should be easier on a donkey since they are smaller than horses. Once the saddle is in place, you can let the girth down on the Off side (the left side is **Near**, the right side is **Off**). Make sure the girth is lying flat and is not twisted.

Fasten the girth gently at first. The girth should be snug the first time you fasten it. Then, lead the donkey about a little. He will have blown out his belly in the "my girdle is killing me" syndrome, and this walking will cause him to settle down. At this time you can tighten the girth to the proper tightness without this problem. If you are taking a long ride you may need to tighten It later also. Also if you are taking a long ride and stop for rest periods, loosen the girth until you plan to go on, then retighten it. The girth should be adjusted so that you can slip three fingers flat, under it with relative ease. Be sure it does not ruffle the hair under it or pinch skin wrinkles. It is wise to get in the habit of pulling the donkey's feet forward (bending at the knee) or otherwise smoothing out skin under the girth before you mount and ride. If the donkey is ridden very long with the hair or skin twisted or wrinkled under the girth or cinch ring the result will be painful. If it continues, he will have a big bloody spot and will need rest for healing.

If you use either a crupper or britching on a saddle, fasten it after you have the saddle set in place. It is best to unbuckle on of the top buckles, gently set the tail in place, and then fasten the crupper. Trying to stuff the tail hair-portion first into a closed crupper and then slide it up into place will not work and ends up with the saddle too far back.

After you have done up all the fastenings, walk around the donkey and check all straps and both sides of the girth, this is very important and if you neglect it, it will be to your cost and the innocent donkey's also. Let the stirrups down on an English saddle just before you mount, and check the length. Make any adjustments on the ground if at all possible. It is relatively easy to tighten the saddle when mounted English, difficult to do so Western. This also requires a well-trained donkey who will stand patiently while you shift and squirm on his back to get room enough to negotiate the straps and buckles.

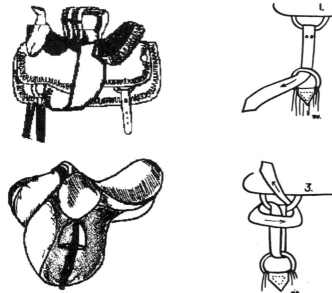

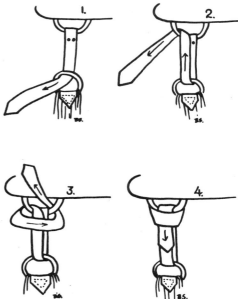

Saddles (Western above,
English below) with stirrups up.

How to fasten the western cinch

TACK CARE

Keep all tack in good, safe condition by treating it properly. Keep the bit clean. Clean leather parts regularly with a good leather conditioner. The nylon articles will benefit from a good washing in the clothes washer. Be sure all tack is hung in a dry place, secure from rats, and if possible of moderate temperature. Cold is better for leather than intense heat. The saddle and pad should be kept clean by brushing and occasional washing of the pad or blanket.

The saddle should not be stood on its gullet or hung from a stirrup, but placed on a rack or sawhorse to keep it in perfect shape. You can set the saddle down balanced on the gullet and horn while you are working (untacking, grooming, etc) but set the blanket under it to prevent scratching up the leather, and store it on the rack as soon as possible. The stirrups on an English saddle should always be run up. On a western saddle, if your stirrups tend to twist, you can turn them the way they would sit with your foot in the stirrup, and set a broom handle in them. This will help the leather hold a better shape.

BAREBACK PADS

A riding saddle pad with stirrups can be used very successfully on donkeys. Pads are really just to cushion your seat bone against the donkey's spine, and to keep hair off the seat of your pants! However, **only experienced riders should use a saddle pad with stirrups**. The most important reason for using stirrups in the first place is to save the mouth of the donkey. If an inexperienced or untaught rider rides bareback, he almost always uses the reins as a handle to keep his balance. Then he may blame the donkey for not responding to the cues he is given. If you must have a green rider on bareback, take the stirrups off the pad. The novice rider, if they start to slip, will often try to use the stirrups to right themselves. Since there is no shaped tree to hold the pad in place, shifted weight in a stirrup causes the pad to slip sideways, often dumping the rider. If a novice needs a handhold, you can use a "necktie" on the donkey. A horse has enough mane to grab for support, but not the donkey. Use a flat strap, old belt, or a real necktie (an old one dad hates and just won't wear) and tie it around the donkey's neck with a non-slip knot (or buckle the belt). It should just be snug enough for you to put your closed fist under. Then, the rider may use this for a handhold, not the reins. It will also help keep the rider's hands down near the neck and not up and flying around his shoulders.

Of course the good rider will get a lot of pleasure out of riding his donkey bareback and may feel free to do so, keeping in mind that the lack of withers makes for a sensation similar (in a fat donkey) to riding on a large barrel! Experienced riders may use bareback pads with stirrups - they will be able to compensate for the shifting that occurs in the pad. You can improve the non-slip of a pad by adding a regular cinch (most just have a flat nylon strap for a girth), but the newer pads with a flexible tree, or no saddle at all, is really best if you are training someone to improve their seat and balance.

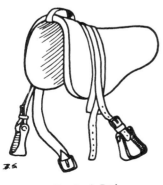

Bareback Pad

Under the belly!

FITTING YOUR TACK

Nowadays there are more than just two or three types of saddles you might wish to use on a donkey. Western saddles may be pleasure, ropers, cutters, barrel racers. All of these styles come in the traditional leather, and many in the new neoprene synthetics. For a child a pony or youth saddle is ideal since it fits most donkeys quite well. The neoprene saddles of this type are also lighter in weight, and easy to care for. Children's saddles can often be passed along, but if you decide to invest in a saddle, make sure of the fit on the animal.

If you are an adult and are buying a saddle we suggest the barrel racer's type with round skirts, as it is light and should fit. You should try a new or used saddle carefully on the donkey before you buy it since donkeys are so different in size and conformation from horses and ponies. Even with a crupper fitted to keep the saddle from sliding forward, the saddle should not be so large as to touch the point of the hip in back, not interfere with the shoulder blade in front. You will find you have the most problem with Western saddles on smaller donkeys.

When fitting a crupper, loosen the tail loop buckle so the crupper can be extended to fit comfortably without bending the tail. Then tighten snug but not tight. If someone constantly twisted YOUR tail to get it into a short, tight crupper wouldn't YOU feel like kicking his head off! The breast collar is a broad piece of leather attached to the saddle by straps attached to the rigging rings, not the cinch rings. The britching is a similar device which goes around the quarters (see diagram). It should be fitted high enough not to interfere with leg movement, but low enough not to work up under the tail. You use either a crupper on britching on a saddle, but on most harness you use both as the britching is the device the animal leans on to stop the cart or wagon. You will not usually need the breast collar unless you are riding in very steep country, as it helps to keep the saddle from sliding toward the rear of the animal. Most saddles do not come with rings for cruppers, so you may need to look into having them added. With breast collars, most are sized for horses. However, as with saddles, they often come in leather and nylon (synthetics) and may be altered to fit the smaller, narrower donkey.

You may need to try several different styles of tack until you find something that suits both you and your donkey. If it is just for pleasure riding and it works, don't worry about using one type of bridle with another type of saddle. It's really only in the show ring where specific tack types count. It's best to try and borrow a piece of tack, or try your friend's tack on their animal to see if you like it. Otherwise, you may become the ultimate Tack Collector - and if you are like the rest of it, you NEVER throw away a piece of usable tack! This may be fine if you breed, show and have lots of animals, but for the two-donkey owner (only one of which is your riding animal.....), three saddles, twelve bits and bridles probably are a bit much and take up more space than your entire wardrobe.... Borrow it, try it, buy it, swap it if it doesn't work!

too tight, twisted

too loose.

CHAPTER SIX

OTHER WAYS TO USE YOUR DONKEY
PACK TRIPS WITH YOUR DONKEY
By Hiram Savage

The main requirement for happy burro packing (the term burro is used most often in the far west where this type of packing is prevalent, and Hiram uses it as a matter of course) is to like and understand burros. If you can do this, everything else is easy. A burro that likes you will follow like a dog. Burros are docile animals, when they step in a hornet's nest, or the pack slips, they don't panic. When they get in a bind they allow you to help them out. Best of all, they are gentle with children. Unless your burro's feet are unusual, you won't have to have him shod either. To carry him, an ordinary pickup with side racks will do, some people even use their vans! You can get as fancy as you want with pack equipment too, but all you really need is a burro pack saddle (which is usually a simple sawbuck type), a breast strap, britching, a thick pad or blanket and a swing cinch with a 35 ft. lash rope, 1" type.

Most outfitters of pack supply places can supply you with a burro sized saddle and pack bags of some sort. Most packers use plywood pack boxes but dandy aluminum, canvas and other types are available. If you have quite a bit of gear, one of those big 11" square tin cans you can buy at recreation stores are great to have along. They are mouse proof, rainproof, and you can sink them in a creek to keep perishables cool. Our pack bags are especially made because standard mule size bags proved too large for the burros. They are canvas and are 20" long 18" high and 10" deep.

How do you get all this load to stay on a burro? The best way to learn about packing is to go with someone who knows how. Failing that, the books VACATIONING WITH SADDLE AND PACK HORSE, PACKING IN WITH MULES AND HORSES, or HORSES, HITCHES AND ROCKY TRAILS, are all good texts if you can find them at used bookstores or maybe through an internet book store. The Hee Haw book service also has a Packing and Outfitting Fieled Manual from the Univ. of Wyoming. The ones one that cover burros areis VACATIONING WITH SADDLE & PACK HORSE and the Field Manual. If you hire burros, you usually get a crash course in packing them and there are several packing courses in Western states also.

On your first trip, keep your load light and take a trail that isn't too steep. Don't make your burro's back suffer from your inexperience! BALANCE is the key to packing. Make up your side loads before you put them on. You can weigh packs on the bathroom scales (and these can also be slipped into your truck - they are small and cheap!). Try estimating loads before you weigh them and you will soon be able to judge within a few pounds. That is important because you don't have scales in the hills. I use the axe to balance out differences in the pack bags. If you have sleeping bags to go on top, don't roll them separately. We lay a 6x6' square poncho on the floor, and fold our sleeping bags into it to form a pack of about 30x36". Then we snap the poncho together over them, tuck in the ends, and there's a neat, waterproof pack cover. You can set it to one side or the other for the final balance.

When you cinch all this down with a diamond hitch you have a load that won't slip. The fit of the saddle may be altered by rasping and sanding to fit individual burros. The fit of the saddle, how tight to cinch, the adjustment of britching and breast collar are essential to the burro's comfort and health and can only be learned by experience. Follow the general rule "keep it snug". By picking an easy trail for the first few outings, you will greatly help your burro (and probably yourself!). If he is not used to the work it is essential that he become conditioned on shorter and easier trails. It is no fun trying to figure a way to come out from way back in the mountains favoring a saddle galled burro and your conscience!

Learning to throw a diamond hitch looks at first like the most complicated part of packing. While it isn't absolutely essential, it is sure a good hitch. It isn't really hard, just be sure that no matter how you learn it, from a book, or from someone else that you only watch one method. If you try it more than one way (and there are half a dozen) you get confused and it is difficult. (One version is shown in the appendix.)

Burros are not stubborn unless they have been mistreated or overworked. We have decided that much of the "stubbornness" attributed to burros is simply because people the world over expect them to do the work of an animal three times their size! All too often, people will say to us, "I guess they can pack three or four hundred pounds". This is pure foolishness. "How much can a burro pack?" is the question we are asked most. Unfortunately, we can't give you a solid figure. We have to counter the question with: how far, how steep, how long, how often, how big is the burro? But there are some guidelines to go by.

Burros, like people, vary in size, strength and physical condition. In considering how much to load on our pack burros I use my years of back packing as a gauge. The country we live in is very steep, rugged and the trails are usually poor. So if you think my estimated loads are too light, keep this in mind. I can easily pack 1/5 of my own weight when I am in soft condition and when hardened for the summer about 10% more. Our smallest burro, *Pedro*, weighs less than 350 lbs., so my formula says he should be able to carry 1/5 of his weight, or 70 lbs. We try to go light the first trip or two when the burros have pastured all winter on flat ground, yet I have put 100 lbs. on *Pedro* the first time out of the season and he did quite well with it. Now let me show you the big difference. We have a big burro, "*Mamma Girl*", nearly twice *Pedro's* size, heavy, well built and only half his age. *Pedro*, well into his 20's will carry his load 10 or 12 miles with no real strain. He'll stop to rest, then go on of his own accord. We found however, that if we put the same load on the big burro, she will be exhausted in five miles! *Mamma* is not faking. When she is toughened up for the season she can carry 200 lbs. with ease. In her case, it is all in her physical conditioning. This holds true for you and your burro alike!

How do you know if your burro is loaded too heavily? He acts the same way you would if your pack was too heavy. If he comes right along, moves easily under the load and doesn't stop too often to blow, or lie down, you can assume he has what he can handle. Ours stop on the steep places when they need to, and proceed when ready.

Right here, I'd like to get in my two cents worth about leading burros. Don't! Not unless you are in populated or restricted areas where you have to that is, or if your animal is new at the game or for some reason particularly headstrong about leaving —for instance if you have brought him away from his companions and he feels he can and should, rejoin them. If the burros you have are your own, and are friends in the pasture they will want to stay together. Ours, like most burros, hate to be led, especially on the trails. They know a trail when they see one! Unlike a horse, the burro thrives on attention and you can't spoil him with it if you are intelligent about it. We let the kids play with our burros by the hour. But, here's how smart burros are. The kids can get on one in his home pasture and try to make him go. Unless he feels like humoring them, he won't budge. Take him through the gate and onto the road. If the rider is strange, he still won't go. But if any of us who have handled or packed them can simply say "come on", off we go. The burro knows he isn't going anyplace in the pasture, it's only a game. If you haul him to a trail his pasture-born security is gone and you are all he has.

He also knows that he is not going to shed his load or eat until we are in camp, so he gets there as fast as possible without killing himself. If a burro balks for no apparent reason you had better check his pack. A cinch too far forward can wear against the inside of his front legs and with his flat back the load often comes forward. At times, the side loads work forward and rub or bind his shoulders. In fact, on our very steep trails we often have to repack. Sometimes we tie the side loads to the britching. If the britching is too low, it can cause trouble by binding his hind legs and making walking difficult if not impossible. Be sure to check this point. Our burros usually stop immediately and refuse to budge if a pack slips or comes loose. If the burro is unused to muddy places or water you may have problems until you can get him convinced that he won't be killed by getting wet. Beating is cruel and useless, but prying might have to be resorted to as a last resort. Best train him at home to cross running water and mud.

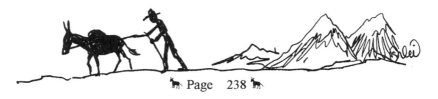

If you are a former back-packer wanting to switch to four feet to carry your load, you already know how to throw out the non-essentials. With lightweight sleeping bags, using plastic for tarp and ground sheet, two can easily go for a week with only 60 or 70 lbs. on a burro. Our essentials break down something like this.

2 down sleeping bags	10 lb.
2 air mattresses	8 lb.
1 camp kit	4 lb.
1 axe, #3 head, 2' handle	31 lb.
plastic tarp	2 lb.
Total equipment	25 lb.

That leaves you at least 20 lb. for food, which is best if you have the mountaineer type dried food. You have to have first aid kit, personal items, extra clothes, burro brush, fly repellant and grain for the burro. I have often taken four kids and one burro for a week, but a couple of us carried our own sleeping bags and personal effects for the first few days. We load the burros light, because knowing they aren't hurting and are enjoying the trip along with us helps us to enjoy our own trip more.

FEEDING

Feeding your pack burros is very like deciding how much they should pack. So much depends on body build, size, strength and how long and hard he is being worked and what he is used to eating. It is best to remember when carrying grain that mixed sweet type feeds with corn in them, have more nutrition and energy per ounce than straight oats, and you can feed and carry less than you can oats. They should have been used to this food however. In our area, there is generally some browse or graze so we just carry grain. We feed two pounds in the morning and two at night on the average. If we use them when it is very cold, we feed 6 pounds per day. If there is no graze available, the new hay and grain combined pellets are ideal. Feeding him too much of a feed he is already used to won't hurt the burro, so I always err on the generous side. If I have to make a positive statement I would say that 6 lbs. of his usual grain for a burro of average size would be more than ample. We are talking all along in this article about a family pet, not a working pack string of burros. There is just no real substitute for knowing your own animal. If he is hungry along the trail he will show it by trying to graze seriously and not just snatching delicious looking tidbits as he goes along, which all burros will naturally do.

GEAR

To adjust the major pieces of gear, in general the saddle should be set as close to the withers as possible. The withers is a little behind the cross on a burro, in the same place a riding saddle would comfortably go. The breast collar is connected to the front of the saddle tree. This is rather high, and many packers put an auxiliary strap connected "Y"fashion to the front cinch ring, which brings the pull more on the shoulders than the neck. When adjusting the breast collar, fit it snugly but not tight. The britching should be adjusted first over the hips so that the ring, from which the britching support straps hang, is located about 12 inches in front of the tailhead, perhaps 10 inches on smaller burros. Secondary adjustments are made on the supporting straps. The final position of the britching should be fairly high on the rump, so that leg motion is easy, but not so high it slips up under the tail. When the saddle is first adjusted the cinch should only be snug. Later, just before the pack is tied on,the cinches should be brought up tight. Check the cinch after the load is packed and the burro has walked a little while. A little too tight on a pack saddle is better for the animal and the pack than too loose. A loose saddle win cause sores, and a pack saddle slipping sideways is not desirable on the trail, as you can imagine! Use a good thick non-slip type pad.

SHOWING YOUR DONKEY

If you can either find, or organize a show for your donkey to appear in, you must first find out the classes and rules. Most donkey classes are something that a well trained donkey like yours can take in his stride. Rarely are they very specialized or difficult. You can also enter 4-H with your donkey if you are a young person, or ask horse show (open horse shows) officials if you can come in some classes (probably pony classes) for fun and experience. Sometimes you have to offer not to be judged, but it may be worth it for the showing experience. There are many more breed-specific (meaning Donkey and Mule) shows now than there were 30 or even 15 years ago, it is fairly easy to find a show near you. If you start out in a Donkey show and then move to Open Shows, you will be among friends who also understand the ways of the donkey and can help you past the embarrassing moments of donkey showing. If you don't know of a local club, you can contact the ADMS for a list of clubs.

PREPARING FOR SHOW

In the spring, you will be faced with a shaggy, dirty donkey. To get him ready for show you will have to get him looking much prettier than that. The way most donkey owners choose to do this is to "body clip" their donkeys. That is, they beg, buy, borrow or (No — not steal), a set of LARGE horse clippers. (The small animal or people-hair clippers you can find in the drugstore will die a quick death upon being asked to body-clip your donkey. They are fine for small areas or for touch-ups, but a big shaggy donkey and small clippers usually results in a burned out motor very quickly.)

They cross tie their donkey, read the directions carefully, make SURE THE BLADES ARE NEWLY SHARPENED and go to work! Do not forget to BATHE and dry the donkey first, or the dirt in his coat after a long winter will dull the sharpest blades. Try to get him used to the noise and on the shoulder, neck or rump where the skin is thickest first. Work with medium strokes, against the hair and "take it all off". Most donkeys get used to this right away, but you will be bound to have trouble with the legs and head and ears. If you have a "twitch" have it ready. This is a stick, upon one end of which is mounted a loop of rope, this rope is deftly twisted about a recalcitrant animals' upper lip and held tight by the stick and a helper while a brave person tries to do the legs, head or ears. The twitch is not supposed to control by pain, but it exerts enough pressure to distract the donkey's attention and make him think that the clippers aren't all THAT bad after all. If this doesn't work get that experienced horse-person I hope you will have assiduously cultivated by this time (maybe your farrier if he is nice) and have him help you. It may indeed take a couple of people who understand handling horses the first time or two.

If you can't clip, take scissors and do his tail from the brush to the root — his mane, inside his ears and maybe his fetlocks and the backs of his legs. Then get him clean and brush, brush, brush. You might consider giving him one of the special supplements that are supposed to make horses shed off early. However remember that donkeys shed off a month to two months later than horses. Here in Texas where we have summers that are broiling hot. Our donkeys may finish shedding in July and start growing hair again in August! We clip them since the shows are usually from May to October. In any case, the idea is to have him neat, clean and as pretty and well cared for looking as possible. (If you are in cooler areas and don't want to blanket, don't body clip. Use your judgement on clipping - you might want to just shorten the hair so he won't be so shaggy, but not clipped bare. Or you can use one of the modified clips that Jackstock people prefer, just the head and upper portion of the neck, the mane and tail.)

On the day of the show bathe him. If you do it the night before put a blanket (get a pony size horse blanket — lightweight — you may have to order it specially) on him so he won't get dirty again when he rolls. At the show you will want to clean his feet and probably paint them with some special "hoof blacking" or if they are white, with clear hoof polish sold in most horse supply stores. Spray him with a special "coat polish", preferably one with fly spray in it also — and he is ready. Be sure your show halter is **neat, clean, and worthy of your donkey,** and keep your tack looking clean and in good repair. Remember this is a **show**, an **exhibition**, and you are here to be seen by the public. If you have a clean, neat nylon halter, that's fine, but if you can get a nice leather halter that sets off the head, by all means go with the leather. Don't go overboard on silver, you never want to detract with it. Be neat, that's what counts the most.

DRESS UP. Look good. If there is a dress code (Western dress including long sleeved shirt, boots and cowboy hat for instance) find out and follow it. The rulebook locally used may state only Western Attire for halter, no English or other style. If not, look your appropriate best! It's easy to round up a pair of dark jeans, a good-looking Western shirt and boots, and a cowboy hat. If you don't have these, you can probably go down to the local Wal-Mart ™ store and get all of the above for about $50. If you plan to keep on showing, it will be $50 well spent, as these will be used as your show clothes - you don't have to have a new outfit for every show!

Never, never, never go in the ring looking sloppy or badly dressed. The same applies to your donkey. You are representing a breed. Donkeys have been derided as worthless for years, so don't let your dress and deportment show the public that you think your animal is not worth taking care of or dressing properly for. When you are in public you are representing all donkeys everywhere, so take it seriously, PLEASE!

A nicely built donkey groomed and turned out for the show. The owners proudly show off ribbons, the handler is attired correctly for the showring of 1993 or 1999. Ties are not usually required with men's western jackets, but certainly add a finishing touch. You can color-coordinate your clothes to set off the donkey as well.

CORRECT SHOWMANSHIP FOR THE DONKEY OR MULE FAN

Many donkeys and mules can only be shown at halter. Also many novices are beginning to show their animals and these people worry about doing things wrong, and perhaps looking stupid. There is more to correct showmanship than just giving your animal a better chance in front of the judge, there is good manners, safety and respect for tradition. This Showmanship Score Card, from the Upstate Old Timers Donkey and Mule Society, will give novices and those that are out of practice some tips on the correct way to do things. Remember, certain customs differ in certain areas, but most of these rules are basic.

A. APPEARANCE OF DONKEY OR MULE
1. Condition: Animal should be in good flesh; over fatness or lack of flesh to be discounted, animal must be sound.
2. Grooming: Coat clean, free from dust, stains, dandruff, loose hair, fly eggs etc. Mane and tail should be shaped according to the taste of the exhibitor and be even, free from burrs, tangles and trash. Hoofs should be trimmed and shaped in accordance with the needs and uses of the donkey or mule. Shoes are not necessary, but if used should fit, be tight and not show undue wear. Clinches should be smooth, hoof dressing may be used. There will be no discrimination against barefoot animals if feet are properly maintained.
3. Trimming: Excess hair should be removed from legs, fetlocks, hooves, heads, jaw, muzzle and ears. Unless animal is one of those which has a several inch coat all over and this is to be retained for protection and beauty. Bridle paths should be cut and mane and tail may be shaped in any form. Total clipping is acceptable. If braiding or banding is used on mane or tail it should be neat, conservative and suitable.
4. Tack: Cleanliness, neatness and appropriateness are what is important. New tack must be properly conditioned. Tack and harness must be in safe condition. Halters used for showing must not be dirty, dusty, worn or obviously ill fitting, much used or sloppy.

B. **APPEARANCE OF EXHIBITOR**
1. **Clothes**: Should be neat, clean, conservative, suitable as personal appointments in a corresponding pleasure class for the type of mule or donkey shown. Ladies who wish to show in conservative skirts with safe shoes (oxfords or strong loafers, not canvas shoes) should ask if it is allowed in halter classes (Most shows will not). Excesses, especially in western or farmer type attire or sloppy and inappropriate street clothes to be discounted. Person should be well groomed, clean and alert at all times.

C. SHOWING THE DONKEY OR MULE IN THE RING.
1. **Leading**: Enter the ring going left to clockwise rotation unless instructed otherwise. Walk on left side of animal, midway between animal's nose and shoulder. The lead shank should be in the right hand, 6 to 12 inches from the halter, do not hold chain, and the bight (excess) should be FOLDED in the left hand.
2. **Control**: The animal must be under control. Jacks should wear bridle with bit, or chain on halter. (This is a standard rule in most books, but it is common courtesy if not mentioned) There should be no crowding or pushing of leadsmen. There should be no interference with any entry in any way. Leadsman should not look at animal except for an instant at a time, head and eyes should be up and forward.
3. **Posing**: On command, line up side by side. There should be no crowding. Do not change position in line without orders unless forced by circumstance to do so. If you must move go behind the line to do so. Take advantage of higher ground by getting animal set: front feet higher, not lower.
4. **Showing**: Stand beside animal or facing it at a slight angle (this depends on local custom) do not do beyond center line to off side of animal. Stand in leading position when judge is working in front of and to left of entry. Positions to take

as to standing with animal vary but keep out of the judges way. When he comes to your side move away and toward the front of the animal so you will never be between the judge and the animal. Never use your feet in positioning the animal's feet. Also do not bend down and place the feet with your hand, this should be accomplished only at home in practice for the show.

5. **Stance**: Set animal with feet placed squarely and in accordance with type and use. Donkeys and mules are not stretched, but stand naturally, square on all four feet like quarter horses.

6. **Remain Showing**: When the judge is observing other animals allow your animal to relax, but you both must remain alert. Set up your animal when the judge is two or three animals away from you. Never allow him or yourself to stand in a sloppy manner, always appear alert even if relaxed. Remember that you are showing until the class is pinned (awards stated) and even then, you should continue to show your animal until the entire class has exited the ring.

7. **Attitude**: Be natural and don't overshow, fuss or exaggerate your actions. Do not undershow either. Remember you are showing the **animal** , to its best advantage so keep your mind on showing at all times.

8. **Individual Performance**: On command, lead animal directly away from judge in a straight line, towards ring steward or pre-selected spot at a walk. Assume proper leading position to do so. Stop at the proper spot momentarily and try to have animal stop with legs in proper position. Execute a pivot to the RIGHT, pushing animal away from you and walking around the outside of the animal. This is for the safety of both yourself and the ring steward or judge. Stop after the pivot to settle animal, 1 or 2 seconds and lead back to judge at a trot in a straight line, unless you have been ordered to walk instead. Stop the animal in front of the judge keeping the stop straight, and pose animal very quickly for final inspection. Stop at least 6 feet from judge. On dismissal, return to place in line. Lead directly through line, pivot and pack into line, or come around and behind the line.

D. SHOWING IN GENERAL

1. Have the animal properly trained to stand well and quietly, back and have mouth examined and feet lifted.
2. Recognize conformation faults and find ways to overcome them.
3. Be ready to answer questions from the judge.
4. Do NOT attempt to show a kicker.
5. Know where the judge is at all times.
6. Do not pay any attention to spectators or other exhibitors.
7. Be Courteous and a GOOD SPORT
8. Respond to official requests quickly and efficiently but without confusion or rush.
9. Show from the moment of entry to the moment of exit, the more "professional" you appear the more honor you do your animal and yourself.

Megan Teel, of College Station TX, Hi-Point Junior Donkey exhibitor at Ft. Worth. A winning pair!

Photo by Don Shugart

LEARNING ABOUT SHOWING

The best way to learn about showing is to first go and observe. Go to Open Horse shows, but also try and go to your local breed shows. You will get to know the people around, and more importantly you will see how your particular type of animal is groomed and handled. If you see a particular animal that places well, watch the exhibitor and see what they are doing.

Showmanship is a class that causes a lot of confusion for novices. It is not actually a halter class, it is a non-riding performance class. The only tack used is a halter, and the person works from the ground, not in the saddle. In showmanship, it is more the person being judged on their performance than the animal. The animal is a prop, but grooming and behavior do count.

Showmanship will usually have a posted pattern, or the ring steward may inform the competitor as they enter the ring. A usual pattern is enter at the walk, stop at the cone (which will be placed in the arena). Execute a turn to the right. Stop and stand square. Proceed to the judge at the trot. Stop square for inspection. Back 4 steps, and walk on to lineup.

While the judge is looking at the animal, the handler should "Quarter". This has a logical pattern, but can be confusing the first few times you do it. The purpose of quartering it to keep the animal set in a frame to move it AWAY from the judge if it should act up. Even after you are finished with your individual inspection, you should always be aware of the location of the judge in the ring and stand in the appropriate quarter. If you observe some handlers standing to the right of their animals, and all the others further down still on the left, look to see where the judge is. He is probably off to one side of the ring, right in the middle of the rows.

To quarter properly, you should practice with another person. The second person should represent your judge. Practice at first with someone who knows how a judge would move - usually an experienced shower. They can both be the judge and instruct you to your moves.

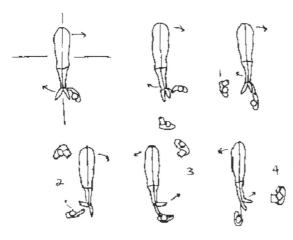

The animal is divided into 4 "quadrants". As the judge steps into each, the handler must be positioned not only to show off the animal, but to keep the judge safe as well. The animal should always be where the handler would PUSH the head (and therefore the hindquarters would swing also) away from the judge. (Arrows show direction for movement of donkey in emergency. You should train your donkey not to move during inspection.)

ROLE OF THE RING STEWARD:

If you participate in showing, you will need to understand the roles of the other people in the ring with you. Besides the other exhibitors, there will be two people in the ring. One is the judge, the other is the Ring Steward. He or she is the liaison between the exhibitors and the judge. The ring steward will direct the flow of "Traffic" in the ring, give out instructions. He/she will relay the judge's requests for gait or direction changes to the announcer. If you have questions, ask them of the ring steward as you enter the ring. You should never speak to the judge in the ring unless he or she asks you a direct question. If you suddenly find you have a question, or an animal that is giving you problems, catch the eye of the ring steward. He or she will be the one to give permission for you to leave the ring.

HALTER CLASSES

Donkeys can be shown by breed/type if desired (Miniature; Mammoth; Standard; Spotted) but experience over the years has shown that the most satisfactory way of grouping asses for showing is by size. The Southwestern Donkey and Mule Society has decided to show donkeys in this manner.

SIZE CLASSIFICATIONS:

Jacks	donkey to 36"
Jennets	donkey 36.01 to 48"
Gelding	donkey 48.01 to 56'
Sex Classifications	donkey 56.01 and up
	ALSO Yearling, and foals

MULES can be shown by type (Miniature; Saddle; Pack; Draft) but the Southwestern Donkey and Mule Society has found that it is simplest to show by size, and separate by sexes when possible.

Mules to 40"	FOALS
Mules 40.01 to 48"	YEARLINGS
Mules 48.01 to 52"	
Mules 52.01 to 56"	Many divisions by age and sex possible.
Saddle Mules 56.01 and over	
Draft Mules 56.01 and over	
(or pack mules)	

OTHER HALTER CLASSES

BROODSTOCK

Mares and foals and jennets and foals (judged separately). In this class the dam and foal are judged as a unit. 75% on conformation, 25% on presentation (grooming etc.) Local rules differ on percentages in this class, so if there are local differences, as always, take them into consideration. It is always a crowd favorite, especially if the jennet and foal have similar coloration and markings.

MATCHED PAIRS

Donkeys or mules, judged on conformation and suitability as a matched team. 50% conformation, 50% on similarity of size/coloration/markings.

COLOR CLASS

Donkeys or mules, the most colorful animal. 75% fancy color, 25% conformation.

PRODUCE OF DAM

One entry fee, two or three offspring allowed. Trophy awarded to owner of dam, ribbons to produce. Dam need not be present but is welcome. Judged as a standard halter class. 50% conformation, 20% way of going and soundness, 20% fitting and conditioning and 10% appointments and showmanship. Each 2 or 3 animals from one dam judged as one entry against other groups of produce.

GET OF SIRE

Two or preferably three get for each sire. Sire need not be present but may be paraded for benefit of audience. Each group of get judged against the other groups. 50% conformation, 20% way of going and soundness, 20% fitting and conditioning, 10% appointments and showmanship.

HEREDITARY UNSOUNDNESS IN GET OR PRODUCE COUNT HEAVILY AGAINST ENTRY.

PLEASE SHOW ALL JACKS IN BRIDLES WITH BITS, OR WITH CHAINS ON HALTERS.

Many other show classes are possible and are held over the country. This set of guidelines is primarily available to help newcomers start shows or to be available as guidelines to help horsemen with donkey and mule shows. For rules or customs in your area, write to the various Regional Clubs. If further information on any classes is desired please contact the American Donkey and Mule Society, 2901 N. Elm St., Denton TX 76201.

TIPS ON GROOMING FOR THE SHOW

Most shows are in the summer season, so clipping coats is not so much a factor of show grooming, but what other preparation should you take to get Molly, Jenny and Jack ready for the showring?

If you do show during the cooler months, you will probably want to do some sort of clipping. Draft mules and Mammoth asses are frequently shown in their heavy coats with only the face/head, ears, and throat area of the neck clipped. In Mammoth Jackstock a tuft is usually left on the end of the ears to make them look longer. This overall clip style is to show the fine clean lines of the face and throat. No additional blanketing of the animal is needed. Of course, the mane should be trimmed (usually upright or roached in these animals,) tail shaped, and hooves polished.

If you decide to body clip, make sure your donkey or mule will have a stall available, and be ready to blanket on cold nights and wet, windy days. Body clipping is taking off the entire long haircoat. Although there are English Hunter and Trace clips worn by horses, they are not that popular with mules or donkeys. Face-only or full body clips are more common. If the animal is body clipped, use a blending comb on your clippers so the donkey won't have clipper tracks in every direction over the body. Take the time several weeks before the show to accustom your animal to being clipped. Also, clipping a week or so ahead of the show will allow some of the uneven patches that invariably appear at the first clip to grow back out again.

The mane and tail have no set styles for mules or donkeys. If your donkey or mule has a mane that is long enough to lie over, if that look is good for your animal and you like that style, go ahead and do it! Remember that the mane will have to be worked with daily to train it to lie flat. It may need to be banded, and a mane tamer (neck wrap) used. Don't comb the mane out, but use a "people" nylon toothed styling brush instead. Always work from the bottom up to the roots when grooming the mane.

There are a number of clipping styles for donkeys or mules. Short upright manes (varying in length from 4 inches down to a ¾" ridge) can be clipped at any time to neaten them up. If the mane tends to fall over to one side, try it a bit shorter, or it may need to be thinned out. The alternative is roaching (shave off) the mane down to the neck - experiment with a photo or trace the shape of your mule's neck from a photo and experiment with different styles to see which will suit him or her best. The length of the bridle path, mane, shape of the hair (if clipped upright in a curve) can all contribute to the overall appearance of the shape of the neck. A long neck can be enhanced by a longer bridle path, and an upright curved mane can help a thin neck.

Donkeys tails have short body hair over most of the length, ending in the longer switch. The top part of the hair may either be trimmed (remember to blend in with the body coat so it doesn't look funny) or shaved if the rest of the coat is also shaved (body clipped). The tassel hair can be left natural, banged across the ends, or may be shaped or belled. The length of the area you shave, as with the bridle path, can enhance the hips. Always take small amount off when trimming - you can always snip a few more hairs off, but you can't stick back on the ones you have already cut.

If your mule or donkey is in a shed, slick summer coat, daily grooming will help keep it looking good for the show season. Limit bathing, as it strips away essential oils in the hair. Try to bathe at least two days before the show to let the oil come back into the coat. Brushing with a currycomb, followed by a brisk all-over with a stiff dandy brush on the dry coat will help the oil spread evenly through the hairs. Keep the animal up if possible right before a show. A quick touch-up with a wet sponge can help remove stains on socks, hocks, or hips. Baby wipes in your show grooming kit can also help with these problem areas.

Hooves should be trimmed and smoothed, and if shod, try not to have new shoes set or to trim too close to the show. Give at least two or three days if possible to let the mule's feet adjust to the new shoes or hoof length.

Hooves should be polished once you reach the showgrounds. Be sure to apply polish on a dry surface such as a concrete barn floor or aisle, or on a piece of board brought along for just such an occasion. Let the polish dry before the animal steps into the grass or dirt. Ideally, black hoof polish should be used on dark hooves, and clear on light or striped hooves. However, there is such a thing as a red/brown for use in sorrels, and the Quarter Horse trend for a long time has been to black all hooves, even those on legs with white stockings. Try this out at home to see which style will look best on your animal. Remember to remove the hoof polish after the show is over to let the feet breathe. Diluted liniment will usually remove the blacking. Wear rubber gloves or put your hand inside a baggie when working with hoof polish - or you will end up with black hands!

Last-minute trims at the show should include ears, manes, tails, and whiskers. If your animal spends most of its time out in the pasture and flies will be a problem, you may not want to entirely clip the inside of the ear. Neatly trimming the long hair and creating a smooth line along the edge of the ear will create a nice picture and still provide some protection for the ears.

Tack is ever changing, but by checking out tack stores and mail-order magazines, you can tell what's hot now and what's not. "Light Oil" finish was popular for a while, now the darker shades of leather are coming back. Silver usually stays in, while double-ear headstalls, horsehair accents, Apache trim, hand-braided reins, etc, may come and go. No matter what style of halter you choose, make sure above all that is properly fits your animal. A too-tight halter will chafe, and does not compliment a nicely shaped head, nor does a halter that is too loose and hangs on the face. Leather is best for halter classes, but a nice nylon halter that fits well can always be used at schooling shows. Most rulebooks state that silver should not be rated over clean working tack - so if you are just getting into showing, don't worry too much about fancy tack at first. As long as the tack is clean, well-fitting and not too gaudy, use what you have while you and your animal gain experience.

This jack has had his head and ears clipped for show, but the body coat left long. He wears a "stud bit" or headstall with a snaffle bit.

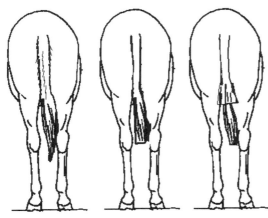

1. **Normal**
2. **shaved, banged**
3. **shaved, belled.**

DOING TRICKS

It can be very enjoyable to have a donkey that will do a few simple tricks, but don't try to teach them unless you are prepared to be patient. Your donkey should now be trained so well that you two have a rapport and understanding which should make these few tricks easy to teach.

STANDING ON A PEDESTAL
by Lily Splane

The pedestal should be made of wood, two to three foot high with a base larger around than the top surface. This trick is first, and may appear to be very simple but will require much patience as it tends to make the donkey feel insecure. He will be required to step up on the pedestal with his front feet and to stand there until a signal is given for him to step down. The chain lead should be snapped into the jowl ring of the halter and the other soft rope should be fastened around one front ankle with all slack drawn up. The donkey is then asked to step up on the pedestal with the halter lead at first, then the ankle rope is jiggled to encourage the donkey to lift his foot. When the donkey responds the foot may be placed on the pedestal at a distance with the ankle rope. Try to relax the donkey and encourage him to shift his weight to the foot on the pedestal, using a voice command. Tug at the halter lead as you ask him to step up by holding his foot stationary with the ankle rope. If he begins to fight, try to insist that he do what you asked. He may fight because he has just realized what you want and is afraid to oblige you. If the donkey may react with fighting, a good precaution is to give one-foot lessons on several preceding days, letting him put one foot, right and then left on the pedestal in practice before asking him on the succeeding day to put both feet up. As soon as he is calm he will probably suddenly decide to go up on the pedestal but will immediately step down. Let him do so and reward him. In doing tricks food rewards are very useful.

Repeat this four or five times a day, preferably not all at once, remembering never to grab at his halter to keep him up, but letting him find out for himself how easy it is. Time and repetition will find him gaining confidence. Gradually the trainer may ask him to stay up for longer and longer periods. As the voice command is used, the donkey should learn to step up with just a jiggle on the ankle rope and halter rope, until the ankle rope can be removed. The donkey may have to have his leg tapped lightly before he realizes he is to respond without any leg cues. Before long he should be performing for the trainer on voice cues alone with an occasional tug on the halter when he resists.

SHAKE HANDS

The easest stimulus in teaching this trick is to pat the coronet or tweak a few hairs in this region. You can use the ankle rope if absolutely necessary, but try to teach without it. Catch the foot as it comes up and reward the donkey with food. Concoct a voice command and begin using this and be sure you deliver it before the reinforcement (twitch, pat, rope etc.). A donkey will often learn this trick quite rapidly, therefore the trainer must control his enthusiasm and not crowd his pupil in his first day. The donkey will learn to pick up his foot on command but the trainer must eventually demand that the donkey put his foot forward into his hand. This may be done by gradually withdrawing your hand until the donkey will put his foot into it no matter where it may be. The point is, that the donkey must put his foot into your hand and know by touch that it is in the right place. It is best to teach first one leg and later the other to keep the animal from becoming totally confused. The best cue for tellng the donkey which leg to lift is to stand on the side you are working from, shift the weight to the opposite leg by turning the head slightly and ask him to shake hands.

THE KISS

There are many ways to teach this trick and this is only one of them. There are two methods often used and these usually work with a donkey. With carrots a donkey can be led up to the trainer's face and given a command, but some donkeys may reach for the trainer's face, not find the carrot and proceed to search for the hand with the carrot! A better method might be to apply molasses, honey or salt water to the face and guide the donkey's nose there, while giving the command. He will lick the solution from the trainer's face, hopefully not applying his teeth to the job. Much repetition is required which will result in a very sticky face, but soon the donkey will lick on command. A kind word and pat is in order for a correct response. In the summer when you are already probably sweating the donkeys will lick you for the salt on your face and you can give up he sticky stuff. Our advice is to try salt water first because if he will lick you for that, you don't have to get all icky with honey or molasses!!!

COUNTING

The donkey should be tied up, preferably in a corner of a stall. This is necessary because the donkey may respond to the cue used by moving sideways. Your training tool would be a nail or your finger if the donkey is sensitive. The donkey is asked to count to one, then pricked GENTLY PLEASE, or touched with the nail. An immediate reaction is usually achieved by pricking just below the elbow or knee. Most donkeys will react by pawing. When he paws the desired number grasp his leg and place it back down, rewarding him as you do so. Repeat, always grasping the leg after he has reached the desired amount and rewarding immediately. After a few times the donkey will paw the desired number when you point your finger at the cue spot, then later will respond to voice command only. Formerly learned numbers should be run through before another number is taught. The voice command should always come before the cue, regardless of whether he has learned its meaning or not. If the donkey will not respond when a new commands introduced just prick him until he has reached the number you desire. Usually a donkey will paw for an unfamiliar command, always stopping at the last number he learned. Then just prick the leg gently once more for one extra paw. This prick is a SIGNAL not a punishment remember! Through repetition the donkey will learn that five is just one more than four because you pricked him to get one more paw. Always pronounce your number commands for counting very distinctly. Keep only from 1 to 10 as more would confuse him. For best results do not ask your numbers in order.

LAY DOWN

Trust is the main factor in teaching the donkey to lay down. A running W or a knee strap may be used, the knee strap being safer and more dependable. The knee strap is wrapped or buckled snug around the pastern, run up to the forearm, the leg is bent at the knee and the strap wrapped over and around the folded leg just above the knee and fastened just at the pastern buckle. The donkey is now left with no support on one side of his forehand. To unbalance and unload the donkey quietly and safely to his knees is our object.. Take the lead of the halter and bring it around to the opposite side of the tied up leg, then drape the lead over the shoulder so the end dangles on the side of the tied up leg. With a steady pull on the lead rope from this side hopefully the donkey's head will come around and he will sway and fall lightly to one knee. BE SURE YOU ARE WORKING ON SOFT GROUND!!!!! At this point the lead is kept tight and a voice command is given for the donkey to lay down. The voice command should be repeated constantly during the operation. Persuade the donkey to hold his position and fold his other leg under him so as to be on both knees, always remembering to keep his head around to keep him from recovering. If it is not possible for you to do this alone, have an assistant lean on the donkey's hip on the opposite side you are on, to persuade him to flop his rear end over on the ground. Usually on the first pull the donkey will flop over voluntarily without much fuss but sometimes they won't! The only way to counteract his efforts to regain his feet is fast reflexes and a good sense of balance on your part!

If he really fights it is best to use a "Running W" and not have a lot of fuss over a simple trick. Once you have succeeded in downing the donkey gently, keep his head folded over onto his shoulder. Talk to him and rub him all over to relax him. When you feel you can, release his head slowly and gently in order to lay it down flat. When he shows any signs of a struggle to regain his feet, pull his head back upon his shoulder and repeat this until he will allow you to straighten his head and he will lay completely flat and relaxed and will show no desire to get up. Pet him and make him as comfortable as possible. Keep him down for 10 to 15 minutes and then release him. If he shows reluctance to get up, stand at his back and reach over and pull at his tail a few times. He will probably move fast to get up (even though you didn't hurt him) so stand clear. This procedure may be done twice daily with lessons far apart. Use your voice command first and then employ your reinforcement if he shows no signs of responding.

Later the knee strap may be removed and the trainer can hold up the leg. Eventually all that will be required is the command and a tap on the leg. It is best to use the same leg at all times. This is a lengthy trick to perfect and will take patience and time. Cruelty is uncalled for and will only frighten him and perhaps prevent his ever learning. This trick can take from 4 to 13 weeks to perfect, so take it easy.

PLAY SICK

When the donkey is very practiced at laying down he may be taught to play sick. By poking the flank immediately after a voice command the donkey will bend his head over onto his shoulder to see what is annoying him. After a few times of poking him in the flank after a command the donkey will respond as desired when you point to his flank and ask him "is this where it hurts". He may also be taught to rise when you "crank his tail" by grasping the tail and gently winding it in a circular motion, it does not hurt, but is so odd that he will get up when you do it. Be careful and don't annoy him too much to cause him to tuck his tail or take a swipe at you with his hind foot — if he does it is your fault.

Once the novice understands what training is and that in its simplicity it is actually only cause and effect and that certain stimuli result in a specific reaction, he may want to experiment with the donkey. When the trainer realizes that there is no end to what he can derive from a simple knowledge of donkey psychology he may want to invent a few of his own tricks and find ways of teaching them. It will take a trainer's imagination to get the results he wants, but the imaginative, open minded, thoughtful trainer will find his experiences, discoveries and pleasure endless. The donkey will enjoy it as much as the trainer will when it is done properly because what the donkey wants more than food or even a dust bath is human love and attention, and in the pastime he can get it in full measure.

JOIN A PARADE
by Joan and Joe Case, Pleasanton, California

Entering your donkey in a parade can be great fun. It can also promote knowledge and appreciation for our long eared friends by exposing them to an extremely varied audience; most of these people would not seek out or attend halter and performance shows or otherwise learn of the donkey's appeal and versatility.

To make a positive impression, however, it is imperative that your animal be well mannered and trust its handler. If you are patient and confident, your animal will soon come to love the fun of going with the family and having an opportunity to show off. Like most animals (including ourselves) donkeys have a good measure of the theatrical ham as part of their ego. It's amusing to watch a tired old brood-jennet straighten her back, suck in her gut, lift her head and ears and move out at a smart walk in a parade. She will be especially elegant if she has a foal at her side to show the world. However, for you, the handler, this jennet-foal combination is fairly sure to create a riot. All children and most adults are drawn to foals like magnets, so be prepared.

How do you find out about parades in your area? A good place to start is to contact your community Chamber of Commerce and those of surrounding towns, and local horse associations and Sheriff's Posses (the mounted kind). Usually you must make out an application form for the parade describing your unit (animal at halter - donkey and cart - etc.) You must also choose the category that you wish to be included in such as various riding classes, pleasure driving, novelty, historical or whatever is offered. Find out about classifications rules and requirements. Many communities organize and judge parade entries by state or local horsemen's association rules. Enter your animal properly, especially if you choose to complete for ribbons or awards (and why not!), because you could be great in one class and a flop in another. As a rule, the novelty class has a lot of latitude for the novice who has had little parade experience or who does not own a well schooled riding or driving animal. In any class rules of safety, decency and courtesy are expected to be followed.

Because parades are intended to be showy crowd pleasers, judging criteria might be quite different than that for shows. Find out in advance if you can. A great deal of emphasis is frequently placed on rigging and costume and there may be less weighing of conformation and ability of the animal. If competition rules are too restrictive for your tastes, you may wish to state "not competing for awards" and simply join, the parade for the fun of going along and giving your animal public exposure and visibility. Assess the additional value to you of choosing to compete rather than to just display. Either way, remember that you must always obey rules of safety, timing, routing, etc. All parades, to be successful and enjoyable require organization and cooperation on the part of everyone.

To make the parade participation really enjoyable for everyone plan your day well, especially if entering competition. First of all, grooming and getting your "act together" always take longer than you expected. Secondly, partial or complete judging may be done in the line up before the parade even starts! This requires that you be in place about an hour to two hours before starting time. Thirdly, awards may not be presented until later in the day. For example a late morning parade that has been organized to kick off a county fair may not present awards until early evening ceremonies. In summary, allow yourself time and include feed and water for both animals and humans.

As a special confidence booster it is a good idea to expose your animal to some of the unusual encounters of a typical parade route before joining in your first parade. No one likes mini-rodeos or balky animals holding up an entire parade. If your animal is slow keep in mind that sometimes you have to "hurry it up" to keep up with units ahead of you, other times slow down or actually stop and wait. Let your animal learn that balloons, white painted lines on pavement, manhole covers, railroad tracks, flags, bands etc. are not hiding "ghosts" that are going to get them. Finding marching bands, fluttering crepe paper floats and mounted horse drill teams to get your donkey used to isn't easy. You might want to take your animal to see a parade start up point and let him smell, see and hear some of these things. Experienced show animals usually take to parades quite well, but an animal fresh out of pasture may take some hardening! Also remember that some routes are quite long and may require a lot of trotting to keep up, so be sure you and your donkey are in proper condition for this exercise. It could be embarrassing to have the parade pass you and your recumbent donkey by and leave you behind in the street while he takes a needed rest! (This happened to us with *Platero* once! Betsy)

If you can join up with your friends whom your donkey is used to riding with (such as your weekend trail riding group) you might have a better time the first trip.

With a little forethought and good training your donkey will become an impressive performer that steals the show. Have fun, and Good Luck!

Bear Track Chuck, a Mammoth Jack, and owner/rider Linda Johnson of Enumclaw WA. *Chuck* is a halter and Performance Champion.

Quarter Moon Angel, Champion halter Miniature Jennet yearling, bred by Quarter Moon Farms, Franklin TX, and owned by the Cawthons of Cele-Bray-tion Acres, Aubrey TX. Proud of our baby? Betcherass we are!!!

COSTUME CLASSES

Some of the more fun classes to participate in at shows are the costume classes. All it takes are a few props, a patient donkey, and a sense of humor. Yet there are never quite as many entries in the classes as there could be. Sit down and put together an outfit for yourself and your donkey and enter at the shows. You can get a lot of use out of one costume, and often you will find yourself adding new items or variations.

There are usually two classes for costume - one is historical, the other Humorous. You can have entries for both and switch back and forth, but you may not want to enter both classes back-to back unless you are really good ar quick change and have a lot of fast, willing helpers.

For historical, you can do a pack burro with a miner, or Mary and Joseph are always a crowd pleaser, especially kids and a small donkey. If you have a Miniature Donkey or small Standard, a kid in a bright wool poncho, a souvenir sombrero, white t-shirt and pants, and flower baskets strapped on the donkey will surely get attention. You can also decorate a small cart with flowers all over, bright feathers and flowers on the harness, and become a Sicilian Flower seller!!!

If you love to make costumes and have a patient donkey, you can do ANYTHING at all in the Humorous classes. We have seen Miniature donkeys inside a body costume portraying everything from red Fire Ants to Lions (with the handler dressed as a ringmaster in tails and big moustache) to Dinosaurs, elephants, and Elvis, complete with sunglasses, sideburns and guitar.

One notable entry in a class featured a honest-to-goodness born-without-a-tail donkey, festooned with felt tails, and three ladies taking turns with the blindfold trying to "pin" on a new one! Donkeys will usually play along patiently, so you can really let your imagination run wild, even with little donkeys (foals or Minis).

Riding donkeys can be just about anything at all, from a monk in the saddle to a pack train to a lady sidesaddle in a big skirt and party hat. Get silly, get fun, just be sure your donkey understands his costume pieces at home before hand!!!

Photo by Don Shugart

Texas Santa uses a donkey instead of reindeer to deliver in the Hot South. *WSF Radar Frequency*, a Large Standard Yearling, wears foam antlers, a big bow on his tail, and a string of sleighbells with his bandana around his neck. ADMS Nationals, State Fair of TX. Shown by Mike Posey. *Radar* is now owned by Larry L'Hereaux.

HOW TO TETHER YOUR DONKEY AT HOME OR ON A PICNIC

Most donkeys learn to graze on a piece of tether line 15 minutes after they are first tied to one. To make a tether, take anywhere from 20 to 75 feet of strong, thick rope or thick smooth chain (for safety) and put a strong swivel snap on each end. Be sure these are quite secure. Then provide yourself with a stake. Those that are made in spiral form for tethering dogs are fine in some soils, useless in loose ones. Other stakes may be found or made that are straight metal and are driven in with a hammer. These should have a swivel ring to fasten the rope to. If the stake doesn't make one yourself with materials from the hardware store. Be sure the stake is quite secure. The donkey can be tethered by his halter. Some people use a front foot, but we don't recommend that for the novice. Fasten the tether to the ring under the jaw. Make sure the donkey is not in reach of small bushes or saplings unless you are there watching him every single minute.

If you tie directly to a tree, for some reason a donkey will get the rope twisted around a bush or sapling and himself much quicker than a large tree and can easily strangle to death. We have always been in awe of the way a donkey will work himself around and around a tree until he is firmly attached with 3 inches between him and the tree and 50 feet of rope wound about the trunk!

You should make sure it is okay to tie to trees in park areas before you do so - some parks will not allow it. If you can tie to the tree, you might run a rope overhead between two trees, and then tether the donkey with a special ring to the overhead line. There are also "tree saver" wraps you can purchase if you are going to make camping and trail riding a regular activity.

NEVER TETHER YOUR DONKEY UNLESS THERE IS SOMEONE NEARBY TO KEEP AN EYE ON HIM AND NEVER LEAVE A DONKEY PERMANENTLY TETHERED AS THIS IS REALLY CRUEL!

To teach your donkey to use a picket rope (tether) tie him to it one day and sit and watch him. Let him get tangled up in it a bit and if he can't get out, **get him out**. You will find that within a few-minutes if he is mature in his judgement and not a real baby he will have figured how to cope with most things a rope does and can get out of most tangles. Some take longer than others but most can manage the rope with perfect aplomb by the third day!

swivel

tether stake

SOME OTHER FUN THINGS

* Go an a picnic and let your donkey carry the basket, and share your lunch.
* Give rides either in the cart or on his back for church and charity — lots of fun, but your feet get to hurting, don't overdo it on him or yourself
* Start a local or regional donkey and mule club or help to organize a playday.
* HOLD A SMALL SHOW, anything from a real play show to the real thing
* Take long walks or jog with him keeping you company, a great way for both of you to exercise.
* Try driving other vehicles or doing chores around the place with the donkey
* Let him haul his own manure!
* Give lectures to local groups and use him as a demonstrator model!
* Visit a Nursing Home!
*USE YOUR IMAGINATION AND HAVE FUN!

FLAPJACKIN'
by Bonnie Shields

How do you say happy birthday to someone who is give or take a few millennium, somewhere around a billion years old? Someone who is famous for her harsh treatment of friend and foe alike. Someone who is so low-down that part of her is even below sea level. Someone who is so beautiful and mysterious and full of life, that millions of people have fallen hopelessly in love with her? It ain't easy pal!

What you have to do is gather up some of her more ardent fans and just sorta "drop by" early in November when her usually hot temper is somewhat mellowed out. Then you line up four or five days of doing some of her favorite things, invite the rest of the world and stand back. What you wind up with is the fantastic event called the DEATH VALLEY 49'ERS ANNUAL ENCAMPMENT, and a whole lot of fun. As far as birthday parties go, this one's a doozy!

The Encampment started way back in 1949, some one hundred years from the beginning of the valley's so-called "modern" history. That original Encampment featured a GEN-U-INE Twenty Mule team pulling the genuine borax wagons over part of the genuine route between Harmony Borax Works and the railroad at Mojave, Calif. Soon, what had been planned as a modest celebration among 49'ers had turned into the "Biggest Birthday Bust" ever, attracting movie stars, the governor and a particularly dastardly nest of the E Clampas Vitis. Before the dust settled on the Valley Floor, 100,000 souls had found their way into this beautiful land! The traffic jam is still spoken of in awed tones.

Unfortunately, the twenty mule team is no longer a part of the festivities, but in every other way, this birthday party has grown in scope. It now includes musical contests, a square dance, lectures, tours, a gold tournament, a major western art show, concerts under the stars, bonfires, tall tales, a trail ride, a parade, and the most popular event of them all, **the Burro-Flapjack Sweepstakes.**

The Churchill Downs of assinine pancake munchin is Stovepipe Wells, at the Northern entrance to the valley. There are no grandstands, no pari-mutual windows, no military bands and certainly no tulips! What there IS, is a determined, red-bearded chiropractor in full kilt, pied-piping a team of mini-mules and a string of "prospectors" and pack burros to the pest. What there IS, is poor Walt Geisen, sweltering in his buckskin splendor, musket in hand, to start each race with the proper bang. What there IS, is about 50 eager, grinning, enthusiastic innocent donkey jugglers from all walks of life. It's men and women competing on truly equal terms, each with their own game plan well in mind. And, each with a donkey in tow, all set to mess up everything and do the thing THEIR way. What there is, my friend, is a ball in the making!

Each contestant pays an entry fee and all burros and camping equipment are furnished by your basic sadistic committee. Contestants draw for their burro and post position. Sorta an assinine version of Russian Roulette, don't you think? But all efforts are made to see that conditions are equal for each contestant. No sweets or special foods or equipment are allowed to ass-sist in the motivation of any participant.)

These are not wild burros but gentle and "Experienced Beasties", with definite ideas on how to run a flapjack race — or how NOT to run one. Their arena is a huge circle, staked out on the desert, lined with folding chairs, cameras, and cheering sweepstakes fans. Out in the center of said circle stands a quite innocent little pole, and Mr. Geisen, musket in hand. Contestants find their post positions around the outside of the circle. Burros are saddled and ready, gear is piled on the ground beside the post numbers. All is ready. The musket is raised, a shot rings out, and it's Katie-Bar-The-Door with a donkey!

First objective is to get the burro out and around that innocent little pole and back to your post position. Simplicity itself, wouldn't you say? Wrong. Hustling donkeys has never been known to be simple, and the hyperactive go-go-go member of this twentieth century is not really up to such things in times of stress. There are problems.

Take, for example, the donkey that decides to go back to the truck, and the truck is in Nevada. Or, the odd burro that develops amnesia and dis-remembers how to exactly lead. Or, the donkey that is overcome with fatigue and must sit down for a minute. Or, the donkey that develops a severe case of stage fright and leaves for home. Or, the donkey that falls instantly in love with the sweet young thing going in the opposite direction. Or---well you get the picture.

But let's suppose your favorite ass has been persuaded to complete stage one, and you're safely back to post position. Stage two should be a snap don't you think? Shure it is. All you have to do is pack all that camp gear on your partner and go WHERE??? AROUND THAT BLASTED POLE AGAIN!!! Oh me, oh my. And, you must complete this little maneuver without losing one little thing, not even your temper, Rotsa Ruck.

Stage number three, you musta made it! It's the big number three. What's number three? Unpacking of course. On purpose. And, not only must you pack all that mess, but you must place everything NEATLY on the ground in preparation for startin your fire and mixing the pancake batter. Should be simple enough. All the donkey has to do is stand there at the end of the rope. You'll do all the work, a snap.

Uh-Oh, what's this? Your partner, who up to this point has refused to get within 30 feet of you has suddenly become pushy and is horning in on the action. Gad, he's rearranging your whole camp! What IS this? And, wait a minute, WHAT IS THIS???? Your neighbor's burro just remembered about the truck and he's taking a popular short-cut right through your pancake batter! Not to mention your backside! It's a good thing ass-handlers are made of sterner stuff--or whatever that stuff is.

No matter, on to the next problem, getting the fire started, without benefit of tinder of course. And, with the generous allotment of matches provided by a benevolent association of Smokey Bear and the local fire brigade, where could there be a problem. Guess? Wouldn't you know, that blasted ass has developed a case of desert heaves and is hanging over your shoulder, hacking his little heart out. Poor dear. In rapid succession, match numbers one and two bite the dust. Asthma my eye! But, quality will out, and that tell-tale wisp of blue lifts the spirit back into the fray. Now it's time for serious work. No more foolin' around, it's flapjack fryin' time in Death Valley. Wait just a minute here. Talk about a fly in the ointment! There's an ass in your batter friend, and out of the corner of your eye you notice that the lead rope is ON FIRE!!!! Ooooooooohhhhh, Shi---, my goodness!

Well, you lucked out this time, for there was just enough batter left to put out the fire on the lead rope and still make one little pancake. Once more you become the center of your partner's universe, and the smell of exotic food cooking in the great outdoors is driving the little booger out of his gourd. He's leaning over the skillet and OH MY GOSH! THE LEAD ROPE IS ON FIRE AGAIN!

Meanwhile, back at the ranch, the judge is casting a tear-smeared eye on the whole mess, for the rules definitely state that you must keep your burro within 15 feet of the fire the whole time. FIFTEEN FEET! Currently, said ass has at least TWO feet in the fire itself, and one on your left leg, and the rope is burning a hole in your shirt, but hang in their partner. The rules state that you must cook that pancake on both sides to the point where you can lift the hot little booger with your thumb and forefinger and hold it up for the judge to see. Unfortunately, this joker can't see a thing rolling around like that and holding his sides. Serve him right if he was ----!

Wait a minute, was that a nod of approval? At least you HOPE it was, cause your right hand and the pancake have just disappeared down a donkey and it's all over but the screaming and a bandage or two. And would someone put out that confounded rope! SHOOEEE wasn't that FUN!

I can't give you any times for the results of this epic event have never been timed. It's never been quite necessary. Suffice it to say that the span stretches from 6 to 8 minutes to all afternoon per customer. And, the contestant who speaks "burro" is definitely at an advantage.

So far the men have dominated the winners circle, to the point where there was serious talk about organizing the ladies into a "team" and going into training. That could develop into an ass-tronomical undertaking, for there's this one factor afoot that has a way with human ambition. Yes, our friend, the flapjack burro, can definitely make asses of us all, should he decide we need it.

So long live Death Valley and the Encampment. And, long live the Burro-Flapjack sweepstakes and our friends two legged- and four. Me' n *Leroy* say Keep Your Traces Tight.

Bonnie Shields

Editor's Note : It's been a while since we heard of this fun sport being a regular at shows, however with a simple set of rules, you can organize your own Flapjackin' competition at local shows. There has certainly been a trend recently towards more "Fun" classes - and this one is a real crowd pleaser!!! Good Luck!

GUARD DONKEYS
Observations from Carol Whiteside, Nancy Falley, and the ADMS.

The use of donkeys to protect stock is based on a theory of two parts. One is that donkey just naturally hate canines, are not afraid of canines, and love to intimidate canines! (Author's note: Ask me about the incident where my donkey gelding pulled me, cart and all, up into a strangers yard while chasing the person's German Shepherd - embarrassing, but a good demonstration!). The other is that donkeys are very sociable animal. They like company and thrive on it, in fact they will associate intimately with almost any other species in the absence of their own kind. This is particularly true if they are trained from an early age to accept another species (such as goats or sheep) as their own.

Remember, all donkeys are not necessarily good Guard donkeys any more than all sheep dogs are good with sheep, or that all hunting dogs will hunt! You should try them out at first and watch them carefully for a while. A plus to donkeys (besides the obvious ones like personality and their loveable appearance) is that IF they don't make good guard material, you can resell them as pets. Remember that donkeys are individuals and as such, like people they take time to adjust to any new situation. You should allow at least a month, or longer to determine whether or not they are a good guard for stock.

If you plan to run a donkey with a herd of sheep, goats, cattle or whatever other animals that need protection, do let them get introduced through a fence first. A week or two would be a good introductory time. The donkey you purchase may have never seen sheep or goats and vice versa, and it is just good sense to allow them them to get used to each other's sight, smell and sound before throwing them together.

Guard donkeys should be selected from medium sized stock. Standards are usually best. The large Mammoths are not as fast and agile as the Standards and cost more. A few people use Miniature donkeys for this work. However, the small size puts these animals at risk against a larger predator or against numbers such as a pack of feral dogs. Don't get old, decrepit, or crippled donkeys, or donkeys with uncorrectable overgrown hooves.

Weanling to yearling donkeys adapt very well, but from age 1 to 3 they can be very rambunctious and have to be watched and managed very carefully. Males, even geldings, are especially bad at this age because they try to play with the sheep — and sheep do not play the same way male donkeys do! They can get severely damaged and do not seem to see the sport in it. It might behoove you to look for older animals as guards. The most successful guard donkeys are imprinted or raised with or near the species they are to guard.

All breeders agree and emphasize that entire jacks should not be used as guards due to overly aggressive behavior. Jacks have too many male hormones and will tend to bite, stomp and kick the stock. No one should have an ungelded jack unless they plan on using him as a stud. Also it is not wise to use a gelding that has been gelded when mature as the male behavior instincts will still lead him to be too aggressive. If you are going to use a male, be sure he is gelded as early as possible and raised with the stock. Also watch him carefully during the crucial 1-3 year old stage as "innocent" play behavior can be lethal to smaller animals. Sometimes 2 young geldings kept with a flock will play together and still will be good to chase predators away. Buying a gelding as a guard would eliminate the problems of breeding. Geldings *must* be checked carefully and should be put with larger stock (and less valuable stock) when checking them out. Geldings can be very aggressive. However many are absolutely excellent and will be better than a jenny as they are usually stronger, louder and more aggressive in chasing away predators. Try to get a donkey that brays loudly (your neighbors will tell you that no donkeys brays softly). This is really important in scaring away predators, particularly at night.

You will find that the female donkey (Jennet or Jenny) is the easiest to work with. They are more gentle with sheep and fully as aggressive with canines, especially if they are nursing foals. If you purchase a pregnant jennet or decide to breed her, it is a good idea to separate her so that she can foal alone. A new mother, especially a first foal mother, may be aggressive toward any unwary animal who approaches her newborn foal, so its just good management to separate the expectant jennet before foaling or as soon after foaling as possible. This aggressive behavior is usually gone after a week. Usually after this time the jenny will settle down to her job of flock protection.

Never run untried donkeys with goats or sheep who have new babies. You must be absolutely sure that the animal is trustworthy with the lambs or kids before you put them with them. Ideally the kids or lambs should be several weeks old before meeting the donkey with a fence between them. This is especially true on the smaller ranch or farm. The closer the confinement, the more careful you have to be. If you have a very protective donkey it might try to protect the baby from its mother and break the mother-child bond that is vital for the survival of the young. Alternatively it might see this newcomer as an "outsider" similar to a predator and stomp it out of existence to protect the herd it is familiar with.

For best results breeders usually put one donkey in with a group of stock in a pasture of less than 80 acres. It is hard for one donkey to patrol large acreage although he and his stock will generally be together. Once the stock get used to their donkey, they will run to him when something enters the pasture which frightens them. It may be with a large flock and several dogs, that while the donkey is chasing some of the dogs the others may be able to bring down a lamb. For this reason some owners keep two donkeys instead of one with success, but this is an experiment that would have to be carried out by each farmer on his own. Sometimes it works well and sometimes it doesn't! The rule of thumb is one donkey per herd if you are running sheep or goats. Some people make the mistake of purchasing two donkeys because they feel the donkey will be lonesome for others of its own kind, which is true, but that very loneliness is what causes the donkeys to bond with the flock. Two donkeys make up a pair of buddies and they will often ignore other animals in the pasture. They might run canines off, but not necessarily away from the animals they are there to guard. Make sure your guard donkey beds down with the stock at night if you can, as dusk, dark and dawn are the main times for predators to attack.

Try not to have other equines (horses, mules or donkeys) in adjoining pastures. If you do, you may find your guard donkey with his head together with a friend across a fence visiting instead of working. A donkey finds stock talk interesting but equine talk fascinating. If it is necessary to run your stock near an equine pasture, have an electric fence run parallel 100 feet or so from the adjoining fence raised high enough so the sheep can get under it but the donkey can't. This will usually solve the problem.

When it is cold, make sure donkeys have easy access to water or they will die. Your other stock may get by on snow or ice but a donkey needs water. Make sure there isn't any ice between the donkey and the water as many donkeys will not walk on ice. Their feet are too small and they can't stand up easily. Be sure to trim their feet regularly.

Feeding your donkey is the simplest chore of all. Unlike a big guard dog which will eat a railroad car of dog food in a lifetime, the donkey eats what you feed the stock whether it's lush alfalfa or stockpiled fescue. If you feed a ration containing rumensin or bovatek, both of which are poisonous to single-stomached animals, drive some posts around the area and erect a single line of 2x4s all around. This permits the sheep to pass under to eat and keeps the donkey out. *Watch the donkey at first!* Some of them are so greedy they will lay down and squirm under to get the food. If this happens you will have to think of something else. Always feed your donkey something every time you feed your stock. He feels more a part of the family and knows he isn't likely to miss a meal if he is always near his stock! Don't over feed your donkey. A few special treats are o.k. to keep your donkey gentle, but if they get fat they get lazy and won't do as good a job of protecting your flock. You want the donkey to feed and graze with the stock all day.

It is also important that the donkey not be allowed to become friendly with either domestic dogs or sheep dogs. Most normal donkeys will leave the sheep dogs alone unless harassed and then the danger is not great if the person is there to call off the dog. If, however the young donkey becomes familiar with domestic dogs and learns to disregard them, he will not tend to fight the wild ones off as well. *NEVER, NEVER, NEVER* harass a donkey or sic a dog on it to make it more aggressive! This may cause it to take out it's aggression on stock as well as dogs or to become so afraid of dogs it cannot function. This is a terribly inhumane thing to do in any case and a person who would do this should not be in charge of animals at all! The natural aggression of donkeys toward strange canines will take care of your problems, provided the flock is small enough and the dogs are few enough for the donkey to chase away.

The main advantage of donkeys over guard dogs, is that unlike the dogs, the donkeys can permanently live, eat and sleep with the flock. The need basically the same type of care, whereas dogs usually have to be accompanied (in some part at least) by humans. The same fence that holds in a sheep will hold the normal donkey. Donkeys usually live three times longer than dogs.

Remember, use some common sense. The best beginning is always *a controlled introduction!* As Robert Mock of Seattle, WA says, "I have heard this story so many times -- Well, the coyotes (or dogs) got into the sheep last night, so I went out and bought this damned donkey. They are supposed to guard sheep, right? We had a hell of a time catching him, fought to get him into the trailer, got him home and turned him in with the sheep. Sheep ran off to the south forty in the trees and haven't seen them since. And, I can't even get near that damn donkey to get him out of the pasture. Guess I'll have to shoot him. They guy I bought him from says it ain't his fault, that I must have done something wrong because all donkeys guard sheep, right?"

WRONG!

(EDITOR'S NOTE: The complaint we have most often is that the person is trying to raise a young donkey with sheep or goats in the proper way. However when the animal (especially the geldings) get to the rough play stage they start taking it out on the flock. Unfortunately they often stay in this frisky stage till age 3. Each animal has to be managed individually in this case. They should become good sheep guards but you need to try various things during this stage if they get too "spirited". Unfortunately it is natural for the animal to want to play at this time in its life but sheep or goats or calves just don't play like young equines! I wish I had a single solution but various things need to be tried at this stage. Some of them include putting two young geldings together. Putting the animal in with the rams or bucks, putting him in only at night etc.)

Sweet William and a friend. Donkeys will bond with another breed if kept with them.

DONKEYS GUARD CATTLE AGAINST PREDATORS
by John Conter, President - American Council of Spotted Asses

About six years ago I was talking with a neighbor rancher, Willie Oblander, out in a field. As we were talking, we could see 5 coyotes that were running loose in his 250 acre calving pasture. He was going to put about 200 bred cows in that pasture the following week. I had a big, strong, spotted jack donkey and we decided to turn him into that empty pasture the next day.

The jack was lonesome. Donkeys are like dogs or people and don't like to be alone. He searched that whole 250 acres looking for someone or something —male or female. He honked and blew and searched some more. By the end of a week not a single coyote could be found in the whole calving pasture! Willie put his cows in there and never saw a coyote during the whole calving season.

A word of caution. We later turned that same jack in with another herd of about 100 cows. He found one cow that must have smelled really good to him! He knocked her on the ground and was trying to breed her when the rancher's son came along and saw what was happening. He grabbed a shovel and hit my jack in the head and drove him out of the pasture. We never put *that* jack in with cows again! Not all jacks will try to breed cows, but some will. It is best to use jennys or johns (geldings) for guard duty.

Since then quite a few ranchers here in Montana have turned one, two or several donkeys in with their cow herd. They run together all year long. The ranchers report excellent results. The donkeys keep out the dogs, coyotes and foxes. They also stomp on snakes, raccoons, rats and even porcupines.

Donkeys are good protectors but they are terrified of bears, mountain lions and wolves (when we get them) and will flee in terror when they are around. But before they rush off they make a hell of a lot of noise to let you know that something is wrong. The call for help gives you time to jump in a vehicle to come and scare off the predator.

Spotted Asses and spotted cows. This is *Crystamarq Mario*, owned by Colleen Covey. *Mario* has been a goat and cattle guard donkey. He is a 48" Large Standard gelding.

WHAT GOOD IS A DONKEY!

by Judy Krol

A good question for the 1990's and beyond.

For those of you who like the sleeker and faster horses and mules, the thought of riding or working with a fuzzy little "hard-headed" burro just seems unthinkable. But just remember, that all of those qualities that make you like mules so well; that make mules so different (and sometimes better than) horses, undoubtedly come from the burro half!

First of all, let's take size. There are the little burros that are commonly used for gardening and packing loads that are very heavy for their size and weight. They flourish off the harsh and barren regions of Mexico, South America, the Middle East, Africa, the Orient and some European countries. These little donkeys are actually the difference between starvation and survival for many families in the less mechanized areas of the world. You, as a well fed, good sized American type would feel ridiculous on one of these little rather stunted donkeys. And you are right, you would be big on the smaller breeds of donkey. But donkeys come in all sizes, shapes and colors, just like horses and mules. They can be fed properly and ridden to good muscle tone to be sleek like a horse or mule.

As for fast, don't tell me that donkeys aren't fast. Maybe you aren't a good enough hand to make your donkey move - but friends - ask ranchers or cowboys trying to catch burros in the Western states of our country if donkeys can run! They will tell you it takes three good ranch horses to run a wild burro down. Or how a wild jack will pursue the fastest mare in a herd and have no trouble catching her. (I have a thoroughbred mare in my pasture that was retired with a fine track record, and when my jack is turned out he plants himself at her flank and there is no way she can lose him.) Swallow your ego, and admit that donkeys have speed, athletic ability (as good as a mountain goat) and stamina.

Let's look at this logically. If you are using a horse or mule for trail riding, or pleasure riding you can use a donkey just as well. You spend most of your time walking or trotting so even if you haven't advanced in training enough to encourage your donkey to lope and run fast you are going to get there just the same as. the horses and mules. So you see - what are DONKEYS good for? So far, pleasure riding, trail riding, farming and packing. There are still quite a few people in the 1990's who back pack and hike into wilderness areas with all they will need for survival packed on these trusty little donkey companions. Granted there aren't as many as in the days of the 49-ers when stories of burros saving their prospectors from death by thirst by digging water holes, or by finding a lost miners way back to camp or even finding a gold mine are now a common occurrence. But there are still a few smart ranchers out in the west who don't want all the burros shot off their grazing leases because they will tell you they have seen old burro find and dig a water hole from a dry creek bed in the worst drought and have many head of cattle. And, after all it was a DONKEY that was credited with finding the Bunker Hill and Sullivan mines of Northern Idaho! Two of the richest gold strikes in history, found by an ass!

Donkeys can be ridden Western and English and I don't think anyone can ever guess at the number of kids around the world who learned to ride on a friendly old pasture burro. In England it is and was common for most children to learn to ride Hunters and Jumpers by first learning on a donkey, and even attending the foxhunt on one before being trusted to horses. So again, it isn't a matter of the talent not being there, it is a matter of you getting that talent to the surface so that your donkey will work for you.

If riding donkeys is not your interest, how about driving? A single donkey to a small cart can be an extremely smart' looking outfit — and great fun. A two wheeled cart, especially if it has motorcycle wheels does not have to stick to the road, and a donkey in condition can take you all sorts of fun places this way. Also donkeys work very well in teams of two or four up in collar harness and make fun trail ride accompaniments or parade entries. Donkeys almost seem to be made for driving and packing, and are ideal for these two uses.

We are all familiar with horse racing and becoming more familiar with increasingly popular mule racing, but did you know they have burro races? Yes indeed, and there is even a group, The Western Pack Burro Association, that promotes these races.

There is even a Triple Crown of burro racing in Colorado each year. It is not a track with perfectly groomed turf, fancy tack and silks and jockeys. Nay, nay--in Fairplay, Leadville and Buena Vista Colorado three separate races are held each year with purses as high as $1,000 for first place. The burros are packed with 35 lbs. of mining gear and led, followed or side by side with a person that must be in as good a shape as the burro! The two of them run together, racing others like them over some of the toughest terrain in the United States. This has been going on for over 40 years and these select few are serious athletes and about their burros and their racing. If you want a good burro that will work in good condition for you ask one of them to help you select it--they know!

Donkeys are also great sports and have their own sense of humor. They play basketball and baseball all over the country--and rather enjoy the attention--now how many horses and mules do you know that participate in professional sports!

So next time there is a donkey and mule show, or an open horse show with pony classes in your area and you are thinking about leaving your pet donkey at home with the thought in your head "What good is a donkey", think again. Remember that they can be trained, ridden, packed, driven, raced, show, make mules, can be loved, hugged and cherished for their whole long life span.

HAVE YOU KISSED YOUR DONKEY TODAY?

Myryha Patton loves Donkeys. Miniature donkeys are loveable to all ages! Quarter Moon Ranch, Franklin TX.

Mammoth pack Ass, ADMS Nationals,Roseburg Oregon. Photo by Monte Snyder

Miniature Donkey to cart. ADMS Nationals, Roseburg OR. Photo by Juanita Snyder.

FEEDING AND MANAGEMENT OF MAMMOTH JACKSTOCK
From the pamphlet: **JACKSTOCK PRODUCTION IN MISSISSIPPI**
Mississippi Agricultural Experiment Station Bulletin 363

FEEDING AND MANAGEMENT OF THE JACK

The grain feed used in maintaining the jack has consisted very largely of oats with a small amount of corn. The amount of grain fed daily during the breeding season was about 1 lb. for 100 lbs. of jack's weight. This amount was found to be too much during the off-breeding season as the jack became too fat. It was necessary to reduce the amount to ¼ lb. to 100 lbs. of weight. Mixed hay, consisting mostly of lespedeza and Johnson grass was fed in amounts varying from 5-12 lbs. daily depending on amount of grazing. Every day during the year the jack had the run of a grass lot of about 1 acre in size. He was usually closed in a box stall 20 ft. x 20 ft. at night and water was always available. Flake salt was given in a box separate from the feed and was the only mineral fed.

SUMMER MANAGEMENT OF JENNETS

From March 20 to about December 1 each year the jennets were maintained on improved permanent pasture and no supplemental feed was given. No minerals were fed except salt. Water was supplied from ponds. During May and June they were usually driven to the barn three times weekly for teasing and checking purposes. During the other months of the grazing season they were checked in the pasture two or three times per week. The individual weight records show that jennets can be carried on good permanent pasture with satisfactory results. They. usually shed their winter coats and show evidence of increased thriftiness in May and June. Jennets are good grazers and their grazing habits seem to be no different from that of other species of workstock. They are less active than mules or horses and seem to be more clumsy. Occasionally one was found on her back in a terrace unable to get on her feet. The habit of rolling in dust or on freshly plowed soil is characteristic of asses, and for this reason, jennets, particulary those heavy in foal should not be grazed on freshly terraced land, particularly if the terraces are steep.

WINTER MANAGEMENT OF JENNETS

During the five winters, approximately from December 1 to March 20, all jennets except four were carried through the winter period while dry or after foals had been weaned, some being pregnant and others not. The dry jennets were group fed grain and hay in a stall 36 ft. x 16 ft. where they were kept at night. During the day, they were turned, into a dry lot where water was available. The daily ration for the wintering period consisted of 6 lbs. corn, 2 lbs. cottonseed meal, and 12 lbs. hay per 1000 lbs. live weight of all jennets. The grain was divided into two equal feeds and fed morning and night while the hay was fed at the evening feed. The ration used maintained the weight of most of the jennets during the winter. It was observed that jennets in groups winter better in the barn than do mares. There was no evidence of injuries due to kicking and fighting as is often the case when mares are wintered in groups under a shed. Jennets with late summer or fall colts were wintered in individual box stalls 12 ft. x 12 ft. and were fed more grain and less hay than the dry jennets. The foals started eating grain when six weeks or two months old. They were allowed to eat grain from the trough with their dams during the wintering period.

FOAL PRODUCTION BY TEN JENNETS

Jennets are usually bred as three year olds and foal the first time at four years of age. Jennets will show oestrus or heat, any time during the year. The heat period and heat cycle of jennets vary considerably with individuals and with the season. Some remain almost constantly in heat during the latter part of the winter period, while during the spring after they have been on pasture a month or more the length of the heat period is considerably shorter. It has been observed that most jennets will show signs of heat (foal heat) 2 to 8 days after foaling, and if not bred or if conception does not take place at that time, will return in heat 22 to 24 days following foal heat, or 24 to 31 days after foaling. Open or unbred jennets will show signs of heat at quite regular intervals, usually 21 to 24 days after the first day of the previous heat period. Jennets that are in heat usually can be easily identified. The opening and closing of the mouth in a chewing motion while around other stock is the most common sign.

During the four years breeding with the 10 mature jennets is was found that on the average, 70% of the jennets remained in heat 2-8 days, but there was considerable variation among the individuals. It was also found that the best time to breed jennets is toward the latter part of the heat period; or better still to breed them the first, third and fifth days if the length of the period is about average. The average length of gestation period of jennets was 367 days, ranging from 346 to 398 days. It should be pointed out that not all jennets show foal heat; and some after showing signs will not return in heat for several months. The usual practice of checking from 18 to 21 days after jennets have been bred does not guarantee that they are or are not in foal. Some of the jennets returned in heat 60 days or more after being bred and considered safe in foal.

GROWING LIVESTOCK
The jennets produced in this study have been developed largely on permanent pasture with a period of about 100 days during the winter in which they were fed harvested feeds. The grain feed for the weanlings, yearlings, and two year olds was corn, eight pounds and cottonseed meal two pounds per 1000 lbs. liveweight. The roughage used was Johnson grass and lespedeza hay fed at the rate of 12 lbs. per 1000 lbs. liveweight. Under this method of management the jennet colts developed normally and as four year olds they apparently possess a sufficient amount of size, bone and the other qualifications necessary to produce good, vigorous colts.

Two of the three foals were born April 22 and May 21. The mothers had been on pasture with no supplemental feed for 30 to 60 days. About August 1, the three jennets and jack foals were moved to a pasture nearer the barn. The foals were separated from the jennets about two hours each day and given a feed of oats. About two weeks time was required for the foals to become accustomed to eating grain. Oats were fed as a supplement to their mother's milk for the remainder of the suckling period. The amount consumed varied from about ½ pound at the beginning to 3 or 4 pounds per colt per day toward the end of the suckling period. On November 26 the foals were weaned and placed in their winter quarters which consisted of an acre grass lot and a shed 10 ft. x 16 ft. which opened to the south. The feed bunk and hay rack were built under this shed. The three foals were wintered together along with a filly of about the same age.

For the wintering period they were fed a grain ration made up of the following mixture:

Oats, 5 parts
Corn, 3 parts
Cottonseed meal, 1 part
Wheat bran, 1 part

The colts readily consumed the above mixture in the amount of 1 pound per 100 pounds of liveweight when fed twice daily. The roughage was principally lespedeza hay, 12 pounds of which were fed per 1000 pounds liveweight. Fresh water was available at all times. On March 20 the three yearling jacks were turned on permanent pasture where there were no other workstock except the horse filly with which they had been previously. From March 20 to October 28 no supplemental feed was given. However the pasture on which they grazed was abundant at all times. On October 28, the three young jacks were separated and placed in individual stalls and have been handled separately since that date. Care was taken at all times after weaning not to allow the young jacks to be near jennets or mules since they were intended (as is most Mammoth jackstock) for mule breeding. It is often the case that when jacks are raised with jennets or even pastured in adjacent pastures they will not serve mares readily unless a jennet is in sight The same experience has been noted in the few jacks that were raised with mules. Even with the most careful attention to this problem some jacks will become "jennet spoiled".

For the most part, the ration fed since the young jacks were stabled has been the same as that fed during their first winter. A two acre grass lot was available for the four jacks. Since only one could occupy the pasture at a time, it has been necessary to alternate them. An effort was made to have green feed available throughout the year. The grain has been divided into two equal feeds and given morning and night, the hay has been fed at night.

CARE OF THE FEET (HOOVES) AND LEGS OF YOUNGSTOCK

When the jacks were from 8 to 12 months old their feet were trimmed and they have been trimmed regularly about ever 6 to 8 weeks. Regular attention given to the feet means straighter legs and feet at maturity. Shoes have not been used. If a jack is allowed the run of a pasture day and night his feet will be in better condition than if kept in a stall. Constant stabling increases the chances of foot infection. On two occasions the feet of two of the jacks became infected with thrush, a disease that attacks the sole of the hoof and if left untreated will cause the entire sole to slough off. The disease is characterized by foul smell and the discolored dead tissue on the infected parts. The treatment usually recommended is that of trimming the infected tissue away and treating the sole with prescribed medicine. If the stalls are cleaned and kept well bedded the trouble is reduced to a minimum.

Occasionally a vigorous growing jack will become crooked in the front legs at about one year of age. This condition is caused by nutritional disturbance in bone formation. A jack foaled on Halloween night was apparently perfectly sound and normal until he was about 1 year old. At about 12 to 14 months of age his front legs began to become noticeably crooked. Up to that age the colt had been fed about all of the grain that he would consume and a good quality of mixed hay. He had been given the run of a good grazing lot where plenty of clovers and grass was available during the season.

Oystershell flour and salt were available after the colt was weaned at about 7 months of age. After the crooked condition became apparent cod liver oil was mixed with the feed and bone meal was substituted for oystershell flour but neither seemed to be effective in correcting the condition.

It is believed by some that big boned vigorous growing jacks should not be developed too rapidly for the first two years. (*Ed. note. This has since been proved by research this jack probably had too MUCH rich food instead of too little*) With the Halloween jack, since he had been raised on his mother's milk and good feed, no other logical reason for the crooked legs can be offered than that he was pushed too fast.

Light roan mamoth Jack, ADMS Nationals, the Celebration, Shelbyville TN.

Photo by Leah Patton

RAISING AND TRAINING JACK COLTS FOR USE IN MULE BREEDING

Unless jacks have been properly trained to serve mares they may be slow, uncertain breeders or even refuse to serve mares at all. The following suggestions and comment appeared in the pamphlet "Jacks, Jennets and Mules", published by The Horse and Mule Association of America Inc., 1945.

1. Take jack foal away from jennet mother at weaning time. Pasture him with a stallion foal if possible. If not with a filly or with several horses of his own age or younger. Stallion foals are best to raise jacks with as fillies and mixed horses may frighten or kick the jack and cause him to fear or dislike horses. A stallion foal will play and romp with a jack foal and teach him to act like a horse.
2. The jack destined to serve mares should never see or smell a jennet until he is completely trained to serve mares.
3. Good pasture is essential to raising a good jack. He should have high quality grain (oats) and hay, but not enough to spoil his appetite for pasture. Year round nutritious pasture is ideal for jacks.
4. Jacks should not be raised with other jacks or any other animal not even cattle as this will often make them indifferent to mares.

ACTUAL TRAINING OF THE JACK TO SERVE
by L. M. Monsees, Missouri Breeder

"When young jacks are well raised, with good feed, ample sunshine and exercise out in pasture with a stallion of their own age they will be ready at 24 to 26 months of age to breed a mare. After the weather is warm, late in the spring, take some small, gentle mare well in heat into the paddock where the jack is. Let the jack out loose but with a halter on, and lead the mare slowly around. If the jack should show signs of wanting to serve the mare stop the mare and let the jack serve her. In a day or two, before the mare goes out of heat, repeat. Do not try for over 30 minutes at a time to get the jack to serve. Try him again the next day, and if at first you don't succeed try again on subsequent days. Jacks that are properly broken will make good prompt service. Never let jacks run with jennets or mules after weaning until they are properly broken to serve mares. After a jack is properly broken to serve mares and likes to serve mares you can then let them serve jennets. Our herd of jacks will serve either mares or jennets, doesn't make any difference to them. Jacks that will not serve mares usually have been let run with jennets and let serve jennets before they were broken to serve mares. The best way to handle a jack during the breeding season is to have him supplied with an acre or two of pasture with PLENTY OF GRASS GROWING IN THE PASTURE. Have a good 14' x 14' box stall with a south door which should be kept open in good weather and let the jack go in or out at will. If the weather is rough, you may close the door, but leave it open in the daytime when it is not so rough. We don't let jacks tease their mares unless out in pasture, we tease with a stallion and confine the mares to be bred."

George E. Hineman of Kansas on pasture breeding:

"We have seen and known of many jacks that were allowed to run in pasture with mares where they did their work of serving well and got a good per cent of colts. Mares unaccustomed to jackasses will fight and kick even when in heat, so we turn a 2 year old male mule that has not been castrated with each 30 range mares about Feb. 1. Such a young mule is a most amorous animal He will keep teasing the mares and trying to cover them no matter how often they kick him. Finally mares in heat win give in and let the young mule cover them. They thus become accustomed to seeing long ears over their back and apparently get so they like it. The young mule can never get them in foal because his semen is not fertile. This way they may be covered several times at each of the three or four periods of heat in March and April; in this way the young male mule wins their confidence and they win accept him as readily as they win a stallion. About the middle of May we take the young mule away and turn a jackass in with each band of mares. They don't know the difference, accept him as readily as they did the young mule but of course the jackass gets them pregnant. In this way we have been able to range breed mares with jackasses with good success. On July 15th we take the jack away and turn a stallion in with each band of mares. He gets in foal nearly all the jackass failed to settle.

"In lot breeding where the jack does not run with the mares, we always use a stallion teaser first to try the mare. We do this for the reason that many mares will not show in heat to a jack. Also a jack will learn to tease the mare and not serve. We always hold our jack back a few feet from the mare until he is ready, then let him serve and take him right away. When a jack is broken to serve in this manner he will be better satisfaction as to serving quickly than when he is allowed to smell the mare. Our jacks in service season are allowed to run on pasture for exercise and grass and go in and out of their stalls as they choose. We feed oats for grain in the breeding season with about one third of the hay ration alfalfa and the balance some good hay such as prairie hay or sorghums. A jack of any kind should not be allowed to be where stock of any kind may come close enough to him to cause him to fret or worry. If a jack worries and becomes heated up it will be found that in testing the semen for a day or so after the jack goes through this heated condition, usually the spermatozoa of the semen will be dead. Keep the jack as quiet and contented as possible if you want him to be a sure foal getter."

WHAT TYPE OF JACK TO USE

Mule dealers who buy and sell thousands of mules are emphatic in declaring that compact, close coupled, heavily muscled jacks of good quality are the ones that sire the best mules out of average work mares ranging from 1200 to 1600 pounds. Small mares, 1000 pounds and under, may well be bred to the largest, heaviest bones jacks available or the progeny may lack size. Very big coarse mares cross best with jacks of extra quality even though they may lack some in size. Long backed, loose coupled, light bodied jacks should be avoided as these faults win appear in mules sired by them. Legs set from front side and rear perfectly should be looked for in a jack. Sickle hocks, cow hocks and a tendency to be splay footed are faults too frequently seen and such jacks should not be used.

Note: mule colts must be kept separate from other animals such as sheep, hogs, cattle or goats as they will harass such stock to death.

The ass breeds more surely in hot weather which is why jack breeding is a Southern enterprise.

A jack must be handled quietly and firmly. A bad disposition in a jack is usually attributable to harsh handling or mismanagement. Jack grooms must above all be patient and willing to help the jack not abuse it. Abuse has created many unmanageable and dangerous jacks.

Artificial insemination has proved extremely successful for larger operations and has raised the level of conception greatly in many instances. It is worth looking into for many breeders.

Well-conformed Large Standard Jacks can make perfectly good mule sires. This jack has style and conformation as well as the added bonus of color. Owned by Robert Sell, NC.

APPENDIX III: TWINS IN DONKEYS

Recent research into twins in equines project the possibility of every 1 in 5 ovulations in larger mares (draft) and 1 in 10 in Arab and saddle-type mares could be double ovulations. Yet less than 3% of all pregnancies result in live, healthy twins. Donkey jennets to produce twin foals, and mares carrying twin mule foals may have a higher survival rate due to the hybrid vigor of the mule. There have even been instances (at least 5 recorded cases) of a mare giving birth to one horse and one mule foal at the same time, having been covered by both a jack and a horse stallion and conceiving from both covers.

In many cases, the twins are aborted before they become very large. Because the equine foal is a highly developed creature at birth (meaning they can stand,walk and run quickly), they are rather large when born. The womb space quickly runs out, and one or both twins may suffer.

Most early-aborted twins go unnoticed, especially if the jennets are kept out on pasture. She is simply re-bred by the jack, and it is never known she conceived twins. Other time, one foal will die early on, the other will survive to live birth. In these cases, the jennet will deliver the second fetus along with the first foal, and it still may be small enough to just be unnoticed. However, there is a certain risk factor that the stillborn twin will die and cause both foals to be aborted late in the term - usually losing the second foal as well.

When both twins are both alive, one may be noticeably larger than the other. If the second twin is very small and weak, the chances of survival are not good. If both are similar in size, they stand a better chance of survival.

Twins do not have to be of the same sex, or of the same color. (Or as above, even the same type!) Female foals may be slightly larger and healthier (theories speculate the female hormones secreted by the dam may help the female fetus grow better). However, if you have had twins once from a jennet, you should takes steps to check each further pregnancy. If twins are born far out in a field, the change of one not surviving due to neglect is possible. Neglect in this case is that of the jennet to see she has two foals, or for the foal to be able to free itself from the sack. If it is cold and wet, the second foal, ignored by the jennet, can die of exposure.

Ultrasound on a jennet suspected of twins is highly recommended. One twin can be aborted, or if this is not the case, then you can at least be prepared for the extra steps you will need when the jennet foals.

A big jennet with healthy, live twins. Owned by L. G. Smith, Benton City, WA.

APPENDIX IV: MANAGING PASTURES

Grass is the natural food for donkeys, and although pasture management varies tremendously over the country some basics may be observed. For detailed information on pasture management in your area contact your local County Agricultural Agent.

Pasture forages grown on properly fertilized and managed soil will usually supply the nutrient requirements of adult donkeys unless they are at hard work or nursing.

Quality of forage determines its nutrient qualities. This is controlled primarily by management.

SOIL TESTS

Soil samples should be taken annually and analyzed to determine lime and fertilizer requirements.

FERTILIZING AND LIMING

Lime is essential for pastures to be at their best. It supplies calcium and magnesium, neutralizes acid soils, stimulates proper decomposition of organic matter, promotes bacterial activity in the soil and increases the efficiency of fertilizers.

Nitrogen, phosphorus and potassium are essential elements for balance fertilization. These elements, plus calcium are the backbone of the soil. Fertilizing according to soil test recommendations will save money and raise superior stock.

LEGUMES

Legumes are added to grass pastures for horses when possible. However donkeys do better on all grass pastures, and although legume mix pastures can be used, they are not at all necessary for donkeys.

STOCKING RATE

It is obvious that overstocking pastures ruins pastures. But pastures should be stocked at a rate that prevents excess accumulation of plant growth. This excess accumulation should be harvested and stored as hay before high fiber, low energy and lowered palatability result.

CROSS FENCES AND ROTATIONAL GRAZING

A farm should have enough individual pastures to keep different ages and classes of donkeys safely separated as well as allowing for rotational grazing.

Every cross fenced or large pasture should have adequate shade and a good source of clean water.

CLIPPING AND DRAGGING

As soon as donkeys are removed in a rotational program the pasture should be clipped (mowed) and dragged. This scatters droppings, decreasing parasites and scatters old growth of grass and weeds allowing new grass to grow.

WEEDS

Often weeds must be kept mowed and even killed with herbicides to maintain peak pasture production.

HAY

Make every effort to have pastures produce both hay and grazing to save money.

RENOVATION

Soil compaction can be relieved by discing and replanting perennial or annual grasses and if a pasture becomes depleted it can be disced and re-established.

OVERSEEDING

Sod-seeding dormant perennial sods with cool season annuals is an excellent method of extending the grazing season and providing high quality forage.

ANNUALS

Oats, rye, ryegrass and crimson clover are excellent cool season annuals.

PERENNIALS

Most all of the improved perennial grasses suitable for horses in your area of the country will do a good job when properly managed.

FESCUE

This is often used, but is dangerous to brood jennets and a young animal on fescue needs supplementation - if you are establishing a pasture it is best not to use it. If your pasture has fescue consult your county agent for proper usage.

IRRIGATION

In some areas irrigation would pay its cost in saved hay and feed and in other cases it would not. A careful consultation on costs and methods is necessary for this method.

APPENDIX V: TEACHING A CALF TO LEAD WITH A DONKEY

Select a donkey of appropriate size. It should be mature and well developed and a jennet or gelding, as a jack may use his teeth. Do not use a jennet in foal. The donkey should be kindly disposed toward the animals it is to lead — if it is afraid or dislikes calves or colts it is unsuitable. The equipment needed is a hackamore type headstall for the calf. If the calf is over 6 months old a ring in the nose should be considered.(Do not tie to the nose ring as primary!) The donkey should have a 3 inch wide supple leather collar with a large ring for the calf's lead. The donkey may also wear a plain halter. A chain 18" to 2' connects the two animals. There should be a swivel in the center of this chain (a strong swivel to prevent the chain from twisting). A chain any longer is very dangerous.

First Day: Put the hackamore on the calf and tie him to a strong post for at least one day, letting him go in the evening. Put a halter on the donkey and tie him close to the calf in the corral. If he is inexperienced you may need to slowly ease them close enough to be attached. Keep an eye on them after they are attached and untied from the rail or post. The calf should be on the right side of the donkey to make sure it will lead on its left side when broken. Keep the animals in a small corral to allow the donkey to get used to the calf and its situation — nothing will be gained if you let them into an area where the greater strength of the calf can give the donkey lots of trouble before he has the situation in hand. Place feed and water in the corral at opposite sides and make sure they will both eat. **UNTIE THEM AT NIGHT!** The ADMS FEELS IT IS INHUMANE TO LEAVE THE TWO ANIMALS TIED NIGHT AND DAY FOR A LONG PERIOD OF TIME. If the calf goes down the donkey may not release the pressure on the chain to allow it to rise, or if the calf gets the donkey situated to where it's wind is being cut off - both situations need URGENT ATTENTION. If the calf is very stubborn and hangs back all the time, its nose band may pull down and get over the nostrils and suffocate him or its tongue may hang out and become very swollen. If so, unhook the calf and allow it to recover and think things over for awhile.

Observe eating, drinking and lying down habits also for the safety of both animals. When they are unhooked at night, keep them in the corral together, but not hooked together. Never leave a distressed calf attached to the donkey, give him varying periods of time to recover and try him again.

In the early stages of training a donkey he may kick the calf quite severely. This does not seem to last for long and if the donkey is prone to this, attach a calf that is of lesser value than your best show calf. Most stockmen feel that the little unshod hooves of the donkey hardly make a dent on a big calf and it will take no harm anyway.

NEVER TEACH A BULL WITH HORNS TO LEAD BY THE DONKEY METHOD — USE YOUR TRACTOR OR SOMETHING.

If a donkey is straining hard and sweating after two or three days of this work turn him out for a while with the cattle and try him again later. An experienced donkey seems to enjoy this work and can even lead two calves sometimes. The problems you will encounter will probably be due to human error and lack of common sense so observe your animals with a stockman's eye, and use good sense.

Thanks to Christine Berry for her guidance in this section.

APPENDIX VI:
MAKING A SADDLE BRITCHIN

MATERIAL NEEDED

1 — 21/2" metal ring
1 — 1" metal ring
1 — 5/8" spring snap
1 — 5/8" conway buckle
2 — 1 1/2" metal "D" rings
2 — 1 1/2" metal thumb snaps
2 — 1" center bar buckles
2 — 1" conway buckles

1 — strap of heavy leather 3 to 4 inches wide
2 — 1 x 7" straps
2 — 1 1/2" x 15" straps
2 — 1 x 23" straps
2 — 1 x 35" straps
1 — 5/8" strap
2 — 1 x 4" straps
1 — piece of leather large enough to cut a 4" circle with a 5/8" tail 11" long
1 — piece of leather large enough to cut yoke to go under back jockey

Rivets, sewing awl, thread, edger and leather punch.

DIRECTIONS

Cut all pieces of leather and edge with an edger.

First step is to undo back saddle strings and remove the back jockey. Cut yoke to fit back of cantle, shaping as in sketch. Attach 1" metal ring with rivet, punch holes for saddle strings and put under jockey, re-string.

The next step is to assemble the round hip piece. The small spring-snap is attached .n the 5/8" tail of the round piece of leather. This piece serves as an adjustment for the back straps. The 5/8" conway buckle is used here, also a leather keeper. The 21/2" metal ring is centered on the 4" dia. leather. The 5/8 x 4" strap is folded over metal ring and riveted to round leather.

Next is to assemble the part of the rigging that stays on the saddle. Take the two 1 x 4" straps and fasten with rivets on the under side of each flank billet, about 5 inches down from the rigging ring. Then attach the 1 ½" x 15" straps in the front rigging rings, turning back and fastening with rivets. Run the straps under flank billet, through the 4" keeper you have attached to billet. Attach 1 ½" "D" ring by turning back leather 2" and fastening with rivets.

Attach the 1" center bar buckles to one end of each of the 1 x 7" straps, turning end back two inches, and fastening with rivets. Measure back 6 inches from each end of the wide strap, mark. Attach the straps just assembled with one rivet at the mark. Next assemble the two 1 x 35" straps with thumb snaps and conway buckles and punch adjustment holes. Center loose end in center of the end of wide strap, over the 7" strap with buckle, letting it extend 2" beyond. Rivet at strain points and hand sew in place. Dress riggin' with Neatsfoot oil and it is ready to use.

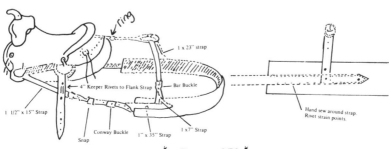

APPENDIX VII:
THE ASS: Anatomical Dissection Notes
by Dr. Suzy Schoener Burnham, DVM,
American Donkey and Mule Society Board Member,
Graduate, Texas A & M University

The specimen chosen for this anatomical dissection was a gelding ass. He was chosen because of his size, being comparable to a Shetland pony, also being used for the class. He was not chosen as an ideal dissection specimen, but rather as a prospect for humane euthanasia. This ass was lame, probably from founder, and had possible rotation on all four feet.

The approximate age was 10+ years.

The weight was 300 pounds.

COMPARATIVE DISSECTION — ASS VS. HORSE
External Features (diagram A)

1. The hair coat of the ass tends to be coarser which was the case with this specimen.
2. The ass has a very short mane, seldom exceeding several inches. The tail hairs are also short, resembling body hair from the dock to nearly 1/2 way to the end of the bony tail (caudal vertebrae). At this point the hair is—longer but still does not reach the length of the tail hair of the horse.
3. The facial hair is coarse, shaggy and the same color as that of the torso. At the muzzle however, the hair becomes finer and is usually a different color. Most commonly white, it is occasionally brown and sometimes black.
4. The ass seldom has a forelock.
5. The belly hair is usually (but not invariably) lighter and white and finer in texture than the torso hair.
6. The ass has a dorsal stripe with a cross stripe across the shoulder and sometimes displays "zebra" stripes on legs and ears. This cross will show up on other colors than dun (gray) quite frequently.
7. The ass has only two chestnuts compared to the horse's four. Two chestnuts of the rear leg are usually absent.
8. The ass also may be without a pair of ergots.
9. The jackass (male) often has vestigial teats on the prepuce of the sheath which will occasionally also be seen on the horse x ass hybrids.
10. The hoof wall of the ass tends to be more vertical than that of the horse, especially in the front hooves. The angle of the entire hoof is steeper. If 50-55 degrees is normal for the horse 60 to even 65 degrees is not uncommon for the ass. (Diagram B)

DISSECTION FINDINGS
The obvious differences between the horse specimens and the ass:

The crest of the neck was massive, extending 8-9 cm. above the nuchal ligament and 5-8 cm. laterally. The crest contained fat and fibrous connective tissue. The FCT was also found in a heavy layer of fat that extended over the back and down the sides of variable thickness like a saddlepad. The dermis over this area was found to be extremely thick. A more normal layer of soft fat was beneath the "insulation pad".

Fat deposition under the abdominal viscera was vast and normally lobular. The animal did not look fleshy or fat but when the dissection was performed it was surprising to see how much fat was stored.

List of outstanding gross findings.

Gross dissection of this embalmed, infused donkey will shed some light hopefully to what is true for all donkeys. This male however was not in good health, was a castrated animal and will therefore certainly reveal some gross pathology that would not usually be seen.

The donkey was humanely put to sleep and immediately preserved with embalming fluid. His heart and arteries were infused with latex rubber. During the course of the semester he was dissected along side a normal pony for comparison. The abnormalities that were found that were probably due to disease (gross path) were the following.

1. A scar was found in the muscle of the heart (an infarct on the myocardium) that itself seemed to be somewhat thickened. The thicker myocardium may be normal. I can't explain the source of the scar.
2. The left kidney had a large cyst that could have been congenital or due to some obstruction during development of the kidney tissue. The kidney with the cyst is visibly larger, probably compensating for the problem. The arteries in association with the kidneys were interesting and since the "peculiarity" was bilateral (both sides) I will not consider it pathological and they will be described later.
3. The adrenal glands displayed some nodular hyperplasia. This also may not be especially pathological, but it is certainly not normal. Without dissecting many donkeys it would not be possible to say what a normal donkey adrenal gland looks like.
4. Rotation and laminitis rings were found in all four feet, and one hoof had an infection inside the sole as well. The third phalanx (coffin bone) was almost pointing vertically downward. This condition in the horse would usually cause a perforation of the sole. The donkey's sole however was much thicker than would be normal. It was a full inch or more thick. Scarhorn had replaced once healthy lamellar tissue.

The anatomical differences that were discovered between the horse and the ass were several and very interesting. Some may explain some of the behavior differences of the donkey, some may be a clue to the physiological differences. The one thing we can be sure of is that much more work is yet to be done, and as I describe each difference I will try to suggest which need to be investigated further. Progressing from muzzle to tail they are as follows:

1. The nasolacrimal (tear) duct of a horse opens on the floor of the nostril, just inside the flare, but on the bottom. The donkey's however opens high laterally up on the flare itself. (Diagram C)
2. This next peculiarity should be of interest to every donkey owner. This is in the back of the pharynx (the area between the nasal sinuses on top and buccal cavity (mouth) below and the esophagus). That is to say - you could get to the pharynx via the nose or mouth on your way to the esophagus and then the stomach (see diagram). In the back of the pharynx the donkey has a recess or diverticulum about the size of a stomach tube. When your vet is tube worming your donkeys he might meet a dead end and wonder what he's done! You'd be wise to warn him of this even if you own a mule, since it is quite possible he may have a similar feature. It serves no obvious purpose but it is significant especially since the tissues from the nasal sinus back toward the epiglottis are very delicate and will bleed easily. An attempt to force the tube through incorrectly would cause damage and bleeding and pain
3. In the area of the larynx the horse has a laryngeal vessicle just lateral to the vocal cord area. In association with this pouch and vocal cord, the donkey has an additional vessicle or pouch. It would be interesting to pass a fibroendoscope while a donkey was braying to see if it has some effect on the production of the blasting cacophony but no one can say for sure at this time.
4. The muscles were very similar in the two species, all the same ones seemed to be present. The shape of two of them were slightly different. The donkey had a more developed and extensive longeus colli m. and seemed to have less of a superficall gluteal m. (see diagram)
5. The **crest** of the specimen donkey was phenominal. There is a nuchal ligament that passes along the dorsal neck from the poll to the withers that acts like a heavy rubber band that supports the heavy head. Over this and to either side is a fibrous deposit of **fat**. The specimen donkey had a deposit over his nuchal ligament that was nearly 8 inches wide! The curious thing about this fat was the amount of fibrous connective tissue infiltration. **It would seem that once deposited it would be very difficult to get rid of it.** Furthermore, this fibrous/fat later extended over the back similar to a saddle pad covering. This layer was dense with connective tissue and may provide a clue to the donkey's survival in the desert, as such a layer would insulate the body against the sun's damaging rays. The fat/fibrous layer is also covered by a remarkably thick

dermis. Neither of which is common to the horse. (diagram D)

6. The kidneys are usually supplied by one renal artery, a branch of the descending aorta. The specimen donkey had two major arteries supplying each kidney. In addition to these the donkey also had the smaller polar arteries.

7. Toward the end of the digestive tract the ingesta is fairly uniform in consistency as it enters the last part of the small colon. The last part of the small colon has haustrations that provide maximum surface area to reabsorb most of the fluid still in the ingesta. The haustra also form the fecal balls. In the donkey the haustrations were not as pronounced at the end of the colon. Instead at this point the fecal balls were already forward and were much smaller than what little haustration there was. This suggests that the water was absorbed earlier in the tract as was found to be true. The haustration was found earlier (and perhaps more efficiently) in the colon. This may sound purely academic but it may lead to some of the differences in the digestion and water retention that we already know are more efficient in the donkey. Anyone that owns a donkey and a horse already knows that the fecal balls of the ass are drier and firmer and smaller than those of the horse, which suggests more efficient use of ingested water.

These findings are not totally complete but provide a basis for further understanding of the relative of the horse that we call the ass, donkey and burro, and may also show why the hybrid mule and hinny differ rather more considerably from the horse than might be expected on first examination

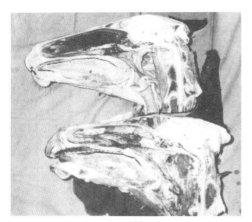

A. Dissection of head.

C. Dissection of kidneys.

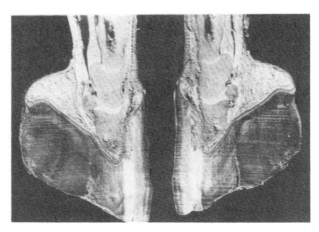

B. Cross section of hoof showing rotated bones due to laminitis and box like shape of donkey hoof.

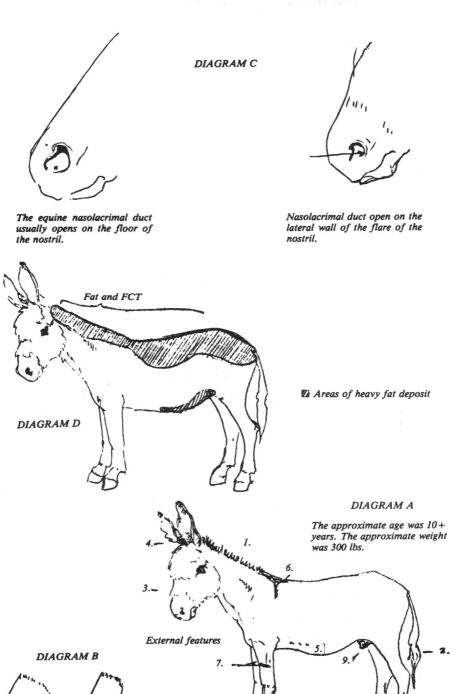

DIAGRAM C

The equine nasolacrimal duct usually opens on the floor of the nostril.

Nasolacrimal duct open on the lateral wall of the flare of the nostril.

Fat and FCT

▨ Areas of heavy fat deposit

DIAGRAM D

DIAGRAM A

The approximate age was 10+ years. The approximate weight was 300 lbs.

1.
4.
3.
6.
External features
5.
7.
9.
2.
8.
10.

DIAGRAM B

horse   *ass*

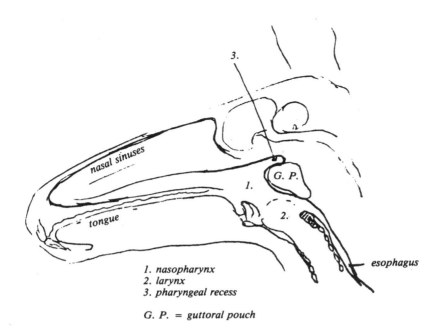

nasal sinuses

tongue

3.

G. P.

1.

2.

esophagus

1. nasopharynx
2. larynx
3. pharyngeal recess

G. P. = guttoral pouch

DIAGRAM E AND F

The longus colli muscle is a thin layer over the "brisket" area extending slightly up along the neck. In the horse, this was narrower and less extensive.

APPENDIX VIII:
PARTS OF THE DONKEY

1. jaw
2. muzzle
3. lips
4. nostril
5. face
6. eye
7. Forehead
8. forelock
9. ear
10. poll
11. crest
12. neck
13. mane (hair)
14. wither
15. heartgirth
16. back
17. point of hip

18. croup
19. point of pelvis
20. tail (bone)
21. tail (hair)
22. hip
23. hock
24. cannon
25. ankle (fetlock)
26. Hoof
27. pastern
28. cannon
29. gaskin
30. stifle
31. sheath (males)

32. flank
33. barrel
34. elbow
35. chestnut
36. ergot
37. hoof
38. coronet
39. pastern
40. cannon
41. knee
42. forearm
43. breast
44. shoulder
45. throatlatch

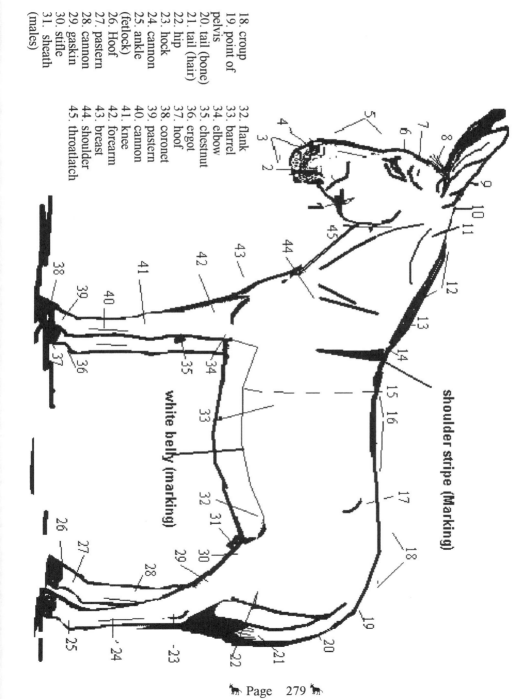

shoulder stripe (Marking)

white belly (marking)

APPENDIX IX: LOVIN' DONKEYS!!!

Missy Hutchins (at 14) and *Platero*.

Farview's Reunion, spotted jack foal

Dash For Cash - photo by Suzy Burnham, DVM.
Left, Colleen Covey and *El Burrito Cupid's Beau*.

Bluestone Maudeen E-2686

Monte Snyder and small friends, Bandon OR .

Mammoth Jack *Cactus Black Jack*,
 ADMS file photo.
Right: *Gentleman Acton Jack*, owned by
Donna Adair, TX.

"*Ahab*" owned by Judy Krohl

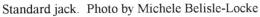

Standard jack. Photo by Michele Belisle-Locke

Part-bred Poitou *Historique of Wishing Star Farms*

Bear Track Chuck

APPENDIX X: BASIC GENETIC PROJECTIONS:

Genetics are easy to figure once you have a grasp of the basic workings. However, often genetics are influenced by a number of extra modifying factors. Bay in horses (and perhaps in donkeys) is one such complicated factor. We will try and keep the language simple, because some of the terms used in factoring genetics are frankly long and complicated. Read the chapter on breeding to get an understanding of basic terms, especially heterozygous & homozygous.

Equines basically have 2 pigments, black and red, that can be modified to produce a vast array of colors. These are base colors. The spotting, (Pinto and Appaloosa), roan and aging gray genes are all additional factors. The base coat color is one gene, spotting is another, roan a third. Therefore if you are breeding black roan spotted to red roan spotted, you have to figure projections for one base color (black x red) and for roan (roan x roan) and for spotted (spotted x spotted) and then see what combinations you can come up with.

In horses red base colors can be diluted to yellow shades such as buckskin or palomino, but there are not yellow tones in donkeys. If there is a dilution gene, the colors are only lightened (sorrel to pink-Light brown to tan-etc.) So at this point we will disregard dilutions.

Slate (gray-dun) is dominant in donkeys. Breed slate x brown and you will get either slate or brown foals. (if there is a recessive brown gene carried by the slate animal (Sl/br x br/br) Sl/br slate

Slate, recessive brown		SL/br (1,2)	Brown,	br/br (A,B)
SL/br (1A)	SL/br (1B)	br/br(2A)	br/br (2B)	
slate	slate	brown	brown	

(We also have the possibility of an animal that looks "Brownish -gray" (Brown/slate) which may be a dilution working, but these are the basic projections for your base.)

You might also have the possibility of a "surprise" sorrel foal - if both parents had the recessive sorrel. If you know the base genes involved (your slate foal had a sorrel sire, and therefore carried a sorrel recessive) and you are breeding to brown out of a sorrel and brown, you can lay out your basic projections:

(Slate)	Sl/so			(Brown)	br/so	
	1	2			A	B
1A		1B	2A			2B
S/br		Sl so	so/br			so/so
Slate		Slate	brown			sorrel

To look at spots, you need to figure your base color (as above) and then the spotting projections Spots in donkeys are caused by a partial dominant. Thus far no homozygous spotted (SA/SA) animal has been confirmed. If there were, all of the foals of the spotted animal would be spotted, regrdless of the other parent's color. (This is how one can guarantee tobiano spotted foals in paint horses) Tobiano is a partial dominant, but can be homozygous)

	Tt		Tt	(Tobiano Horse, both heterozygous)		
	TT		Tt		Tt	tt
	Tobiano	tobiano		tobiano		solid

OR

		TT Tobiano (homozygous)			tt solid	
	Tt	Tt		tT		tT (all tobianos)

Unfortunately, although it would be wonderful for the spotted donkey breeder, the spotted ass pattern works this way.

SA/sa (sa being solid)   SA/sa

SA/SA	SA/sa	SA/sa	sa/sa
Possible lethal	spotted	spotted	solid
No foal			

Frosted spotted white is a "stacked" gene color. There is a base color and spotting, and roan/graying.

After you figure base color, then spotting and then roan, you can combine all to see your possibilities.

FSW,   spotted   roan   solid
In all base colors, (non-frost)(non-spot) (non-roan, non-spot) (all base colors)

If you add in things like "extensions", you can figure the workings for colors like bay. Bay horses (red body-black legs mane & tail) can come from a black sire bred to a sorrel mare who carries one "extension gene" (the red body is kept, and the black is only on the extensions). If we have bay donkeys and true dun, you have to add these factors in on top of the base color projections and in addition to any overlay genes such as dilution, spotting, roan/graying. Due to the number of combinations, some projections can get extremely complicated. Others, such as sorrel x sorrel (a plain simple recessive), are easy.

If you remember that the key often lies in the second generation (especially when breeding for a recessive) you can at least lay out your basic projections for your foal colors.

There is no way to absolutely predict foal color (this foal will be a red roan) but you can lay out your projections. If you must breed for color choose good conformation first, and then get out the pen and paper and plot your gene crosses. Then hope for the frosting on the cake - the color you were wanting the most!!!

Half Ass Acres Kojack, EC 13522. This is a 31 3/4" spotted jack. He is base dark brown in addition, a wonderful bonus since dark-spotted small Miniatures are still few in number and highly sought for breeding. He is owned by Ronnie & Peggy Paul, Sugar & Spice Farms, Lake Jackson TX.

One of the more misunderstood equine colors in the pinto. Most people could tell you that this is a white –and-color "patched" appearance. What many do not realize is that there are distinct patterns within the general definition of PINTO.

It should also be noted that Pinto is the correct term for any equine bearing these general markings, while Paint is not. The Native Americans may have referred to their mounts as "painted" ponies, but in the modern world, the word Paint is reserved for horses that have not only pinto markings, but distinct bloodlines as well. A horse must have Paint, Quarter Horse, or Thoroughbred ancestry to qualify as a Paint horse. Since donkeys do not meet these criteria, technically they cannot be termed Paints. To have a better understanding of the Pinto patterns, the horse patterns and terminology must be explored as well. First, discard the terms *piebald* (meaning a black-and-white) and *skewbald* (any other color and white) as they are British terms, and do not recognize any pattern involved.   Pinto can also be roughly defined as horses with patched color (*broken-coloured* in anywhere other than the US) that is not of Appaloosa appearance.

There are four true coat patterns in Pinto (and Paint) horses, although the American Paint Horse Association (APHA) uses only two terms. The four coat patterns are Tobiano, Overo, Sabino and Splashed White. Tovero can be labeled a fifth pattern, but is actually a combination of the tobiano and non-tobiano coats. Many breeds carry the genes for pinto patterning, and whether it is a Shetland or a Clydesdale, each of the coat patterns has similar basic appearances. The descriptions used by the APHS are rather misleading, and we prefer to show each pattern in a progression form, rather than relying on a single example to show the overall appearance.

TOBIANO: The horse has a solid colored head with normal face marking (star, blaze, none). ALL FOUR legs will have a degree of white marking below the knee/hock (cases of Tobianos with only 3 white legs are virtually non-existent, the smallest degree may only be a coronet marking, but white is present). White appears to "flow" from the topline down. The white usually appears first at the wither or neck, then over the tailhead or croup. A horse with a white hip will usually have a two-toned tail. The marking may not be similar or identical on both sides of the same horse. Edges of the markings are usually fairly smooth, and may have a "Blue border" (blue zone, mapping,) or roaned edge. In the minimal markings, the animal will have a small white area on top of the neck, and four white legs. The pattern may at one point look as if half of the horse is white, and half dark, with even markings. In the maximal white markings, the head will still remain mostly dark, and color is retained on the flanks.

The tobiano gene is a partial dominant. Only one dose is required to produce a tobiano-marked animal. (Tt). The animal may also possess a complete dominant, or be homozygous for the tobiano gene (TT). In these cases, all offspring of the TT animal will be tobiano in pattern, regardless of the color or pattern of the other parent. (There are tovero, which are tobiano and overo combinations, and even pintaloosa animals, which have both pinto and appaloosa markings). Recent research points to the visual indicator of the TT (homozygous) tobiano as being the "paw prints" or "ink spots", small random dark markings in the white areas of the patterning.

OVERO: The horse will be of any solid color, with an extensively marked face (usually bald or apron, more than a blaze). White appears on the belly or midline, spreading up and outward. Secondary patches begin on the neck.

White will NOT cross the topline (back) unless the animal is of extreme white markings, but it can cross on the neck/mane in moderate cases. One or more legs will be colored (normal stockings will appear, but the upper leg is colored). Blue eyes are common. Edges of the markings may be hard and crisp (frame overo) or jagged and lacy with roaning (rosette). As yet it is unknown whether additional genes control the variation of frame and rosette.

Overos are usually fairly symmetrically marked on each side, with the exception of the white marks on the lower legs. The facial marking may also by asymmetrical, but the basic placement and size of the white on the body will be similar on both sides. Research has shown that the overo pattern is a single partial dominant, with a homozygous dose of the overo resulting in a lethal gene (discussed further at the end of this article).

OVERO

SABINO: This pattern is often called Sabino Roan, as it can have true roaning in the coat. This is the color seen most commonly on Clydesdales. The face has normal WIDE blazes, (not apron or bald unless the animal is extensively white). Three or four stockings will occur, higher than the knees and hocks in almost all cases. White flecks, or roaned-edge patches start in the flank and belly. The white will spread up and out from the flank, appearing secondary over the neck, and in extreme cases encompassing nearly the entire body with the exception of the croup and topline. The amount of white on both sides of the body is often nearly symmetrical, in that the rise will be the same, but the roaning on each side may not be consistent.

Sabino is often found as a "cropout" in Quarter horse bloodlines. Research (particularly by Dr. Phil Sponenberg, DVM) has recently theorized that the sabino pattern may be a natural progression of the normal "random" white markings found in horses, and may be influenced by a number of genes. Sabino appears to be at least a partial dominant. In addition, whether animals mated have 3 or 4 white stockings each may influence the amount of white on the offspring. The APHA lumps Sabino in the Overo in the registry category. They are NOT the same. The white stockings are the quickest way to tell Sabino from Overo.

SABINO

SPLASH WHITE: This is the rarest form of pinto. The horse looks literally as if it has been dipped, head down, into white paint. Extensive white is on the head (apron or paper face) and the white appears as hard-edged. This color is very similar to the visual progression of sabino, if one were to include the rise of the roan as progression. Stallions who are splash white have also sired overo, sabino and splash foals (which supports the theory of sabino being a natural extension of other genetic factors). It is the end-progression of the splashed white where the visual differences between sabino and splash are seen best.

SPLASH WHITE

TOVERO: The combination of the tobiano and overo patterns. Unusual markings including white EARS may be seen. Since the APHA lumps all non-tobiano animals together as OVERO, most horses with who are tovero may not be actually tobiano/overo genetic combinations. Some may be odd variations on the tobiano pattern (an apron face) or be tobiano/sabinos. (Remembering that sabinos are classified as overo and may be naturally-progressing white, one can visualize how the leg and face markings would begin to spread past the norms defined in the tobiano pattern).

TOVERO

Medicine Hat: Many of the extreme-white overos fall into a special subcategory, the elusive and legendary Medicine Hat Pinto. The Medicine Hat had a "bonnet" over the ears and a chest "shield". These pintos were once believed by the Native Americans to have special magic powers to protect the rider from harm. Below are examples of horses that could be termed Medicine Hats (another variation of the name was War Bonnet). Not all are overos, some tobianos (rarely), toveros and extreme sabinos may have the correct markings.

Medicine Hat   Moroccan

Moroccan: At the turn of the century and up into the 1950's, you could find horse breed books listing a variant of the tobiano or occasional tovero pattern. The animals had colored heads, and the rest of the body was white. A very few had small patches on the chest or flank. In essence, the Moroccan pattern was an extreme-white end tobiano horse simply having markings arranged in the correct way.

SPOTTED ASS (Donkey spot). This pinto pattern is as unique to the donkey as any of the other patterns are to the horse. The spotted pattern is found in Asses (donkeys) of all sizes from Miniature to Mammoth. The spotting can overlay any of the base colors, and most will keep their mealy points (light points: muzzle, eye rings and belly). However, animals with the recessive genes for No Light Points often show the black muzzle clearly, depending mainly on the amount of actual white markings on the head. Crosses (dorsal and shoulder stripes) will show on the darkly colored portion of the animal. If the dark color is interrupted by white, the cross may show as "broken" only on the dark areas.

The Spotted Ass pattern, if compared visually to horse patterns, resembles overo or tovero to an extent. It also resembles quite closely the spotting pattern found in Longhorn cattle. The minimal expression of the spotting pattern in donkeys is a white blaze on the forehead and nasal ridge. The blaze is often exaggerated as it blends visually into the white points of the muzzle. Close examination can determine where the pink skin of the actual blaze may extend into a snip, race or lip (or any combination) or if the blaze ends at the muzzle hair. Socks, or broken/partial leg markings are also seen in the minimally marked animal. Unlike horses, the blaze and sock in the donkey are an indicator of the spotted gene. Thus far the extent of random white markings in donkeys (unrelated to spotting) is limited to a forehead star and in one bloodline, a white snip.   White hip markings appear, with secondary patches on the neck. Color will stay around the eyes, on ears, down the topline, and on one or more legs. Even nearly-white animal may have dark mascara on the eyes, and dark spots on the cannon bones (fore) and hocks. Blue eyes are unusual in spotted donkeys, but have been seen.

The Spotted Ass pattern looks to the eye as if the donkey were a white animal with dark spots filled in and laid on top of the white background. Because actual small round dark spots are seen, some people believe that donkeys come in leopard Appaloosa. Comparisons to the Appaloosa leopard complex show this is not true. Donkeys who have small round spots scattered over a dark background may be referred to as "tyger spotted", but are still genetically pinto-spotted and not appaloosa.

In these animals with over-lay and tyger type spotting, it is not unusual to see dark spots inside the white blaze over the forehead area. The leg markings may also be jagged and uneven (lightning marks). Thus far all variants of the donkey-spot pattern have proven to be partial dominants, as with overo in horses. This indicates also that the tyger spotting may to the donkey spot as rosette overo is to frame, a variation with an additional controller.

SPOTTED
ASS

MULE SPOT: Mules have the genetic possibility of exhibiting all of the color patterns of the horse and donkey. However, nature has not seen fit to produce mules in any of the exact patterns of either parent. The patterns are most commonly enlarged, or strangely "Skewed" (displaced) in the mule. Research into this phenomenon is by no means complete, but observations can be useful if breeding for color in mules is desired.

APPALOOSA MULES: Mules from appaloosa dams are often the loudest. However as with appy horses, some mules may be solid colored with no white or appaloosa characteristics. (The key to understanding the leopard complex might be to direct research further into mules.) Those that do achieve color often do so with outstanding (or outlandish according to tastes) results. Leopard-type appaloosa mules may have huge spots or hundreds of spots. The blanket pattern may be only a few small white splashes, with gigantic spots over it, or may encompass most of the body, with leopard, roaning, and snowflaking all present.

Another way to get good color in a mule colt is to breed to a spotted jack. If the mule gets the spotting gene from the jack (a 50/50 chance with the heterozygous spotting gene) the markings are definite modifications (skewing) of the donkey spot pattern.

Appaloosa mules

Tobiano pinto mares rarely throw color to the colt. Mules from tobiano mares most commonly have only 4 white stockings (or sock and stocking combinations) and a white tail splash. In comparisons of mules from tobiano dams, less than ¼ normally have what could be considered to be tobiano markings. Of this percentage, only 1 in 100 will ppear to be an exact tobiano pattern. Most mules that are patched similarly to tobiano have some sort of displacement of the arrangement of white.

TOBIANO
MULES

MODIFIED
DONKEY
PATTERN

The overo pattern does not appear to affect the mule colt. Of the recorded foals of overo mares (when bred to non-spotted jacks) no mule showed the overo or any other spotting pattern. Those mule foals with pinto marking out of overo mares also had spotted jack sires.

Mules may often have dark leopard-type spots overlaying the dark areas of pinto markings. While the background of many mules is untraced, the workings of genetics in pintaloosa horses seem to indicate some of these mules are from spotted ass x appaloosa matings.

Mixed pattern Mules   Appaloosa Mules

The question has also arisen regarding Lethal White Foal Syndrome. Recent research as uncovered that this genetic trait is linked to the homozygous overo in Paint horses. It appears to be from frame x frame matings, although since the APHA still categorizes all non-tobianos together, other patterns have not yet been completely ruled out. Foals born from these overo x overo matings (O/o x O/o = O/O) are born all white, and die within a few hours of birth. (Since the overo is only a partial dominant, the heterozygous Overo (O/o x O/o) matings can still produce O/o normal overo, as well as solid colored, foals.)

The Spotted Ass pattern, like the Overo , is also a partial dominant. Extensive research by the ADMS has as yet failed to turn up a jack or jennet that could be confirmed as a homozygous (SA/SA) spotted animal. If there were a homozygout, all foals, regardless of the color of the other parent, would be spotted. Even in extreme-white animals, solid foals still occur. Additionally, spotted x spotted mating still continue to produce solid-colored foals. There is no evidence that the spotted gene is recessive – spotted animals will always have one spotted parent (even when the spotting is hidden by the Frosted (graying-type) gene or the animal is the minimally marked Masked Spotted Factor with only a white blaze). Evaluation of the matings of spotted to spotted animals show preliminary figures indicating the SA/SA is possibly a lethal gene, and the ratio of colored offspring vs. solid is consistent with this theory as well.

It is always stressed by the ADMS, and should be any breeder's policy, that no matter how fascinating and fanciful the color, conformation should never be sacrificed for color. Careful selection of brood stock for conformation and temperament should be fundamental, since understanding the workings of color can easily introduce and "fix" genetically a color or pattern into a herd. 🐎

APPENDIX XII:
Mule, Donkey, Hinny, Jenny - Which one is Which?

"I just got a donkey - or at least I think it is a donkey. My friend says it's a mule. But it's female - mules are male and hinnies are female, right?"

Whoops! People who are not familiar with mules often have a difficult time when it comes to understanding the donkey, mule, and hinny. The facts of the matter have been complicated over the years by different uses of the gender terms, and by hearsay from those who have heard the wrong information and continued to pass it along. Have you ever played "Pass the Message"? One person tells a short story to the next, and it is relayed down the line. By the time it gets to the tenth person in line, the original meaning may have been completely lost. Such, unfortunately, is often the case with information about donkeys and mules.

A donkey is a purebred animal (we are not talking specific breeds such as Poitou or Maltese) - donkey bred to donkey is always a donkey. Within it's own species, it is a purebred. Even a Miniature bred to a large Standard (!!!) would produce a donkey, not something else. The entire male donkey is properly termed a jack, although in countries other than the US, the term stallion is also used. The female donkey is the jennet; jenny or mare are other terms. Castrated male donkeys are called geldings.

For the record, the terms burro, ass and donkey are all correct. Ass is correct for any type of donkey and is proper when used with the terms Mammoth or Poitou. Burro is usually reserved for the Mexican or Spanish type of wild or feral donkey, now seen mainly through the Bureau of Land Management. The terms Sicilian and Sardinian once referred directly to those donkeys of small stature that were imported from those islands. Neither term has anything to do with color - a slate (gray-dun) donkey with a cross on its back is not a "Sicilian" unless it is specifically from that area. Miniature Mediterranean, or simply Miniature, are the preferred terms for donkeys under 36", of any origin, regardless of color.

The mule is the product of breeding a jack donkey to a mare (female) horse. The mule can be either male (called a horse mule) or female (called a mare mule). Due to the imbalance of the chromosome count (the donkey has 62, the horse has 64, and the mule ends up with 63) the mule is sterile. (There have been a few cases of mare mules that have conceived and even given live birth, but these cases are less than 1 in 1,000,000 and are under close scientific scrutiny. No male mule has yet been shown to have sired a foal.) The mule is sexually normal, meaning they have all the proper reproductive equipment, they just do not produce viable sperm or eggs. Male mules do have testes, and produce testosterone, the male hormone. They do not know that they are not full stallions and cannot sire young. The uncastrated mule will act in every way as a stallion would, although they have been known to be single-minded in their sex drive to the point of being dangerous. For this reason, all male mules should be castrated, preferably as soon as possible and hopefully long before the age of two. Colloquial terms for horse mules are "johns" or geldings, mare mules are sometimes called mollies.

The hinny is the "opposite" cross as the mule - the horse stallion bred to a donkey jennet. The hinny has sometimes been said to be slightly more horselike in conformation than the mule, but in actuality, with the use of better mares for mule production, it is often nearly impossible to tell a hinny from a mule visually. Knowing the parentage for sure is really the only way to be sure. Hinnies are both male and female, and for all practical purposes are identical to mules. This also hold true for fertility and the need for castration of the male.

Some female mules and hinnies have been spayed in order to help with hormone problems and to make a more stable mount. Many females - equine or not - have some hormonal problems, and spaying should only be an alternative if necessary. The operation is expensive, and your local vet may not be up on the procedure. There are some hormone therapies that can be used on mares (of any equine species) that can help, but also being sensitive to her moods and reactions plays a large part.

Draft Mule owners have often stated that they prefer mare mules over the horse mule because their face and body lines are smoother. The horse mule often has the more prominent brow ridges from the donkey jack, giving his face a coarser appearance. There are few draft Hinnies, simply because of the difference in size of the parents, and also due to the fact that is simply easier to produce a mule. Independent studies have shown that the conception rate for donkey jennies is lower overall that that of horse mares. Also, conception of a hybrid is more likely to occur when the chromosome count of the female (horse mare = 64) is higher than that of the male (donkey jack = 62). In breeding for hinnies, the male would have the higher count and therefore conception is less likely.

Although it is difficult to visually distinguish between the hinny and mule, it is rather easy to tell a donkey from a mule or hinny at a glance. There will always be a few exceptions, such as very "horsey" donkeys with good hip, loins and withers that resemble a good saddle mule, or the mule that takes more after the donkey parent. Try using this "Rule of Thumb" to tell donkeys from mules.

Cover the head and face of the photo with your thumb. Now look at the overall shape of the animal. Is it long and lean, with a straight neck and back, small, angular hip and little withers? Are the hooves small, round, and upright? Does the short body hair cover most of the tail, with only a long-haired tassel at the end? If the answers are yes, then you are probably looking at a donkey. (Prominent testes on a jack or a milk-filled bag on a nursing jennet can also be a clue.)

Look at the second animal on the page, covering the head again. Is the neck slightly more filled out? Is there a definite wither rise, and a dip in the back? Is the hip rounder, with more of the double-curve seen in the horse? Are the legs and hooves more horselike? Is the tail hair fuller and longer, starting up where the tail joins into the body? (This can be difficult to tell if the tail is shaved or belled, but the overall amount of hair in the switch will be greater than that of the donkey tail switch). This animal is probably a mule.

The shape of the face and ears are also useful in determining the species. The donkey has a deeper, thicker jaw and face, the ears are larger and fuller. The mule has a longer, more horselike face, the ears are not quite as long as the donkeys, and have more of the thin lines of the horse's ears. Donkey do not have a true forelock (the hair that falls down between the ears over the forehead) although a few have fine enough long manes to comb some forward. The mule can have a forelock, but long mane and forelock hair in the mule tends to be unruly and look sloppy on some animals. Most donkeys and many mules wear their manes and forelocks roached (shaved to the neck) or in a small, stand-up fringe.

One last clue that can be useful if the animal's color is right. Most donkeys sport what are termed Light Points - that is the muzzle, eye rings and belly are a shade or white, greyish, or pale cream. In the mule, these light points are usually modified to a tan color (in chestnuts) or even a rich brown (in dark bays, browns, or blacks). The entire light belly is usually not seen in the mule, instead the modified light color is reflected as light areas around the elbow and flank.

Above - **Donkey** (*NTRS My Birthday Angel* owned by Myryha Patton.
Below - **Mule**. (*Leading Lady*, with Cliff Rich)

APPENDIX XIII:
HYBRIDS OF THE DONKEY

In addition to the mule and hinny, the Donkey can be crossed with other Equines to produce hybrids. Wild Ass x Donkey hybrids have been known, but recently the trend for Zebra Hybrids has been rekindled. For those who favor horses and mule, the Zorse (zebra x horse) is popular, but the donkey can also be crossed to the zebra to produce the Zebrass (Zonkey).

Most Zonkeys are from Standard or Large Standard jennets, with the zebra as the sire. Since tame zebra mares are needed for raising more tame zebra stock, few zebra hybrids are the reciprocal cross of the Jack on an a Zebra mare.

The hybrid resembles very much a donkey with zebra striping over the entire body. The ear shape and build will also depend on the type of zebra used. For Zorse crosses, the Plains types of zebra (Burchells, Grants, Damaraland) have proved to be best, while the Plains or Grevy's zebras can be used on Donkeys.

While more donkeylike in nature, the zebrass or zonkey still requires extra care and handling, as one parent is, after all, a wild animal. The zebra hybrids are not for everyone, but those who are dedicated to them love them!

The ADMS has a registry for Zebra Hybrids. For more information, contact the ADMS at 2901 N. Elm St., Denton TX 75201.

Liberty *Acres Sargent*, a zebrass gelding.

A reciprocal cross zebrass colt - Zebra dam, zebrass foal, and jack sire. Red Peterson, owner/breeder.

Photo by Cynthia Ford Dubois.

APPENDIX XIV - USING THE TWITCH

A Twitch can be a useful aid in restraint when working with nervous or upset, animals. You should always try to do your work with the minimum amount of restraint at first, only using extra aids or force as necessary.

You can purchase a twitch at a tack or feed store, or you can make one. The simplest ones are made of a thick ½" or so cord and a short length of broom handle or other smooth wood. Store-bought ones are usually made with s-link chain (to lie flat).

The upper lip of the equine, when pinched, acts as a kind of tranquilizer, causing the animal to relax and quiet down. You can grab the upper lip and hold tightly onto it in a pinch, but if the donkey wiggles or jumps, your hand is not usually strong enough to hold on with.

Use the twitch only on the upper lip. Grab the lip, slide the chain or cord over, and twist it tight (but just tight enough to hold, not to cut off circulation!). If you are using a regular twitch, one person holds the twitch while the other does the work (injection, hooves, clipping, etc). There are also humane twitches that look kind of like a nutcracker, with locking rings or loops so you can fasten it to the halter. This way you can work alone on the animal. Whichever type you use, always make sure the animal is securely tied to a stout post!!!! While you can do all sorts of things to the animal, you may not have a lot of control of the hind end! The twitch just keeps their mind off what you are doing, not necessarily their tail or their passion for sidestepping.

Only leave the twitch on for as long as necessary, remove it as soon as possible. Rub the lip with your hand to let some feeling come back into the lip also. Never run the chain through the mouth and twist – you can cause injury to the teeth or jaw. Only apply to the upper lip. Smaller animals may wriggle out of twitches, and you may have to devise a smaller one with a cord for the really small donkeys. Learn how to use one before you need it, because WHEN you do need it, you will need it RIGHT THEN!!!!

Always use a halter with the twitch, not just a twitch alone. Tie the animal, and have an assistant hold the twitch.

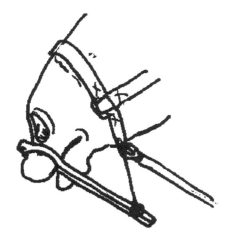

This is a humane clamp-type twitch. It has a small string with a snap to wrap around the handles, holding it clamped, and then snaps to the halter ring to free up the hand of the worker.

APPENDIX XV: RIDER SEAT AND HAND POSITION

It is always best to have someone who is an experienced rider work with you if you cannot have some kind of riding lessons or have no riding experience at all. If you are just going to be riding for fun and never plan on showing, the overall picture presented by the rider is not that essential, but remember that it is easier to learn correctly than to try and re-learn and correct bad habits. No matter what your riding style, you should look comfortable, not stiff or saggy in the saddle. The trends of the heads-down western horse with a head-up, stiff armed rider are not very good form, and won't help you and your donkey.

The line of the head, body, and heel should be long and centered. There should be a straight line from the bit to your elbow. "Broken" wrist lines not only look bad, but lesson your degree of control and are hard on your wrists. Keep your heels pressed down (further flexion is used in English than Western). If you let your heels float up higher than your toes, you cannot use the stirrup properly for position and balance. Remember also that a good rider can ride any course, whether trail or jumping, without stirrups. In an excellent rider, you would never notice a change in leg position whether or not stirrups were used. Don't try to wrap your legs around the donkey. Your leg should hang down along the side. Wrapping your legs will usually cause your ankles to warp in, and you lose balance and leg cues. Your toes should point forward, not out sideways. This puts the inside of your calf properly along the animals sides, which is best for your balance and for leg cues to the animal. Watch riders in Equitation classes at open shows. You will see riders that look stiff and "funny", those who look relaxed, and those that look uncomfortable. Concentrate on those that look relaxed and seem to be enjoying themselves!!! They are usually in the mid form, not too extreme with stiff backs and broken angles, or trying to think every second about their position. Above all, learn what you can, but have fun!

The English rider has a shorter stirrup, with the heels pressed well down. Both English and Western riders should sit tall, with the chin level, and the heel down. The lines should be natural but not slumped. The third rider has the chin too high, and the arm angles are broken, not a smooth line as the arm of the second. This looks stiff and unnatural.

APPENDIX XVI: THE LEGEND OF THE DONKEY'S CROSS

HOW THE DONKEY CAME TO HAVE HIS CROSS

Everyone knows that the little gray donkey carries a cross on his back. Most people don't know the legend of the donkey's cross.

The Story is told that the little donkey that had been Jesus' mount on Palm Sunday, came to the hill of Calvary.

Seeing the tragic event occurring there he wished with all his heart he had been able to carry the cross for Jesus as he was the proper one to carry heavy burdens.

The donkey turned his back on the sight, but he could not leave because he wished to stay until all was over because of his love for Jesus.

In reward for the loyal and humble love of the little donkey the Lord caused the shadow of the cross to fall across his back and left it there for the donkey to carry forevermore as a sign that the love of God, no matter how humble one may be, carries a reward for all to see.

HOW THE DONKEY CAME TO HAVE HIS CROSS (Version II)

There is a charming Mexican Peasant legend about how the donkey came to have a cross on its back.

This legend is particularly charming to those of us who have raised babies.

The story has it that Maria was holding the baby Jesus before her on the donkey during the flight into Egypt. The baby was still very young, and he wet the back of the donkey where he was sitting.

Because of this the donkey carries a cross on its back.

Guiseppe A-6137

APPENDIX XVII: AMERICAN DONKEY AND MULE SOCIETY BREEDER'S CODE OF ETHICS

The American Donkey and Mule Society, is the only National Breed Organization in the United States for Donkeys and Mules of all types and zebra hybrids. It administers the **Miniature Donkey Registry, The American Donkey Registry, The American Mule Registry, The American Zebra Hybrid/Bloodstock Registry and the American Mule Racing Registry.**

The American Donkey and Mule Society requests that all breeders subscribe to the following Code of Ethics to promote and foster the highest standards among breeders, owners and fanciers, and to encourage sportsmanship and cooperation in the advancement and protection of all donkeys, mules and hybrids.

RECORDS: I am familiar with and follow the registry requirements for my breed.

I will keep accurate records and retain those records for a minimum of 5 years. These records will include registry paperwork and health and breeding paperwork for all animals in my herd. I will notify the registry of the death of an animal and will work with the registry to keep records current.

I will report any person who falsifies a registration or knowingly misrepresents a pedigree to the Registry.

BREEDING: I shall plan each breeding with the paramount intention of improving the breed.

I will select the sire and dam with an eye to conformation, temperament and good health with a careful study of the breed standard and the principles of genetics.

I will refrain from close breeding without careful study of pedigrees and individual animals.

I will not breed any male or female until they are both physically and mentally mature. I will not breed any female before the age of two years, with age three preferred.

Before entering into any breeding arrangement I will scrutinize the pedigree, conformation and health of both the sire and dam, keeping in mind the ideal of the breed. I have an obligation to refuse the breeding if in my opinion it is not in the best interest of the breed.

As a responsible owner of a sire, I understand that should I refuse a breeding I will fully explain my reasons to the owner of the female.

I subscribe to the policy that only sires and dams free of defects such as cryptorchidism, under and over bite, dwarfism and other genetic defects shall be used for breeding.

Being a responsible breeder I will refrain from using a breeding animal, although free from the above defects that consistently produces afflicted offspring.

HEALTH: I shall maintain high standards of health and care for my animals and will keep their feet properly trimmed. I will guarantee the health of animals I sell to others.

SALES: I will be discriminating in the sales of my animals and concerned with the type of homes in which they are placed. My animals will not be sold to wholesalers or meat buyers and I will humanely euthanise animals that must be put down.

I will transfer all applicable registration papers at the time that the purchase agreement is completed and is suitable to all parties.

I will not advertise animals as "registered" and then present the new owner with a filled out application and expect him to register the animals himself.

Upon the sale of an animal I will provide the new owner with a diet record, an inoculation and parasite control record and a health guarantee.

I will refrain from releasing any young animal until it is at least 4 to 6 months old and properly weaned.

I will inform all buyers that donkeys need companions, preferably other equines in order to be happy inasmuch as they are herd animals not solitary creatures.

ADVERTISING: I agree that all advertising of animals will be factual and honest both in substance and implication.

I will avoid encouraging buyers regarding the breeding potential of an animal without explaining that the breeding of any animal involves certain responsibilities and is not to be taken lightly.

I will make sure that all show winnings listed in advertising are accurate.

EXHIBITOR/BREEDER RELATIONS: I understand that exhibiting animals is a sport and that I am expected to express good sportsmanship in all activities.

As an exhibitor I will refrain from unnecessary criticism of other people's animals, or of the judge.

I will not represent any animal I sell as being a sure winner, knowing that judges differ in their opinions.

I will not demonstrate behavior that could be defined as serious abuse or harm to an animal either in training the animal or in showing it.

IMPLEMENTATION:

In as much as a Code of Ethics is a guideline, not rules, regulations or legal documents, they do not carry an enforceable punishment. They should be enforced by breeders and buyers upon each breeder in a civil and responsible manner. Buyers should read the Code of Ethics and determine if it is being followed before buying an animal.

FARM REQUIREMENTS:

FOOD AND WATER: Clean water must be available at all times. Care will be taken that water supplies are unfrozen in winter, and clean at all times. Animals should be neither too obese or too thin and proper rations should be available every day.

SHELTER: All animals will have access to clean, dry shelter from rain, wind and snow and shade from heat.

CONFINEMENT: Fences will be sturdy, well built and safe for the type of animal enclosed within. Space will allow for adequate freedom of movement and exercise.

SAFETY AND PROTECTION: More than one jack over 6 months old will not be allowed to be pastured with a group of females. Caution will be taken at all times that under age females will never be available to be bred. Jacks will be confined so that they will not damage each other or jennets or kill foals.

HEALTH CARE: I will take care that Vaccinations and Coggins tests will be administered in accordance with local and state requirements and health needs. An internal and external parasite control program will be maintained. Sick animals and newly introduced animals will be isolated from the general population. Health papers and Coggins tests must be required for any animals brought to the farm for breeding or training. Hooves of all stock will be kept properly trimmed.

WASTE DISPOSAL: Waste must be removed in accordance with accepted local and state requirements. Also waste must be handled in accordance with veterinarian prescribed health practices. Barn and stall areas must be cleared of waste daily.

RECORD KEEPING: Health and breeding records will be kept for each animal. All breedings will be recorded and a sire's breeding certificate made out at the time of breeding. A sales record showing to whom each animal (registered or non-registered) is sold will be kept. All animals should be easily identified by the owner, and if possible should be identified with methods that anyone can use such as neckstraps, freeze brands, microchips etc. Ear tags are not recommended by the registry for donkeys or mules.

Farm owners must meet all local, county and state government requirements for farm or stable operations.

Breed type and conformation are apparent in this mother/daughter (left) small Standard donkey pair.

APPENDIX XVIII: TRAILERING LARGER DONKEYS

Many people who own Large Standards and Mammoth Jackstock have reported that no matter how carefully they tie the animals in the trailer, they always brace against their leads, and have big rubbed spots on their rump or tail when they get to the destination.

There are a few solutions, but the best seems to be to blanket the animal and let it ride loose in the trailer. Riding loose has some drawbacks, but so does riding tied. Riding loose they can pick their own place to stand and lean without creating a double friction on tail and with the headrope. It has the disadvantage of having to get control of the animal and get a lead rope on them before you open the door, and if there were an accident you would have loose animals. However, an animal tied even with a release knot may not be able to get back up if it should lose its balance and fall. If you must tie, always use trailer ties with panic snaps, and make sure the leads are not long enough for an animal to get the leg over. (Ed note - we once took a small jack (on the left side) and jennet (on the right) in a single-wide horse trailer. Both were tied up to the ring in the horse-height manger. The ropes were not slack enough for them to get their legs over - but when we opened the trailer, the donkeys had somehow switched sides. The jack was now on the right, the jennet on the left. We can only guess one set back on the rope, the other sat down, and when they came up again, they were reversed on sides!!!) There have also been sad cases where the trailer door popped open, and the animal (horses too), on a too-long rope, has been dragged behind the trailer!!! (HORRIBLE!)

If you are trailering a jennet and foal, make sure the partition between the animals is solid all the way down. The foal should be left loose if it is a long journey, as it will want to lie down and will probably travel better this way. If the stalls are completely divided, the jennet can still see her baby but can't step on him. When you make your stops, be sure and let the foal nurse. Stock trailers or two-horse with full swing partitions are best for hauling jennet/foal pairs.

Any kind of trailer can have good points and bad. It is not necessary to have a slant-load or special trailer for your donkeys, but make sure than even with a stock trailer that there is ample headroom. A big donkey with big ears will often bend his eartips over in a low-roofed trailer, as well as feel cramped.

Non-slip floors are essential, as is padding (like rubber mats) for long trips. If you use rubber mats, you may want to put down some shavings. If the animal has to urinate and gets splashed, some will not go in the trailer again.

There is no set rule for how long one can trailer, or how long you should go between stops. Stopping about every 2 1/2 -3 1/2 hours for 15-45 minutes is usually a pretty good system, and easier on the human passengers too. This seems to help the big donkeys as well. Check for rub marks. If you use a butt bar or chain, try some extra padding on it. Plan your trip route ahead, and see where unloading stops are if necessary. If you are making a long trip but have a stock trailer where the animal can move freely at night, you may not have to worry about unloading him, just make sure he has food, water, and a level spot to spend the night.

If using a trailer that has windows (like the slant-loads) be sure to travel with the window grills closed, or with screens in place. Do not let the animals ride with their heads out the windows. Also, NEVER load an animal into a trailer that is not already hitched to a vehicle!!! (or at least firmly chained so it will not tilt if you are leaving it in pasture for training.)

The animal who is trained to load properly and will step up willingly into the trailer will ride better! Teach your donkey to load early! If you must trailer donkeys who are untrained (at loading or at halter), keep a halter on, but observe the animal's actions before tying them! If they fall on a short lead, they may injure themselves if they do not know how to stand tied!

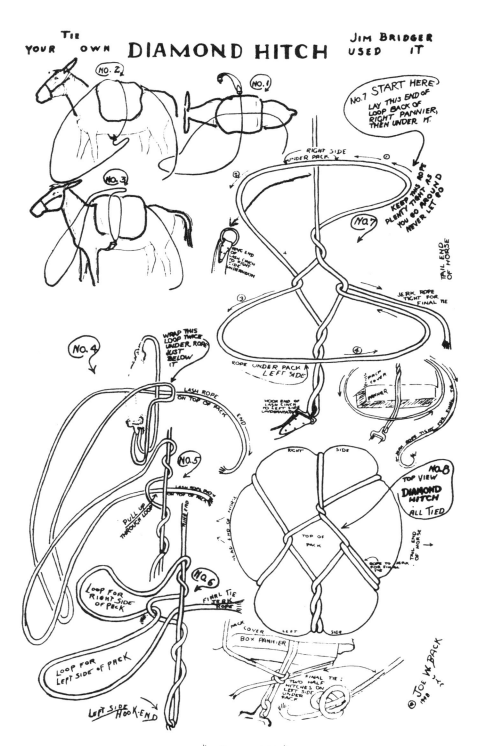

APPENDIX XX: CLUBS AND ORGANIZATIONS

(Please note these addresses and phone numbers are current as of January, 1999, but area codes and addresses may change. For a more complete listing of clubs, contact the ADMS.)

American Donkey and Mule Society (ADMS)
2901 N. Elm St.,
Denton TX 76201
(940) 382-6845 phone
adms@juno.com

The National Miniature Donkey Association (NMDA)
6450 Dewey Rd.
Rome NY 13440
(315) 336-0154

The American Council of Spotted Asses (ACOSA)
PO Box 121,
New Melle MO 63365

Canadian Donkey & Mule Association
RR#2, Site #1, Box 15
Rocky Mountain House,
Alberta, Canada T0M 1T0

American Livestock Breeds Conservancy
Box 477
Pittsboro NC 27132
(919) 542-5704

photo courtesy of Keith Whiteman

American Long-Ears Society (ALES) (for Model/figurines)
5614 Crown Point Rd.
Coos Bay OR 97420

Carousel Farms Hope, Mammoth
Jennet. Owned by Linda Johnson,
Enumclaw WA.

ADMS Nationals, Roseburg OR.
Photos by Juanita Snyder

Kids and Donkeys, a great combination. Myryha Patton with her 45" jennet *Angel.*

Bye now!!! You've reached the end! Hope this has helped you to learn about our favorite subject - DONKEYS!!!! *Angel, Rabbit* and *Mario,* Wishing Star Farm, TX.

About the Artists

Cindy Pollock was a young artist when she did the original art for this book in 1980. Her plans at that time included studies in art and equines. Her artwork has not only been shown in DEFINITIVE DONKEY, but THE BRAYER, BROOMTAIL, ANIMAL KINGDOM NEWS, and various club newsletters including that of the British Mule Society. She was last known to be in Phoenix AZ, and wherever she is today, we wish once again to extend our thanks for her dedication to the original art for this book!

Bonnie Shields is familiar to everyone who loves mules and donkeys as the TENNESSEE MULE ARTIST, and the illustrator for THE DONKEY AND MULE AS A BACKYARD HOBBY, and many other books, magazines, pamphlets etc. Her latest triumph is to be accepted as a contributing artist to the Leanin' Tree, company which produces greeting cards, and to be voted into the WOMAN ARTISTS OF THE AMERICAN WEST, a group of great prestige. She has also served on the Board of Directors for the ADMS.

When you draw mules for a living you get asked lots of questions — like WHY! Well, there's some folks say I got kicked once and ain't been right since, and they pretty well got it figured right. These ole mules just aimed for the heart and let me have it. I love mules. That's why I draw 'em.

I was born and raised in southern Indiana around fine gaited saddle horses and standard breds, but no mules. It wasn't until I moved to Middle Tennessee in 1965 that me and the mule met. We've neither one been the same since.

As for my art, I've been drawing and painting all my life, and I'm not tellin' how long that's been. Studied art at Georgetown College in Georgetown, KY. and at the Ringling School of Art in Sarasota, Fla. Most of my professional efforts, BM (before mules), were in newspaper advertising and layout and in free lance commercial work.

My hero mule, *Leroy*, passed away last year, but I am now living in the high Sierra country of Bishop, Calif. — with a few thousand other mules. And I'm happy to report a mule at any altitude is still very much a mule. God Bless 'em All!"
Bonnie Shields

Leah Patton terms herself a "jennet of all trades". when it comes to the ADMS. Following in Betsy's footsteps, Leah does any and everything in the ADMS office - from phone answering, putting together the magazine, processing the registrations, and working on the color research for ADMS. On the weekends she is either showing, inspecting, or at the farm working with her own stock. Basically, you name it, she does it.

Her newest addition to her animal menagerie is the American -bred Baudet du Poitou gelding *"Thor"*. *Thor* is kept at the ADMS office and is being shown by Leah in Texas. She has shown her own and other stable's mules, donkeys and horses. Her three-year old daughter Myryha has already debuted in the showring, on appropriately, a borrowed saddle mule. Leah, her husband Chris, and family also have 4 horses 4 donkeys, 1 small mare mule, and 15 head (at the moment) of Longhorn and high-percentage cross cattle. As if all of this isn't enough, not only does she have regular art clients and has just released no less than 15 (of a planned 26) Equine Clipart collections, including the first-ever All-Donkey collections. She is a published sci-fi/ fantasy writer and writes freelance for several other magazines besides the BRAYER. She has co-authored a book on color and conformation in equines, and is currently revising this book with expanded donkey color genetic information. This is in conjunction with Dr. Phillip Sponenberg of the University of Virginia.

Don't hesitate to ask for Leah if you call the ADMS office - she's there regular and sometimes odd hours and is always willing to answer questions about her favorite subject - EQUINES!!